REINHOLD PHYSICAL AND INORGANIC CHEMISTRY TEXTBOOK SERIES

Consulting Editor: Professor Harry H. Sisler, University of Florida, Gainesville, Florida

Principles of
Chemical Thermodynamics

REINHOLD

PHYSICAL AND INORGANIC

CHEMISTRY TEXTBOOK

SERIES

_____

The challenge of chemical education in the world of today demands a willingness to try new approaches, a willingness to fit new teaching methods to a great variety of situations, in short, a willingness to bring to the teaching of chemistry the same experimental attitude that characterizes the research laboratory. It is our aim that the Reinhold Physical and Inorganic Chemistry Textbook Series will provide a variety of modern textbooks which will help to meet this challenge. Some of these texts will present scientific viewpoints controversial among chemists of today. Others will present new and unique arrangements of subject matter. Still others will be new with respect to the teaching methods to which they are adapted. In all these textbooks, however, a sincere effort will be made to avoid the triteness of repeating the presentations of textual materials already available. We shall be happy if the books in this Series serve sometimes as a stimulus, sometimes as a guide, but always as an aid to the teacher and the student who look boldly to the future of chemical science.

Harry H. Sisler
Consulting Editor

Principles of

Chemical

Thermodynamics

Charles E. Reid

Associate Professor of Chemistry
University of Florida
Gainesville, Florida

REINHOLD PUBLISHING CORPORATION, NEW YORK
CHAPMAN & HALL, LTD., LONDON

Copyright © 1960 by

REINHOLD PUBLISHING CORPORATION

Library of Congress Catalog Card Number 60-11082

Preface

THERE IS NO DEARTH of textbooks on chemical thermodynamics; at least ten are currently in print. It therefore seems reasonable that the author of a new one should state reasons justifying his adding to this profusion. Basically, the reason for this book is my conviction that no previous text fully exploits the pedagogical advantages of a logical and critical presentation of the principles of thermodynamics and its application to chemistry. More specifically, some of the features which make this book distinctive (though it is probably not actually unique in any one of them) are:

(1) Entropy is treated postulationally, with no attempt to make it depend on heat engines. The chemist's confidence in the applicability of thermodynamics to chemical equilibria is not dependent on its prior use by mechanical engineers, and so it appears better to avoid an approach which presents chemical thermodynamics as an appendage of heat engine theory. A more obvious advantage is a considerable saving of time, which can be spent on more relevant material.

(2) A chapter on statistical thermodynamics is included, and molecular concepts are used freely whenever they serve the purpose of clarity. There are many reasons why every thermodynamics text should include an introduction to statistical methods, but let one suffice here: many students, particularly those not specializing in physical chemistry, take only one course in thermodynamics and must receive their formal instruction in this topic in the first course or not at all.

(3) Although the terminology is not original and will certainly not resolve the confusion attending thermodynamic nomenclature, it has been chosen so as to be readily understandable to those accustomed to any of the more common systems. Unfortunately, it is still necessary for serious students of thermodynamics to learn a variety of conflicting nomenclatures, and little or no progress seems to have been made toward setting up a generally recognized standard. The use of the letters U, H, A, G, and S conforms to the recommendations of the American Standards Association.* However, lower-case letters are used for molar quantities

*Bulletin No. Z 10.4, 1943.

rather than, as ASA recommends, for specific quantities; the latter are of so little use in chemical work that it appears unwise to confine the very useful lower-case letters to them. Moreover, small capitals, which are recommended for molar quantities, are certain to be confusing when written by hand, whether by the lecturer on the blackboard or the student in his notes.

(4) The recommendations of Guggenheim** in regard to dimensional consistency have been followed with some modification. Guggenheim recommends that such expressions as "ln p" be avoided, "ln (p/atm)" being used instead. The reason is that "p/atm" is a dimensionless number, while p is a physical quantity; and it is only for dimensionless numbers that logarithms have a meaning. The modification used here is to replace "atm" by a general symbol p_u representing whatever pressure unit is needed for any particular application. This is in accordance with a policy followed in this book of encouraging students to become familiar with the use of cgs, mks, or related units, such as the joule and bar, as well as the more customary but less logical calorie and atmosphere.

Finally, it should be added that this book is intended for an introductory thermodynamics course — the type of course commonly given to graduate students in chemistry, though not beyond the ability of qualified undergraduates also. For this reason it stresses principles and makes no attempt to be comprehensive in covering applications. The background expected of the student is a year each of calculus and physical chemistry. From a strictly logical viewpoint, this book does not depend on the latter, though few students would be ready to follow it without this background.

No attempt will be made to list all the people who have helped or encouraged me in this work, but a few should be mentioned. At an early stage of the writing Mr. (now Dr.) George B. Savitsky read and criticized the first four and sixth chapters. Later Dr. Pierre Van Rysselberghe, of Stanford University, read the first nine chapters and provided a very thorough criticism; many of his suggestions are incorporated into the final form of the book. Finally, there was the help of my wife, not only in much of the typing, but in other ways too numerous to list.

Gainesville, Fla.   Charles E. Reid
March, 1960

**See Reference 2, Chapter 4.

Contents

List of Symbols

THIS LIST does not include symbols used only at a single point and described there, nor symbols used to express a mathematical fact without the need for physical interpretation, as when the equation

$$\int_0^\infty e^{-\alpha x^2} \, dx = \tfrac{1}{2}(\pi/\alpha)^{\frac{1}{2}}$$

is used simply to state a fact which is true for all positive values of α.

A Helmholtz free energy, or work function ($U - TS$)

B Coefficient in one form of the Debye-Hückel limiting law, $\ln \gamma = -Bm^{\frac{1}{2}}$

C Heat capacity, usually with a subscript p or v to indicate constant pressure or volume; molar concentration; number of components

D Dielectric constant

E Electromotive force (emf), also called "chemical tension"

$\mathcal{E}$ Emf of half-cell

F Faraday's constant, 96,487 coulombs/g eq wt; variance

G Gibbs free energy

H Enthalpy

I Ionic strength, $\tfrac{1}{2}(C_1 z_1^2 + C_2 z_2^2 + \ldots)$; moment of inertia

J In Chapter 6, quantum number of a rotator; in Chapter 11, Jacobian

K In Section 6–14, $9N/\nu_m^3$; elsewhere, with suitable subscript, equilibrium constant

M Molecular weight

N Number of atoms, molecules, etc.

N_a Avogadro's number

P Vapor pressure, or partial vapor pressure; number of phases

Q Heat added to a system

R The molar gas constant, equal to $\lim_{p \to 0} (pv/T)$; number of extra restrictions on a reacting system

S Entropy

T Temperature (on an absolute scale)

U Energy, also known as internal energy

V Volume

W Work done on a system

Y Any extensive thermodynamic property (in Chapter 7); a reactant (in Chapters 5 and 8)

Z Partition function; product of a reaction

Af Affinity

$\overline{Af}$ Electrochemical affinity

a Activity; molar Helmholtz free energy

c Molar, or partial molar, heat capacity; in Chapter 9, concentration in ions per cc

d Differential operator

e Base of natural logarithms, equal to $\sum\limits_{k=0}^{\infty} (1/k!)$

f Fugacity

g Molar, or partial molar, Gibbs free energy; gravitational acceleration

h Molar, or partial molar, enthalpy; Planck's constant (mostly in Chapter 6)

k Boltzmann's constant, 1.380×10^{-16} erg/degree

l Relative partial molar enthalpy

m In Chapter 4, mass; elsewhere, molality

n In Chapter 6, number of systems in a given state or energy level; elsewhere, number of moles

p Pressure

q Heat per mole added to a system

r Radius

s Molar, or partial molar, entropy; also, entropy per system in an ensemble, or entropy per unit area in a surface

t Time

u Molar, or partial molar, energy; energy of one system in an ensemble; or energy per unit area in a surface

v Molar, or partial molar, volume

x Mole fraction

y In Chapter 6, $\exp(-h\nu/kT)$; in Chapter 7, molar, or partial molar, value of Y; elsewhere, stoichiometric coefficient of reactant

z Partition function for a single molecule; stoichiometric coefficient of a product; charge on an ion.

α Coefficient of expansion, $(\partial V/\partial T)_p/V$

γ In Chapter 6, probability that a system will be in a designated state; in Chapter 10, surface tension; elsewhere, activity coefficient.

Γ In Chapter 6, probability that a system will be in a designated energy level; in Chapter 10, with subscript, surface excess of component per unit area

Δ Final value minus initial value

ϵ Charge on a univalent positive ion (the same, except for sign, as the charge on an electron); in chemical equations, the symbol for an electron; with subscript, energy of a system in the state or energy level indicated by the subscript

θ Temperature on an arbitrary scale; reduced temperature (T/T_c)

Θ Characteristic temperature of Debye crystal, $h\nu_m k$; with subscripts f or b, freezing-point depression or boiling-point elevation, respectively

κ Compressibility, $-(\partial V/\partial p)_T/V$; in the Debye-Hückel theory, $[\,(z_+{}^2 c_+{}^0 + z_-{}^2 c_-{}^0)4\pi\epsilon^2/DkT]^{\frac{1}{2}}$

μ Chemical potential

$\bar{\mu}$ Electrochemical potential

ν In Chapter 6, frequency; in Chapter 9, number of ions into which a formula unit of a salt dissociates

ξ Degree of advancement

π In Chapter 4, reduced pressure (p/p_c); in Chapter 7, osmotic pressure; elsewhere, ratio of circumference of circle to diameter

ρ Density (in Chapter 9, charge density)

σ In Chapter 6, $h^2/8\pi^2 IkT$; elsewhere, area

Σ Summation sign

ϕ Reduced volume (v/v_c)

Φ Actual potential difference between electrodes, or electric tension

ψ Schrodinger function; electrostatic potential

ω ⎧Number of states (generally, Ω represents the number of states in
Ω ⎩a larger, ω that in a smaller, group of states)

Superscripts and Subscripts

f Formation (as in heat of formation)

fus   Fusion

i, j In Chapter 6, states; elsewhere, usually components

p Constant pressure

r In Chapter 6, energy levels

sp   Specific

u A unit value, such as a unit pressure, p_u

v Constant volume

vap   Vaporization

X Excess quantity in surface

$'$ When appended to u, h, a, g, or s, standard value referred to zero pressure of a gas; C', number of constituents

$''$ Standard value referred to infinitely dilute solution

$*$ Value for a pure substance

0 As a superscript, standard value (of one of the three types above); as a subscript, temperature of absolute zero

$+$ Positive ion

$-$ Negative ion

chapter 1

Mathematical Preparation

IT IS ASSUMED THAT ANY STUDENT of chemical thermodynamics will have had at least a beginning course in calculus and will be familiar with the concepts of differentiation, integration, and partial differentiation. This chapter treats a few advanced topics of special importance in thermodynamics. It may be studied at first, or skipped and referred to as needed; those who have taken advanced calculus may not need it at all. A few additional derivations, less important than those given here, are treated in the appendices.

1–1. Thermodynamic Notation for Partial Derivatives

One of the complications arising in the thermodynamic use of partial derivatives can be illustrated by a geometric example. In Figure 1, the area of the rectangle can be expressed by any of the following formulas, among others:

$$A = bh \tag{1-1}$$
$$A = st \tag{1-2}$$
$$A = b(s^2 - b^2)^{\frac{1}{2}} \tag{1-3}$$
$$A = b^2 t(b^2 - t^2)^{-\frac{1}{2}} \tag{1-4}$$

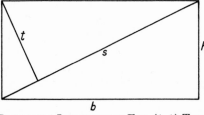

FIGURE 1. RECTANGLE ILLUSTRATING EQS. (1–1) THROUGH (1–4).

What then is meant by $\partial A/\partial b$? We get different results by differentiating Eqs. (1–1), (1–3), or (1–4) above. A special notation is used to avoid this ambiguity; the derivative is enclosed in parentheses, with the variable or variables which are held constant indicated by subscripts. Thus differentiation of Eq. (1–1) gives

$$\left(\frac{\partial A}{\partial b}\right)_h = h \qquad (1\text{–}5)$$

while Eq. (1–3) yields

$$\left(\frac{\partial A}{\partial b}\right)_s = (s^2 - b^2)^{\frac{1}{2}} - b^2 (s^2 - b^2)^{-\frac{1}{2}} \qquad (1\text{–}6)$$

The first of these represents the variation of area with base when the height is kept constant; the second, when the height is varied with the base so as to keep the diagonal constant.

Thermodynamic quantities are usually dependent on two or more variables, but these may be selected more or less arbitrarily. Thus energy may be expressed as a function of temperature and pressure, temperature and volume, or any of several other combinations. Then partial derivatives such as $(\partial U/\partial T)_p$ and $(\partial U/\partial T)_v$ may be of interest.

1–2. Change of Variable in Differentiation

Suppose that we wish to find $(\partial f/\partial x)_z$ when f is expressed as a function of x and y. The straightforward way is to find y as a function of x and z, substitute $y(x,z)$ into f to obtain a function of x and z, and then differentiate. Ordinarily this is not possible in thermodynamic applications, because the forms of the functions are unknown or excessively complicated, and an alternative procedure is necessary.

Differentiation of $f(x,y)$ gives

$$df = \left(\frac{\partial f}{\partial x}\right)_y dx + \left(\frac{\partial f}{\partial y}\right)_x dy \qquad (1\text{–}7)$$

Now since y is a function of x and z, it may be differentiated similarly, yielding

$$dy = \left(\frac{\partial y}{\partial x}\right)_z dx + \left(\frac{\partial y}{\partial z}\right)_x dz \qquad (1\text{–}8)$$

Substituting Eq. (1–8) into Eq. (1–7) gives

$$df = \left[\left(\frac{\partial f}{\partial x}\right)_y + \left(\frac{\partial f}{\partial y}\right)_x\left(\frac{\partial y}{\partial x}\right)_z\right] dx + \left(\frac{\partial f}{\partial y}\right)_x\left(\frac{\partial y}{\partial z}\right)_x dz \qquad (1\text{–}9)$$

However, when f is expressed as a function of x and z and differentiated, the result is

$$df = \left(\frac{\partial f}{\partial x}\right)_z dx + \left(\frac{\partial f}{\partial z}\right)_x dz \qquad (1\text{–}10)$$

Comparison of Eqs. (1–9) and (1–10) shows that

$$\left(\frac{\partial f}{\partial x}\right)_z = \left(\frac{\partial f}{\partial x}\right)_y + \left(\frac{\partial f}{\partial y}\right)_x\left(\frac{\partial y}{\partial x}\right)_z \qquad (1\text{–}11)$$

and

$$\left(\frac{\partial f}{\partial z}\right)_x = \left(\frac{\partial f}{\partial y}\right)_x\left(\frac{\partial y}{\partial z}\right)_x \qquad (1\text{–}12)$$

An alternative derivation of Eq. (1–11), though less rigorous than the above one, is so simple that it is useful as a mnemonic. Equation (1–7) is a general equation applying to any variation of x and y; in particular, it applies to those variations of x and y which keep z constant. But if Eq. (1–7) is divided by dx with z held constant, the new derivatives are partial derivatives at constant z, and the result is Eq. (1–11).

Equation (1–11) reduces to another important relation when f and z are identical. The derivative on the left vanishes, since it becomes a derivative of z at constant z; there remains

$$0 = \left(\frac{\partial z}{\partial x}\right)_y + \left(\frac{\partial z}{\partial y}\right)_x\left(\frac{\partial y}{\partial x}\right)_z$$

or

$$\left(\frac{\partial y}{\partial x}\right)_z\left(\frac{\partial z}{\partial y}\right)_x\left(\frac{\partial x}{\partial z}\right)_y = -1 \qquad (1\text{–}13)$$

This form is easy to remember, because we can start with any derivative and form the other two by cyclic permutation of the variables.

1–3. Change of Variable in Integration

A common error, more of notation than of understanding, which should be avoided is failure to change the limits of an integral when the variable of integration is changed. So long as a new letter is used for the new variable, the error seldom occurs. Thus to evaluate

$$\int_0^1 (1 - x^2)^{\frac{1}{2}} \, dx$$

we may make the substitution $x = \sin \alpha$, noting that when $x = 0$, $\alpha = 0$, and when $x = 1$, $\alpha = \pi/2$. The integral then becomes

$$\int_0^{\pi/2} \cos^2 \alpha \, d\alpha$$

It is common in thermodynamics to make such a change without giving the new variable a special symbol, and then it is often not recognized that a corresponding change of limits is needed. Thus:

$$w = - \int_{V_1}^{V_2} \frac{RT}{V} \, dV = -RT \int_{\ln V_1}^{\ln V_2} d(\ln V)$$

Here the variable is changed from V to $\ln V$, and the limits are changed correspondingly. Alternatively, the last integral may be written

$$-RT \int_{V=V_1}^{V_2} d(\ln V)$$

to indicate that the limits apply to a variable other than the variable of integration.

1–4. Exact Differentials and Line Integrals

Expressions of the type $P(x,y) \, dx + Q(x,y) \, dy$ are of frequent occurrence; such an expression may or may not be the differential of some function of x and y. If it is, it is called an *exact differential*; in this case

$$df(x,y) = \left(\frac{\partial f}{\partial x}\right)_y dx + \left(\frac{\partial f}{\partial y}\right)_x dy = P \, dx + Q \, dy$$

Since dx and dy are independent, the coefficient of each must be the same in the two expressions; that is,

$$P = \left(\frac{\partial f}{\partial x}\right)_y \qquad Q = \left(\frac{\partial f}{\partial y}\right)_x \tag{1-14}$$

If the first of these is differentiated with respect to y and the second with respect to x, the result is

$$\left(\frac{\partial P}{\partial y}\right)_x = \frac{\partial^2 f}{\partial y \partial x} \qquad \left(\frac{\partial Q}{\partial x}\right)_y = \frac{\partial^2 f}{\partial x \partial y}$$

Under certain conditions of continuity, which are usually of little concern in thermodynamics, the order of differentiation is immaterial, the two partial derivatives being equal. We then have

$$\left(\frac{\partial P}{\partial y}\right)_x = \left(\frac{\partial Q}{\partial x}\right)_y \qquad (1\text{--}15)$$

This important relation is often called the *reciprocity relation*. It can be proved that this is not only a necessary but also a sufficient condition for $P\ dx + Q\ dy$ to be an exact differential.

If we attempt to integrate such an expression as $P\ dx + Q\ dy$, it is generally found that the integral is meaningless until we specify a *path of integration*; that is, a relation between x and y which we can (at least in principle) substitute into $P\ dx + Q\ dy$ to convert it into an expression in one variable. As a rather trivial example, let $P = y$ and $Q = 0$; then

$$\int_{x_1,\ y_1}^{x_2,\ y_2} (P\ dx + Q\ dy)$$

becomes simply the area under the curve connecting the points (x_1, y_1)

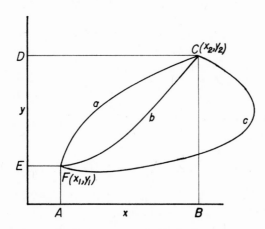

FIGURE 2. DIAGRAM ILLUSTRATING VARIOUS PATHS OF INTEGRATION.

and (x_2,y_2) (Figure 2). Obviously this has no meaning until the connecting curve is specified, curves a, b, and c, for example, yielding different areas. On the other hand,

$$\int_{x_1, \, y_1}^{x_2, \, y_2} (y \, dx + x \, dy)$$

includes the area below the curve and that to the left of it; that is, the area $ABCDEF$. Now this is independent of the path, provided that, if a path such as c is chosen, the signs of the various areas involved are properly assigned. The reason is that $y \, dx + x \, dy$ is the differential of xy, and so the integral becomes simply

$$\int_{x_1 y_1}^{x_2 y_2} d(xy) = x_2 y_2 - x_1 y_1$$

This is true whenever $P \, dx + Q \, dy$ is an exact differential; the integral between any two points is the same for all paths connecting them, provided no two of the paths enclose a point of discontinuity.

1–5. Homogeneous Functions

A function of one or more variables $f(x_1, x_2, \ldots, x_k)$ is said to be a *homogeneous function of degree n in the x's* if

$$f(ax_1, ax_2, \ldots, ax_k) = a^n f(x_1, x_2, \ldots, x_k) \qquad (1\text{--}16)$$

For example, each of the functions on the right side of Eqs. (1–1) through (1–4) is a homogeneous function of degree 2. It follows by setting a equal to zero in Eq. (1–16) that $f(0, 0, \ldots, 0) = 0$ unless $n = 0$. Differentiation of Eq. (1–16) with respect to x_i yields

$$\frac{\partial}{\partial(ax_i)} f(ax_1, ax_2, \ldots, ax_k) \frac{\partial(ax_i)}{\partial x_i} = a^n \frac{\partial}{\partial x_i} f(x_1, x_2, \ldots, x_k)$$

or

$$f_i(ax_1, ax_2, \ldots, ax_k) = a^{n-1} f_i(x_1, x_2, \ldots, x_k) \qquad (1\text{--}17)$$

where f_i has been used to indicate the derivative of f with respect to its ith variable. This shows that the derivatives of homogeneous functions are also homogeneous, but of degree one lower than the original function.

An important property of these functions is described in *Euler's theorem on homogeneous functions*. This states that

$$\sum_{i=1}^{k} x_i f_i(x_1, x_2, \ldots, x_k) = nf(x_1, x_2, \ldots, x_k) \qquad (1\text{--}18)$$

To prove this we note that the equation

$$df(y_1, y_2, \ldots, y_k) = \sum_{i=1}^{k} f_i(y_1, y_2, \ldots, y_k) dy_i \qquad (1\text{--}19)$$

applies to all variations of the y's, and in particular to those in which

$$y_i = x_i \alpha \qquad dy_i = x_i d\alpha \qquad (i = 1, 2, \ldots, k)$$

the x's being constant. Since the functions f_i are of degree $n - 1$, substituting these values reduces Eq. (1–19) to

$$df = \sum_{i=1}^{k} \alpha^{n-1} f_i(x_1, x_2, \ldots, x_k) x_i \, d\alpha \qquad (1\text{--}20)$$

We then integrate this equation, using 0 and 1 as the limits for α; the corresponding limits for f are 0 and $f(x_1, x_2, \ldots, x_k)$. This gives

$$f(x_1, x_2, \ldots, x_k) = \sum_{i=1}^{k} x_i f_i(x_1, x_2, \ldots, x_k) \int_0^1 \alpha^{n-1} \, d\alpha$$

$$= \frac{1}{n} \sum_{i=1}^{k} x_i f_i(x_1, x_2, \ldots, x_k)$$

which is the same as Eq. (1–18). This proof fails if $n = 0$, but in this case $f(\alpha x_1, \alpha x_2, \ldots, \alpha x_k) = \alpha^0 f(x_1, x_2, \ldots, x_k)$ and so is independent of α. Its derivative with respect to α is therefore zero, and Eq. (1–20) reduces to

$$\sum_{i=1}^{k} x_i f_i(x_1, x_2, \ldots, x_k) = 0$$

Therefore the theorem is true in this case also.

1–6. Lagrange's Method of Undetermined Multipliers

It often happens in statistical thermodynamics that we need to find not the maximum value that a function can assume, but the maximum that it can assume under certain restricting conditions. If the restricting conditions are expressed as equations, it may be possible to use them to

eliminate some of the variables from the original function, and the maximum with respect to the remaining variables can be found. To take a
trivial example, the maximum value that $\sin x + \cos y$ can take (for real
values of x and y) is obviously 2, which it assumes when $x = \pi/2$ and
$y = 0$. But if we impose the restriction that x must equal y, it cannot take
this value; the maximum under this restriction can be found by noting
that now the function takes the form $\sin x + \cos x$, which has the maximum value $2^{\frac{1}{2}}$ when $x = \pi/4$. Often, however, the elimination of variables
by means of the restricting equations is impracticable; in these cases the
problem can often be solved by a procedure known as *Lagrange's method
of undetermined multipliers.*

If no restricting conditions are involved, the problem of finding a
maximum or minimum of a function of several variables is in principle
simple. Differentiation of $f(x,y,z)$ in the usual manner gives

$$df = \frac{\partial f}{\partial x} dx + \frac{\partial f}{\partial y} dy + \frac{\partial f}{\partial z} dz \qquad (1\text{--}21)$$

For a maximum or minimum, df must be zero for *any* choice of values of
the differentials dx, dy, and dz. By selecting $dy = dz = 0$ and $dx \neq 0$, we
immediately find

$$\frac{\partial f}{\partial x} = 0$$

Similarly it can be shown that the other partial derivatives must vanish,
giving three equations from which to determine the values of x, y, and z
at the maximum or minimum. It should be noted that this gives only a
necessary condition, not a sufficient one, for a maximum or minimum;
but in applied mathematics the existence of the maximum or minimum
is usually evident on physical grounds.

If, however, we try to repeat this argument when a restriction is
present, we find a serious difficulty. If the restriction is written in the
form $g(x,y,z) = 0$, differentiation gives

$$\frac{\partial g}{\partial x} dx + \frac{\partial g}{\partial y} dy + \frac{\partial g}{\partial z} dz = 0 \qquad (1\text{--}22)$$

If we now select $dy = dz = 0$, this equation gives $dx = 0$ (unless $\partial g/\partial x = 0$),
so that the argument used above breaks down.

To eliminate this difficulty we multiply Eq. (1–22) by a quantity

λ, whose value is for the moment undetermined, and add the result to Eq. (1–21), obtaining

$$\left(\frac{\partial f}{\partial x} + \lambda \frac{\partial g}{\partial x}\right) dx + \left(\frac{\partial f}{\partial y} + \lambda \frac{\partial g}{\partial y}\right) dy + \left(\frac{\partial f}{\partial z} + \lambda \frac{\partial g}{\partial z}\right) dz = 0 \quad (1\text{–}23)$$

If we now choose $dz = 0$ and $dy \neq 0$, then dx will also not equal zero. The term in the second parentheses (the coefficient of dy) can be made to vanish by a suitable choice of λ. This leaves only

$$\left(\frac{\partial f}{\partial x} + \lambda \frac{\partial g}{\partial x}\right) dx = 0$$

and since $dx \neq 0$, the term in parentheses vanishes. By similar arguments the other terms in parentheses in Eq. (1—23) are seen to vanish also. Thus the conditions for a maximum of the function $f(x,y,z)$ under the restriction $g(x,y,z) = 0$ are

$$\frac{\partial f}{\partial x} + \lambda \frac{\partial g}{\partial x} = 0 \qquad \frac{\partial f}{\partial y} + \lambda \frac{\partial g}{\partial y} = 0 \qquad \frac{\partial f}{\partial z} + \lambda \frac{\partial g}{\partial z} = 0 \quad (1\text{–}24)$$

These three equations, together with the restriction equation $g(x,y,z)=0$, can be solved for the four unknowns λ, x, y, and z to determine the point at which $f(x,y,z)$ has its maximum.

This method is easily extended to problems involving more than one restriction, provided that there are fewer restrictions than variables. Two restrictions suffice for the applications in this book. Suppose, then, that we wish to find the maximum value which the function $f(x_1,x_2, \ldots, x_n)$ can assume under the restrictions $g(x_1,x_2, \ldots, x_n)=0$ and $h(x_1,x_2, \ldots,x_n)=0$. In differential form, the problem states that we must find the conditions which make

$$\frac{\partial f}{\partial x_1} dx_1 + \frac{\partial f}{\partial x_2} dx_2 + \ldots + \frac{\partial f}{\partial x_n} dx_n = 0 \qquad (1\text{–}25)$$

at the same time that the restricting equations

$$\frac{\partial g}{\partial x_1} dx_1 + \frac{\partial g}{\partial x_2} dx_2 + \ldots + \frac{\partial g}{\partial x_n} dx_n = 0 \qquad (1\text{–}26)$$

and

$$\frac{\partial h}{\partial x_1} dx_1 + \frac{\partial h}{\partial x_2} dx_2 + \ldots + \frac{\partial h}{\partial x_n} dx_n = 0 \qquad (1\text{–}27)$$

hold. The restricting equations are multiplied by λ and μ, respectively, and added to Eq. (1–25). This gives

$$\sum_{i=1}^{n} \left(\frac{\partial f}{\partial x_i} + \lambda \frac{\partial g}{\partial x_i} + \mu \frac{\partial h}{\partial x_i} \right) dx_i = 0 \qquad (1\text{--}28)$$

Now it is possible to make all but three of the terms in this sum vanish by selecting the corresponding dx's equal to zero; e.g., we may choose $dx_4 = dx_5 = \ldots = dx_n = 0$. However, dx_3 (for example) cannot also be zero, for if it were, Eqs. (1–26) and (1–27) would reduce to

$$\frac{\partial g}{\partial x_1} dx_1 + \frac{\partial g}{\partial x_2} dx_2 = 0$$

and

$$\frac{\partial h}{\partial x_1} dx_1 + \frac{\partial h}{\partial x_2} dx_2 = 0$$

These equations could be solved (unless their determinant is zero) and would yield the result $dx_1 = dx_2 = 0$. We could then learn nothing from Eq. (1–28). We still have λ and μ to manipulate, however, and proper choice of these will make two more terms of the sum in Eq. (1–28) vanish. For example, we may (in general) solve the equations

$$\lambda \frac{\partial g}{\partial x_2} + \mu \frac{\partial h}{\partial x_2} = - \frac{\partial f}{\partial x_2}$$

and

$$\lambda \frac{\partial g}{\partial x_3} + \mu \frac{\partial h}{\partial x_3} = - \frac{\partial f}{\partial x_3}$$

for λ and μ, and these values will make the coefficients of dx_2 and dx_3 vanish. This leaves none of Eq. (1–28) except the single term in dx_1. Since $dx_1 \neq 0$, we have

$$\frac{\partial f}{\partial x_1} + \lambda \frac{\partial g}{\partial x_1} + \mu \frac{\partial h}{\partial x_1} = 0 \qquad (1\text{--}29)$$

Similarly the other terms must vanish. This provides a set of n equations, and the restricting conditions furnish two more; thus there are enough equations to determine the $n + 2$ unknowns $x_1, x_2, \ldots, x_n, \lambda$, and μ.

PROBLEMS

(1) Apply Eq. (1–11) to the function A (Section 1–1) so as to obtain a relation between $(\partial A/\partial b)_h$ and $(\partial A/\partial b)_s$. Verify this relation by substituting values for the derivatives involved.

(2) Similarly verify Eq. (1–11) for the variables A, s, t, and b. (To find $(\partial b/\partial s)_t$ eliminate A from Eqs. (1–2) and (1–3), square the resulting equation, and differentiate with respect to s, regarding t as a constant.)

(3) Verify Eq. (1–13) for the variables A, s, and b.

(4) Show that A in each of the Eqs. (1–1) through (1–4) is a second-degree homogeneous function of the variables on the right, and verify that Euler's theorem applies.

(5) Show that the expression $2xy\,dx + x^2\,dy$ meets the requirement (Eq. (1–15)) for an exact differential. Then calculate

$$\int_{0,\,0}^{1,\,1} (2xy\,dx + x^2\,dy)$$

along each of the following paths: (1) the straight line $y = x$; (2) the parabola $y = x^2$; and (3) the x-axis from the origin to the point (1,0), followed by the line $y = 1$ from the x-axis to the point (1,1).

(6) Show that $2xy\,dx + x^2\,(y - 1)\,dy$ is not an exact differential and that its integral from (0,0) to (1,1) has a different value along each of the paths in problem 5.

(7) A hill has the shape of the curve $z = -2x^2 + 6xy - 5y^2 - 4x + 8y$, and a path crossing it appears straight when viewed from above, following the equation $y = 2x$. Find the highest point on the hill, and the highest point on the path.

chapter 2

Introduction and Basic Concepts

IT MAY BE SAID of most branches of science that no exact definition of their fields, no precise delineation of their boundaries, is practical, and thermodynamics is no exception. In general, it deals with the conditions under which physical and chemical systems can be in equilibrium. The study of systems not in equilibrium is largely excluded, except to predict the direction in which they will change. Etymologically, however, these are the systems to which the word should refer, the term *thermostatics* being more appropriate for systems in equilibrium. The usage is well fixed, nevertheless, and such phrases as *thermodynamics of irreversible processes* are used when nonequilibrium systems are to be treated. Furthermore, thermodynamics in its classical form is a treatment which starts with macroscopically observable quantities, such as pressure and temperature. If the treatment starts with a molecular or atomic viewpoint, it is referred to as *statistical thermodynamics*. It is possible to treat either classical or statistical thermodynamics without making use of the other, but such a treatment has little to recommend it.

This textbook deals primarily with classical thermodynamics, but statistical methods are freely used to aid the student's understanding of the concepts and to present a more nearly complete view of current thermodynamics.

Many of the quantities dealt with in thermodynamics (for example, temperature and heat) are familiar, and yet their exact definitions are rather elusive. A frequently used way around this difficulty is to give up any attempt at exact definition and to rely on intuitive understanding of these concepts. This was, of necessity, the approach by which thermodynamics was originally developed. However, a more rigorous formulation not only helps to guard against misconceptions but is more economical in that less material of little direct relevance to chemical thermodynamics is needed. For these reasons a rigorous treatment, based partly on Born's formulation of the first law,[1] is used here, with references to the historical approach confined to illustrative material.

2–1. Basic Definitions

A *system* is the matter (and perhaps radiation) in any spatial region under consideration. Both the region and the matter in it may vary, but they must be definable at any given time. A system cannot consist of only part of the matter in a given region, such as all the sodium ions in a solution of sodium chloride. A system is *closed* if no matter enters or leaves it during any change under consideration; otherwise it is *open*. Only closed systems will be considered in Chapters 2 through 6.

The definition of a *state* of a system depends on the purpose in mind; for most chemical problems specifying the pressure, volume, and amount of each substance suffices to fix the state. This is not necessarily the most convenient way, however, and other methods are often used. For some applications other information may be needed; for example, electrical potential or, in the case of solids, mechanical stresses.

A *property* is any quantity related to a system which is fixed when the state of the system is specified and can, at least in principle, be calculated from a knowledge of the state without reference to the history of the system.

The walls or boundaries enclosing a system are said to be *insulating* if the system can be affected only by (a) motion of the walls, or (b) long-range forces such as electrical, magnetic, or gravitational forces. A system so enclosed is said to be *adiabatically* enclosed, and any change occurring in it is called an adiabatic change.

Finally, thermodynamics makes use of several concepts which are borrowed from other branches of physics or mathematics, and for which no specifically thermodynamic definition is given. Among these are pressure, volume, and work.

2–2. The First Law of Thermodynamics

Suppose that a system undergoes an adiabatic change from an initial state, 1, to a final state, 2. Usually, the change will involve motion of the insulating walls, and accordingly an amount of work W is performed on the system. (If work is done by the system, W will be negative.) More generally, other forms of work (electrical, magnetic, etc.) may be involved instead of, or in addition to, mechanical work; all these must be included in W. It is always found that this amount of work is the same regardless of the manner in which the change from state 1 to state 2 occurs, so long as the change is adiabatic. In this fact is the essence of the first law. From this we can state that there is a property, U, of the system whose difference in the two states is the amount of work involved in an adiabatic change from one of the states to the other; that is,

$$W = U_2 - U_1 \qquad (2\text{--}1)$$

The quantity U, which is defined, except for an additive constant, by this equation, is called the *energy* of the system. Clearly this provides a means of measuring the energy difference of two states if and only if it is possible to transform the system adiabatically from one of the states to the other. Although it is possible to conceive of changes in which the possibility of doing this would be at least doubtful, all changes of interest in chemical applications can, in principle, be carried out adiabatically. However, the direction of the change cannot be chosen arbitrarily; that is, if we can transform the system adiabatically from state 1 to state 2, in general we cannot so transform it from state 2 to state 1.

If a system is changed from state 1 to state 2 but not adiabatically, the work done on it will be different from $U_2 - U_1$; in fact, it may have any arbitrary value. If the difference between $U_2 - U_1$ and W is designated by Q, so that

$$U_2 - U_1 = Q + W \qquad (2\text{--}2)$$

then Q is called the *heat input* to the system. It is in this form that the first law is generally used. It should be emphasized that Q and W are not properties of the system, but merely represent different means of adding energy to it. That energy which is added as work makes up the term W, while the heat, Q, is simply energy added in other ways. This distinction is valid only during the process of adding energy; once the energy has been added, it cannot be divided into two parts, one of which is heat and the other work.

It may be worthwhile to point out that W is often used for the work done by, not on, the system. The alternative choice was made here so that both Q and W, when positive, represent energy added to the system. The energy defined by Eq. (2–1) is often called the *internal energy*. This equation fails to define U completely in that an arbitrary constant is involved;

that is, only differences are defined, and the zero point may be set arbitrarily. This is necessarily true of any definition of energy; the point will be more fully discussed in Chapter 5.

From a statistical viewpoint, the energy defined by Eq. (2-1) includes the kinetic energy of molecules, the vibrational energy of atoms within them, and the potential energy resulting from their interaction. Chemical bonding energy must be included if chemical reactions are under consideration, and may be included in any case. On the other hand, the binding energy of nucleons within the nuclei, the energy equivalent of the rest mass, and electrostatic potential energy are not usually included in chemical applications, but they are necessary in applying thermodynamics to nuclear reactions and electrochemistry respectively. In general, all forms of energy which may change during the process under consideration must be included in U; the inclusion or omission of others is optional. In chemical work U is usually conceived of as excluding gravitational potential energy and kinetic energy resulting from motion of the system as a whole; it is for this reason that it is sometimes called the "internal" energy. However, since the exclusion of these forms of energy is ordinarily merely a matter of convenience, the use of the more complicated name does not appear advisable, except perhaps in such cases as the study of fluid flow, where the bulk kinetic energy is considered separately from other kinds of energy.

Heat is energy transferred to (or from) the system by collisions of its molecules with randomly moving molecules in the walls of the container. If the motion of wall molecules is not random, the wall as a whole is moving, and work is involved in addition to, or instead of, heat.

If Eq. (2-2) is applied to an infinitesimal process, it becomes

$$dU = dQ + dW \qquad (2\text{-}3)$$

Since Q and W are not properties of the system, dQ and dW are not differentials of properties; that is, they are not exact differentials, and their integral between two states depends on the path. For this reason special symbols are used instead of the d's in some texts.

If no work is done, $dW = 0$, and Eq. (2-3) becomes $dU = dQ$; therefore the increase in energy is equal to the heat input in this case.

If a system exerts a uniform pressure, p, on its container, and if a portion of the container wall of area $d\sigma$ is moved inward a distance dx, the work done on the system is $p\, d\sigma\, dx$. (Strictly speaking, this should be the scalar product of the vectors $p\, d\vec{\sigma}$ and $-d\mathbf{x}$.) But $d\sigma\, dx$ is $-dV$, where V is the volume of the system. Thus for an infinitesimal volume change

$$dW = -p\, dV \qquad (2\text{-}4)$$

provided no other form of work is involved. (For the moment we neglect the question of whether the system will exert the same pressure on a moving wall as it does on a stationary one; certainly the difference will be negligible if the change is very slow.) Substitution into Eq. (2–3) leads to

$$dU = dQ - p \, dV \qquad (2\text{–}5)$$

2–3. The Enthalpy

It has been shown that dU represents the work input in an adiabatic process, and the heat input in a change involving no work (e. g., a constant-volume process). It is often important to have a similarly simple expression for the heat input in a constant-pressure change. This can be derived by noting that at constant pressure $p \, dV = d \, (pV)$. Then Eq. (2–5) gives

$$dQ = dU + p \, dV = dU + d(pV) = d(U + pV) \qquad (2\text{–}6)$$

The quantity $U + pV$ is important enough to be given a special name and symbol. The usual symbol for it is H. Among the names that have been given to it are *heat function at constant pressure, heat function, heat content, total heat*, and *enthalpy*. The first of these correctly describes the principal use of this quantity, but it is too cumbersome in actual use; *heat function* is a reasonable shortened version, more convenient but less accurately descriptive than the longer name. *Heat content* and *total heat* are unacceptable because they suggest the erroneous idea that a definite portion of the energy can be regarded as heat.* Throughout this book the name *enthalpy* will be used; this should be pronounced with a primary or strong secondary accent on the second syllable to avoid confusion with the word *entropy*.

Since $H = U + pV$, it follows that in general

$$dH = dU + p \, dV + V \, dp = dQ + V \, dp \qquad (2\text{–}7)$$

2–4. Thermal Equilibrium

If two systems are adiabatically enclosed except that they are separated from each other by a conducting (i.e., noninsulating) wall, it will generally be found that their states change for a while, ultimately becoming stationary. The two systems are then said to be in *thermal equilibrium*.

---

* A related fallacy, which should be carefully avoided, is that in which pV is regarded as an "external energy" which, when added to the "internal" energy, U, gives the "total energy" or "total heat," H. Actually, U is the entire energy; pV is not an energy term, though having the same dimensions; and H is merely an abbreviation for $U + pV$.

Now suppose that two systems, A and B, are each in thermal equilibrium with a third system, C, and that A and B are then placed in thermal contact with each other; i.e., they are placed so that they are separated only by a conducting wall. Will these two systems then be in thermal equilibrium with each other? It is an important principle of thermodynamics that they will be; *any two systems in thermal equilibrium with a third system are in thermal equilibrium with each other.* It follows that there is some property whose value is the same for all systems in thermal equilibrium with each other. This is the fundamental basis of the concept of temperature; systems at thermal equilibrium are said to be at the same temperature. Knowledge of this law is by no means new,[2] and yet it is disregarded in many treatments. In order to emphasize that it should come before the first and second laws, Guggenheim designated it by the rather curious, though logical, name of the *zeroth law of thermodynamics*.

2-5. Reversible and Irreversible Changes

The change described in the paragraph above, in which two systems in thermal contact come to equilibrium, is called an *irreversible*, or *natural*, change. Irreversible changes occur when systems not in equilibrium change toward equilibrium. Conceptually, another type of change is also possible; that is, a change in which a system already in equilibrium changes through a continuous succession of equilibrium states to a final equilibrium state. Such a change cannot actually occur, since a system in equilibrium has no tendency to change. It is, like frictionless planes and weightless pulleys, an unattainable but useful idealization. This type of change is called a *reversible*, or *quasistatic*, change. In actual practice, a reversible change

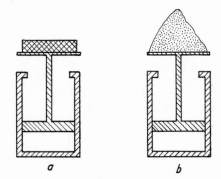

a b

FIGURE 3. SCHEMATIC DIAGRAM OF APPARATUS FOR CARRYING OUT IRREVERSIBLE AND REVERSIBLE CHANGES.

can be approximated by an irreversible change carried out very slowly, with the state of the system kept very near equilibrium; it can then be reversed by a small change of conditions.

For example, suppose that compressed gas is contained in a cylinder by a piston, which is held down by a weight (Figure 3a). If the weight is suddenly slipped off, the gas and the piston are left far from equilibrium. The rapid expansion that takes place, bumping the piston violently against the end of the cylinder, is an irreversible change. If, instead, the weight consists of a pile of sand (Figure 3b), and it is removed one grain at a time, the system is never far from equilibrium, and the process closely approximates a reversible change. Clearly the reversible change does more work than the irreversible, since a greater average weight is raised; if both processes are adiabatic, the energy will be lower at the end of the reversible change than at the end of the irreversible one, since more energy has been removed as work.

2–6. Extensive and Intensive Properties

It is often convenient to classify properties according to the manner in which they depend on the size of the system. For example, if the amount of matter in a system is varied at constant temperature,** pressure, and composition, the volume varies proportionately, while the density remains constant. A more rigorous formulation of this idea will now be given.

In chemical thermodynamics, as in other chemical work, the most suitable unit for expressing the amount of substances is the mole.*** Accordingly the compositions of systems will be expressed by their mole numbers $n_1, n_2, \ldots$, indicating that the system contains n_1 moles of substance 1, etc. Now if the temperature and pressure of a system are kept fixed and the amount of matter in it is varied so that the ratios of the

---

** It should be noted that at this point temperature has not been defined; nevertheless, Section 2–4 gives meaning to the phrase "at constant temperature."

*** The mole may be defined (1) in the traditional chemical manner, as that amount of a given substance such that its mass bears the same ratio to 1 g as the mass of one molecule, atom, ion, or formula unit (as may be appropriate) of the substance bears to one-sixteenth the average mass per oxygen atom in naturally occurring oxygen, this ratio being called the *molecular weight* (or *atomic weight*, etc.); (2) as N_a individual objects (molecules, photons, etc.), where *Avogadro's number*, N_a, is the number of oxygen atoms in 16 g of oxygen; or (3) for gases, as the amount of a gas that has the same value of

$$\lim_{p \to 0} (pV)$$

at a given temperature as 32 g of oxygen has at the same temperature.

mole numbers remain constant, those properties which, like volume, vary in direct ratio to the mole numbers, are called *extensive properties*; those which, like density, do not change are called *intensive properties*. A more mathematical definition is: *An extensive property is a first-degree homogeneous function of the mole numbers, at given temperature and pressure; and an intensive property is a zero-degree homogeneous function of the mole numbers, under the same conditions.* Extensive properties are also additive; that is, their values for an entire system are the sums of their values for its parts.

In this book capital letters will generally be used for extensive properties and quantities, and lower-case letters for intensive properties and quantities. When a property of an entire system is extensive, its value per mole is intensive (Eq. (1–17)); in this case corresponding letters will be used; for example, the enthalpy is an extensive property, and is denoted by H; the molar enthalpy, or enthalpy per mole, is intensive, and is designated by h. A few exceptions are made to avoid conflict with strongly established usage; e.g., T for temperature, R for the molar gas constant, n_i for the mole numbers, and N_a for Avogadro's number.

2–7. The Second Law

The second law is the law which specifies that the direction of change of an isolated system is always toward equilibrium. Awareness of this law arose out of the studies of Carnot and others on the limited efficiencies of heat engines. Since this statement does not lend itself to quantitative development of thermodynamic theory, other statements are actually used. One of these is Clausius's statement: *Heat cannot be conveyed from a lower to a higher temperature except by the expenditure of work.* This statement appears close to common experience, but closer analysis shows that there are logical objections to it. Most treatments based on this statement leave temperature undefined, relying on an intuitive understanding of it. Actually, our method of recognizing that one system is at a higher temperature than another is basically dependent on observing that heat flows from the first system to the second. Sometimes a provisional definition of temperature, based on the behavior of an ideal gas, is used. However, an ideal gas is simply a gas that follows a certain relation of pressure, volume, and temperature, and so this involves arguing in a circle. There are ways to avoid these difficulties, but it should be clear by now that this treatment is not so simple as it appears at first.

Clausius's statement is easily shown to be equivalent to that of Planck: *It is impossible to devise a machine whose only effects are the removal of heat from a reservoir and the raising of a weight.* This statement avoids the difficulty in Clausius's principle, and a logical presentation of thermodynamics can be based on it. The main objection to it is that it requires a long and tedious development before material relevant to chemical thermodynamics is reached.

A more abstruse treatment is that of Caratheodory, based on his statement of the second law: *In the neighborhood of any given state there are other states which cannot be reached from the given state by adiabatic transformations.* Despite its logic and elegance, the mathematical difficulty of Caratheodory's approach has kept it from becoming popular. Various simplified versions of it have been presented.[1,3]

The second law is stated here as a mathematical postulate, so chosen that relatively direct development of further theory is possible. This may at first seem more artificial than traditional treatments. However. it should be remembered that confidence in any scientific discipline rests not on its postulational basis, but on the experimental verification of its many ramifications. For this reason the statements of the basic laws may well be chosen primarily for convenience.

The form of the second law which will be used in this book is as follows: *There exist an intensive property, T, (which is always positive)[†] and an additive-extensive property, S, such that*

$$dQ = T \ dS \text{ for reversible processes, and}$$
$$dQ < T \ dS \text{ for irreversible processes} \qquad (2\text{--}8)$$

It will be shown later that this statement provides a complete definition of the two properties T and S, except for an additive constant in S, and that T has all the characteristics customarily associated with the intuitive concept of temperature. This, then, will be taken as the thermodynamic definition of temperature, not in contradiction to the intuitive concept, but supplementing the latter and providing it with a quantitative basis. The measurement of the thermodynamic temperature is discussed in Section 4–2. The property S is called the *entropy*; its interpretation and measurement will be the subject of several later sections, and of much of Chapter 6.

It may be noted that $1/p$ is an integrating factor for the infinitesimal quantity dW, converting it to the exact differential $-dV$. The second law provides a similar integrating factor, $1/T$, for the quantity dQ, and this

† For a rather freakish exception, see Problem 5, Chapter 6.

converts it to the exact differential dS. Both these relations hold only for reversible processes; however, in many processes the flow of heat is far from reversible, while the volume change is nearly reversible; so that $dW = -p \; dV$ is often applicable even when $dQ = T \; dS$ is not.

For reversible processes Eqs. (2–5) and (2–7) can be rewritten

$$dU = T \; dS - p \; dV \qquad (2\text{–}9)$$

and

$$dH = T \; dS + V \; dp \qquad (2\text{–}10)$$

The requirement of reversibility means that no chemical reactions occur, or that the system is always in equilibrium with respect to such reactions.

For those who prefer a more traditional approach, the derivation of Eq. (2–8) from Planck's statement of the second law is given in Appendix 1. It should be emphasized, however, that starting with this statement instead of Eq. (2–8) in no way strengthens the basis of thermodynamic reasoning.

2–8. The Carnot Cycle

In 1824 N. L. S. Carnot published his studies on an idealized cyclic process in a gaseous system consisting of four reversible steps: (1) isothermal expansion; (2) adiabatic expansion, lowering the temperature; (3)

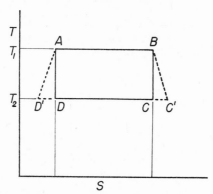

FIGURE 4. TEMPERATURE-ENTROPY DIAGRAM FOR A CARNOT CYCLE (SOLID LINES) AND A SIMILAR BUT IRREVERSIBLE CYCLE (DOTTED LINES).

isothermal compression at the lower temperature; and (4) adiabatic compression, returning the system to its original state. This may be generalized to any reversible cyclic process in four steps, alternately isothermal and adiabatic.

In Figure 4, the initial isothermal step may be represented on the temperature-entropy diagram by the line AB. Clearly the heat absorbed in this step is $Q_{AB} = T_1 (S_2 - S_1) = T_1 \Delta S$. The adiabatic step, according to the definition in Section 2-1, involves a change in which the system is affected only by motion of the wall or by long-range forces; in other words, only by those effects in which work is done on or by the system. An adiabatic change is, therefore, one for which no heat exchange is involved. If it is also reversible $T\ dS = dQ = 0$, and so the entropy is constant. Such a change is often called *isentropic*; it is represented by BC on the diagram. Since BC and DA are both isentropic, the entropy change along CD must be the same, except for sign, as that along AB. Therefore $Q_{CD} = -T_2 \Delta S$. Since the final state is the same as the initial one, $\Delta U = 0$. Therefore

$$-W = Q = Q_{AB} + Q_{CD} = (T_1 - T_2)\Delta S$$

This shows that work is done by the system. The *efficiency* is given by

$$\epsilon \equiv \frac{-W}{Q_{AB}} = \frac{T_2 - T_1}{T_1} \tag{2-11}$$

If a similar process is carried out with states A and B the same, but with irreversible adiabatic steps, then for these steps $T\ dS > dQ = 0$, so that the entropy increases in both steps. This gives a diagram such as $ABC'D'$, and

$$Q_{C'D'} = T_2(S_{D'} - S_{C'}) < T_2(S_D - S_C) = Q_{CD}$$

Therefore

$$-W' = Q_{AB} + Q_{C'D'} < Q_{AB} + Q_{CD} = -W$$

Since Q_{AB} is the same for both cycles, the efficiency of the irreversible cycle is lower than that of the reversible cycle.

Equation (2-11) is often derived without using entropy and is then used as the basis for introducing this concept. The fact that the efficiency of a reversible machine depends only on the temperatures between which it works is known as *Carnot's principle*.

Carnot's cycle is the idealized version of all heat engine cycles; if reversed, it is an idealized refrigeration or heat pump cycle.

PROBLEMS

(1) A process involves the performance of electrical work in the amount W' on a system. Show that if the process is carried out

(a) At constant volume, the heat absorbed is $\Delta U - W'$;

(b) At constant pressure, the heat absorbed is $\Delta H - W'$;

(c) Adiabatically, the pressure-volume work done on the system is $\Delta U - W'$.

(2) In a phase change, the temperature at which the change occurs is dependent only on the pressure. Show that if such a change occurs reversibly at constant pressure, $\Delta S = \Delta H / T$.

(3) The *heat capacity* of a system is defined as the ratio of the (infinitesimal) amount of heat absorbed to the corresponding temperature increase when a specified process is carried out (for example, a constant-pressure process). Show that the heat capacity at constant volume, C_v, is equal to $(\partial U/\partial T)_V$, and the heat capacity at constant pressure, C_p, is equal to $(\partial H/\partial T)_p$. Show also that, in general, if the process is at constant X, where X is any suitable thermodynamic function, $C_X = T(\partial S/\partial T)_X$. What is the significance of this when X is the entropy?

(4) Show that

$$C_p - C_v = -\left(\frac{\partial p}{\partial T}\right)_V \left[\left(\frac{\partial H}{\partial p}\right)_T - V\right] \tag{2-12}$$

and

$$C_p - C_v = \left(\frac{\partial V}{\partial T}\right)_p \left[\left(\frac{\partial U}{\partial V}\right)_T + p\right] \tag{2-13}$$

Hint: Differentiate $H = U + pV$ and apply Eq. (1–11).

(5) Show that if a system is heated at constant volume, the entropy change is given by

$$dS = \frac{C_v}{T} dT \tag{2-14}$$

and if at constant pressure, by

$$dS = \frac{C_p}{T} dT \tag{2-15}$$

REFERENCES

1. Born, M., *Physik. Z.*, **22**, 218, 249, 282 (1921).
2. Buckingham, E., "The Theory of Thermodynamics," p. 1, New York, N.Y., The Macmillan Co., 1900; Planck, M., "Treatise on Thermodynamics," English ed., p. 2, London, Longmans, Green & Co., 1903.
3. Buchdahl, H. A., *Am. J. Phys.*, **17**,, 41, 44, 212 (1949). Chandrasekhar, S. "An Introduction to the Study of Stellar Structure," Chap. 1, University of Chicago Press, 1939. Reprinted by Dover Publications, Inc., New York. Eisenschitz, R., *Science Progr.*, **43**, 246 (1955). Landé, A., "Handbuch der Physik," Vol. 9, p. 281, Berlin, Julius Springer, 1926.

chapter 3

Conditions of Equilibrium and the Free Energy Functions

IN THIS CHAPTER the criteria for equilibrium of systems under various conditions will be derived, and it will be shown that this leads naturally to the introduction of two new functions, both of which are simple combinations of previously introduced functions. Also certain equations and methods involving these functions will be derived.

Throughout this chapter, unless otherwise stated, it will be assumed that no form of work other than pressure-volume work is involved.

3–1. Equilibrium at Constant Energy and Volume

If a system is isolated so that no change in its energy can occur, then for any change that takes place in it, $dU = 0$. If the volume is also constant, $dV = 0$, and no pressure-volume work is done. Then, since the absence of other forms of work is assumed, the first law shows that $dQ = 0$. Then, according to the second law, $dS > 0$. (The equality sign is not used, since any change under these restrictions must be irreversible.) The entropy, therefore, increases whenever any change occurs; and it follows that when the entropy has its maximum possible value, no further change can occur, and the system is in equilibrium.

3–2. Equilibrium at Constant Temperature and Volume

At constant temperature, $T\ dS$ becomes $d(TS)$ and at constant volume $dQ = dU$. Then the second law requires that $dU < d(TS)$ or $d(U - TS) < 0$. The quantity $U - TS$ is an important new function; it will be designated by the letter A and the name *Helmholtz free energy*. Then from $dA = d(U - TS) < 0$, it follows that the Helmholtz free energy decreases during any naturally occurring change at constant volume and temperature, and the system is in equilibrium when this function has its minimum value.

If a change at constant temperature and volume is reversible, the inequality in the above derivation must be replaced by an equality, with the result that $dA = 0$, and A is constant for such processes.

Another important property of the Helmholtz free energy is readily derived from the fundamental relation $dU = dQ + dW$. At constant temperature $dQ \leqslant T\ dS = d\ (TS)$. Therefore $dU \leqslant d(TS) + dW$, from which it follows that $dA \leqslant dW$. That is, the work done on a system undergoing a change at constant temperature is equal to the increase in Helmholtz free energy if the change is carried out reversibly, and is greater than this otherwise. If dW is negative, the interpretation of this is that the work done by the system is equal to the decrease in Helmholtz free energy for a reversible process, and is less otherwise. This includes all forms of work; if the volume is constant, no pressure-volume work is done, and dA (or ΔA if the change is not infinitesimal) if the minimum of other forms of work that must be done on the system during the change; if dA is negative, then $-dA$ is the maximum work that the system can do.

3–3. Equilibrium at Constant Temperature and Pressure

It is shown in Section 2–3 that the heat absorbed in a constant-pressure change is dH. If the temperature is also constant, $T\ dS = d(TS)$. Then by the second law, $dH < d(TS)$, or $d(H - TS) < 0$. Thus the quantity $H - TS$ plays the same part in processes at constant temperature and pressure as A does at constant temperature and volume; the letter G and the name *Gibbs free energy* will be used for it. Other expressions for it are $U + pV - TS$ and $A + pV$. For conditions of constant temperature and pressure, the Gibbs free energy is constant for reversible processes, decreases for irreversible processes, and has its minimum value at equilibrium.

The Gibbs free energy has another widely used property. If a change is carried out at constant temperature and pressure, the work done on the system is equal to or greater than dA according as the change is reversible or irreversible. If the volume changes slowly enough so that the pressure-volume work can be considered to have its value $-p\ dV$ for reversible changes, then the work of other forms done on the system is equal to or greater than $dA - (-p\ dV) = dA + d(pV) = dG$. Alternatively, we may say that the work other than pressure-volume work done by a system undergoing a change at constant temperature and pressure is $-dG$ if the change is reversible, and is less than this otherwise.

3–4. Some Important General Relations

The relationships among the functions U, H, A, and G, may be summarized as follows:

$$H = U + pV \tag{3-1}$$

$$A = U - TS = G - pV \tag{3-2}$$

$$G = H - TS = A + pV = U - TS + pV \tag{3-3}$$

Throughout the remainder of this section, except for Eqs. (3–19) and (3–20), it will be assumed that the composition of the system remains constant during any indicated changes. If desired, this can be shown explicitly by adding the subscript n_i to each derivative, indicating that the number of moles of each substance i is constant. These equations also hold if chemical equilibrium is maintained at all times.

Differential expressions analogous to Eqs. (2–9) and (2–10) are readily derived for dA and dG. Thus since

$$dU = T\ dS - p\ dV$$

and

$$d(TS) = T\ dS + S\ dT$$

subtracting gives

$$dA = -S\ dT - p\ dV \tag{3-4}$$

(This method of replacing $T\ dS$ by $-S\ dT$ is called a *Legendre transformation*.) Similarly, from

$$dH = T\ dS + V\ dp$$

and

$$d(TS) = T\ dS + S\ dT$$

we have by subtracting,

$$dG = -S\ dT + V\ dp \tag{3-5}$$

Several important relations can be derived by applying the properties of exact differentials to these expressions for dU, dH, dA, and dG. Thus Eq. (1–14) yields

$$\left(\frac{\partial U}{\partial S}\right)_V = T \qquad (3\text{–}6)$$

$$\left(\frac{\partial A}{\partial T}\right)_V = -S \qquad (3\text{–}10)$$

$$\left(\frac{\partial U}{\partial V}\right)_S = -p \qquad (3\text{–}7)$$

$$\left(\frac{\partial A}{\partial V}\right)_T = -p \qquad (3\text{–}11)$$

$$\left(\frac{\partial H}{\partial S}\right)_p = T \qquad (3\text{–}8)$$

$$\left(\frac{\partial G}{\partial T}\right)_p = -S \qquad (3\text{–}12)$$

$$\left(\frac{\partial H}{\partial p}\right)_S = V \qquad (3\text{–}9)$$

$$\left(\frac{\partial G}{\partial p}\right)_T = V \qquad (3\text{–}13)$$

The reciprocity relation (Eq. (1–15)) leads to *Maxwell's equations:*

$$\left(\frac{\partial T}{\partial V}\right)_S = -\left(\frac{\partial p}{\partial S}\right)_V \qquad (3\text{–}14)$$

$$\left(\frac{\partial T}{\partial p}\right)_S = \left(\frac{\partial V}{\partial S}\right)_p \qquad (3\text{–}15)$$

$$\left(\frac{\partial S}{\partial V}\right)_T = \left(\frac{\partial p}{\partial T}\right)_V \qquad (3\text{–}16)$$

$$\left(\frac{\partial S}{\partial p}\right)_T = -\left(\frac{\partial V}{\partial T}\right)_p \qquad (3\text{–}17)$$

Substituting Eq. (3–12) into Eq. (3–3) gives

$$G = H + T\left(\frac{\partial G}{\partial T}\right)_p \qquad (3\text{–}18)$$

If this equation is now written for both the initial and final states of a system undergoing an isothermal change, such as a chemical reaction, and the first equation is subtracted from the second, the result is

$$G_2 - G_1 = H_2 - H_1 + T\left[\frac{\partial\,(G_2 - G_1)}{\partial\,T}\right]_{p_1,p_2,n_{i1},n_{i2}}$$

or

$$\Delta G = \Delta H + T\left(\frac{\partial \Delta G}{\partial\,T}\right)_{p_1,p_2,n_{i1},n_{i2}} \qquad (3\text{–}19)$$

The subscripts in these equations indicate that the differentation with respect to T is performed with the initial pressure, final pressure, initial composition, and final composition all held constant. Eq. (3–19) is generally called the *Gibbs-Helmholtz equation*, although Larmor[1] long ago pointed out that it, or an equation closely related to it, was first derived by William Thomson, Lord Kelvin. Another form of it is

$$\Delta H = -T^2 \left[\frac{\partial(\Delta G/T)}{\partial T} \right]_{p_1, p_2, n_{i_1}, n_{i_2}} \tag{3–20}$$

3–5. Temperature and Heat Flow

It was stated in Section 2–7 that the temperature, defined there in mathematical terms, has the characteristics associated with the intuitive concept of temperature. This will now be demonstrated by showing that the property T of Eq. (2–8) possesses two of the most familiar properties of temperature.

The first of these is that the direction of heat flow is always from higher to lower temperature. Consider a system enclosed by rigid adiabatic walls and consisting of two parts, which are not in equilibrium with each other, though each is in internal equilibrium (Figure 5). Now let a small quantity

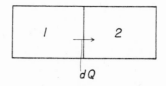

FIGURE 5. DIAGRAM ILLUSTRATING FLOW OF HEAT FROM
ONE PART OF A SYSTEM TO ANOTHER.

dQ of heat flow from part 1 to part 2, so that $-dQ_1 = dQ_2 = dQ > 0$. Since each part is in internal equilibrium, the entropy changes within the parts, at least for infinitesimal changes, can be calculated by the equation for reversible processes ($T\ dS = dQ$). However, the system as a whole is not in equilibrium, since its parts are not in equilibrium with each other; therefore, the inequality for irreversible processes ($T\ dS > dQ$) applies to the over-all entropy change. This gives

$$dS = dS_1 + dS_2 = \frac{dQ_1}{T_1} + \frac{dQ_2}{T_2} = dQ\left(\frac{1}{T_2} - \frac{1}{T_1}\right) > 0$$

the last inequality following from the fact that the system is adiabatically enclosed. But since $dQ > 0$, it follows that

$$\frac{1}{T_2} - \frac{1}{T_1} > 0, \text{ or } T_1 > T_2$$

as was to be proved.

It was also stated in Section 2–7 that the second law demands that spontaneous changes must be in the direction of equilibrium. The meaning of this may be vague in some cases, but it is perfectly definite in the one discussed in the paragraph above: The cooler part, to which heat flows, must have its temperature raised, and vice versa. To show that this actually occurs, consider a system enclosed by rigid adiabatic walls and in equilibrium throughout. If now a rigid conducting wall is introduced so as to divide the system into two equal parts, the equilibrium will not be disturbed, and the parts will have equal energy and entropy. Now if an amount of energy dU passed from part 1 to part 2, so that $dU_1 = -dU$ and $dU_2 = dU$, the changes in entropy would be given by the Taylor series expansion

$$dS_1 = -\left(\frac{\partial S}{\partial U}\right)_V dU + \frac{1}{2!}\left(\frac{\partial^2 S}{\partial U^2}\right)_V dU_2 - \ldots$$

and

$$dS_2 = \left(\frac{\partial S}{\partial U}\right)_V dU + \frac{1}{2!}\left(\frac{\partial^2 S}{\partial U^2}\right)_V dU^2 + \ldots$$

the derivatives being evaluated at the initial state of the systems. Now this would be an unnatural change, taking the system away from equilibrium; since natural changes under these conditions increase the entropy, this would decrease it. But the entropy change is

$$dS = dS_1 + dS_2 = \left(\frac{\partial^2 S}{\partial U^2}\right)_V dU^2$$

neglecting higher powers of dU. Since dS is negative and dU^2 is positive, $(\partial^2 S/\partial U^2)_V$ is negative. But

$$\left(\frac{\partial^2 S}{\partial U^2}\right)_V = \left[\frac{\partial}{\partial U}\left(\frac{\partial S}{\partial U}\right)_V\right]_V = \left[\frac{\partial}{\partial U}\left(\frac{1}{T}\right)\right]_V = -\frac{1}{T^2}\left(\frac{\partial T}{\partial U}\right)_V$$

use being made of Eq. (3–6). Since this must be negative, $(\partial T/\partial U)_V$ must be positive, so that the temperature increases when energy is added to a system at constant volume. In other words, the heat capacity at constant volume is always positive.

The heat capacity at constant pressure is always positive also, and it always exceeds that at constant volume. There is one exception: they are equal when the coefficient of expansion is zero, as for water at $3.98°$ C. This can readily be seen from Problem 7.

3–6. Pressure and Volume Changes

An argument similar to the above shows how volume must vary with pressure at constant temperature. In this case the system must be enclosed in rigid conducting walls and submerged in a constant-temperature bath. The wall dividing the system into two equal parts is now regarded as movable. If the dividing wall moves so as to increase the volume of part 2 by dV at the expense of part 1, the change in Helmholtz free energy is given by

$$dA_1 = -\left(\frac{\partial A}{\partial V}\right)_T dV + \frac{1}{2!}\left(\frac{\partial^2 A}{\partial V^2}\right)_T dV^2 - \cdots$$

$$dA_2 = \left(\frac{\partial A}{\partial V}\right)_T dV + \frac{1}{2!}\left(\frac{\partial^2 A}{\partial V^2}\right)_T dV^2 + \cdots$$

and

$$dA = \left(\frac{\partial^2 A}{\partial V^2}\right)_T dV^2$$

neglecting higher powers. But this is again an unnatural change, and dA is negative for natural, or irreversible, changes; it must therefore be positive for this one. Since dV^2 is certainly positive, $(\partial^2 A/\partial V^2)_T$ is also positive. But by Eq. (3–11) $(\partial^2 A/\partial V^2)_T = -(\partial p/\partial V)_T$, and so $(\partial p/\partial V)_T$ is negative. That is, increase in pressure at constant temperature always leads to decrease in volume, and the *compressibility*, defined as $-\dfrac{1}{V}\left(\dfrac{\partial V}{\partial p}\right)_T$, is always positive.

3–7. Stable, Metastable, Unstable, and Neutral Equilibria

In the preceding sections it has been shown that equilibrium is characterized by a maximum or minimum of one of the thermodynamic properties; for example, at constant temperature and pressure, the Gibbs free energy has a minimum value at equilibrium. Now in Figure 6, showing

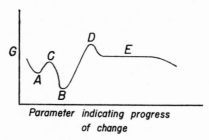

Parameter indicating progress
of change

FIGURE 6. GRAPHICAL SKETCH ILLUSTRATING TYPES OF EQUILIBRIUM.

the Gibbs free energy plotted against some suitable parameter, points A and B are both minima; A represents the type of equilibrium called *metastable*, while B represents *stable* equilibrium. If a system in state A is disturbed slightly, it will return to state A; if the disturbance is sufficient to carry it over the maximum point C, it will settle down to state B. In a more general sense, any point at which the derivative of G is zero may be considered an equilibrium point. These include the *unstable* equilibria at the maxima, C and D, and the *neutral* equilibrium at the flat portion, E. Any disturbance of a state in unstable equilibrium causes the system to move further from the unstable equilibrium point rather than returning to it; for this reason unstable equilibria are experimentally unattainable. If a system is in neutral equilibrium, a disturbance, if not too great, leaves it still in equilibrium, with no tendency either to deviate further from its original state or to return to it.

A familiar example of a metastable equilibrium is a liquid cooled below its freezing point; in most cases a slight disturbance suffices to set off a change to the stable solid state. Ammonium nitrate is another example; in this case the barrier, corresponding to the point C, is so high that the substance was long considered stable. However, a severe shock can cause it to start decomposing chemically, and the violence of its decomposition has been demonstrated by several tragic explosions. The distinction be-between stable and metastable equilibrium is based largely on convenience and is somewhat arbitrary. This is well illustrated by hydrogen gas; certainly it is ordinarily considered stable, though the nuclear reactions which can convert it to helium release a vast amount of energy.

Neutral equilibria are exemplified by a liquid in equilibrium with its vapor. The system can assume any state from pure saturated liquid to pure saturated vapor without change in the Gibbs free energy, and in any such state it has no tendency to change in either direction as long as the temperature and pressure are held at suitable values.

The concept of *false equilibrium* is often useful; this means a state in which the thermodynamic criteria are not met, and yet no change occurs. Whether a given equilibrium is regarded as false or metastable usually depends on whether the change which might take the system away from the equilibrium state is described in macroscopic or molecular terms. Consider, for example, the condensation of a supersaturated vapor. If the extent of the change at any stage is indicated by the percentage of the original vapor that has condensed, then the Gibbs free energy falls linearly with increasing percentage, and the condition of the supersaturated vapor will be described as a false equilibrium. However, suppose that we follow the progress of condensation from a molecular viewpoint, observing, at least conceptually, the clustering of molecules into a group, which grows larger by the addition of more molecules until it can be regarded as a droplet of liquid. If we now plot the Gibbs free energy against the number of molecules in the group, a maximum will appear at, for example, fifty molecules,[2] and the equilibrium will be described as metastable.

Similarly, for many chemical reactions, a description in macroscopic thermodynamic terms will not take account of activation energy, and failure of the reaction to proceed will be ascribed to false equilibrium. However, in a description in terms of a molecular parameter, the activation energy appears as a barrier, and the equilibrium is viewed as metastable.

3-8. Nomenclature and Units

Helmholtz coined the name *free energy* in 1882 and applied it to the function A. Despite some confusion between A and G by early workers, this term was for many years used generally for this function, and it still is in most European work. Other names that have been used for it include *available energy*, *work content* (which is unacceptable for the same reason that "heat content" is unacceptable for H), and *work function*. The latter two derive from the relation of A to the work involved in an isothermal change; this also accounts for the letter A (from German *Arbeit*).

Lewis,[3] and later Lewis and Randall,[4] chose Helmholtz's term *free energy* for G, and this choice has been widely followed by American chemists and chemical engineers. Unfortunately, this has led to much of the confusion of terminology that still plagues thermodynamicists. Partington[5] similarly transferred Kelvin's term *available energy* from A to G.

Gibbs, the first person to realize the importance of G, used this function freely but did not suggest a name for it; most later writers have attached the name of Gibbs to it in one way or another. The name *thermodynamic potential*, which is occasionally used, is unsatisfactory because all of the functions U, H, A, and G, are thermodynamic potentials for certain conditions.

The time is long past due for some internationally recognized organization to agree on a recommended set of names for these functions. The set *energy, enthalpy, Helmholtz function* (or *potential*), and *Gibbs function* (or *potential*) has been suggested by several authors and has much to recommend it. Another set, tentatively recommended by the Commission on Symbols and Terminology of the International Union of Pure and Applied Chemistry, assigns to A and G the names *free energy* and *free enthalpy*. The emphasis that this set places on the analogy of A and G to U and H is a strong point in its favor, but the use of the adjective "free" (or similarly of "available") is open to objection. Consider, for example, the reversible isothermal expansion of an ideal gas, which is treated in the next chapter. The work done is $-\Delta A$ (or $-\Delta G$, since they are the same in this case), and it is in this sense that this amount of energy is considered "free". However, the energy of the gas is unchanged; the energy for performing work comes entirely from the source of heat which maintains the constant temperature. Thus it seems misleading to regard any part of the energy of the gas itself as "free," and yet the "free energy" of the gas, whether defined to mean A or G, is certainly not in general zero. As Zemansky[6] has pointed out, the practice of naming thermodynamic functions by their use is appealing, but not usually satisfactory. The retention of the term *free energy* in this book is a concession to widespread usage; when combined with the names of Helmholtz and Gibbs, it yields a pair of rather cumbersome, but certainly unambiguous, names for A and G. The use of the term *free energy functions* for A and G collectively is convenient, though not free from objection.

The units most often needed in thermodynamics are those of pressure, volume, energy, temperature, and entropy. The first three are based on units of length, mass, and time, and in most scientific work the well-known centimeter-gram-second (cgs) units are used, or the increasingly popular meter-kilogram-second (mks) units. Unfortunately, little use has been made of either the cgs or mks system in chemical thermodynamics, except for volume.

The cgs unit of volume is the cubic centimeter. The larger unit, the liter, was intended to be 1000 cc; actually, it was defined in a more roundabout way. The gram was defined as the mass of 1 cc of water at 4°C, and a liter as the volume of 1000 g of water at this temperature. Because of inaccuracy in making the original standard gram, the liter turned out to be 1000.028 cc. Work accurate enough to make this difference significant is rare.

The cgs unit of pressure is the dyne per square centimeter. Because this unit is too small for most purposes, a unit of 1,000,000 dynes per sq cm was chosen, and this is called a *bar*; it is approximately equal to the pressure of the atmosphere at sea level. For lower pressures the millibar and the microbar ($=1$ dyne per sq cm) are available, and for larger pressures the kilobar. The use of bars and millibars is almost confined to meteorology; chemists generally still use a system of units based on the height of a column of mercury which can be supported by the measured pressure. The main unit is the *atmosphere,* conceived of, rather vaguely, as equal to the average atmospheric pressure at sea level at 45° latitude, but defined as 760 mm of mercury at 0°C. The dependence of these units on the properties of a particular substance, their lack of any simple relation to the cgs units (1 atm = 1.01325 bars), and the inconvenient factor 760 are serious disadvantages. Furthermore, the abbreviation "mm of Hg" is cumbersome, while if it is shortened to "mm," it suggests a distance rather than a pressure. For these reasons the abandonment of the atmosphere — millimeter of mercury system is much to be desired.

The cgs unit of energy is the *erg,* or $g \cdot cm^2/sec^2$; the practical unit is the *joule,* which is 10^7 ergs. Before it was known that heat is a kind of energy, it was natural to choose a heat unit based on the change of temperature of some specified system. Accordingly the *calorie* was defined as the heat required to increase the temperature of 1g of water 1°C. Later (in the 1840's) Joule and others determined the amount of energy (in mechanical units) which would accomplish this same increase. Rowland refined these measurements to such a high degree of accuracy that the need for a separate heat unit disappeared. Nevertheless, use of the calorie, now redefined as 4.1840 joules, has continued. The name *calorie* has also been applied to a unit 1000 times as large as the above one. This larger unit is sometimes distinguished by calling it a *large calorie, kilogram calorie,* or *kilocalorie;* the "calorie" of nutritionists is actually a kilocalorie. The International Committee on Weights and Measures has recommended that the calorie be abandoned and all energy measurements made in joules; this logical practice is followed in parts of the International Critical Tables, and only habit has prevented its unanimous adoption.

In the mks system, the fundamental unit of force, which is called the *newton*, is 1 kg·m/sec². Comparing it with the cgs system, we find

$$1 \text{ newton} = 1 \frac{\text{kg·m}}{\text{sec}^2} = \frac{(1000 \text{ g}) (100 \text{ cm})}{\text{sec}^2} = 10^5 \text{ dynes}$$

The energy unit is

$$1 \text{ newton·meter} = (10^5 \text{ dynes}) (100 \text{ cm}) = 10^7 \text{ ergs} = 1 \text{ joule}$$

Thus the joule becomes not only a practical unit, as in the cgs system, but a fundamental one. The fundamental mks pressure unit, however, is not suitable as a practical unit, since

$$1 \frac{\text{newton}}{\text{meter}^2} = \frac{10^5 \text{ dynes}}{(100 \text{ cm})^2} = 10 \frac{\text{dynes}}{\text{cm}^2}$$

Since this is too small for convenience, the retention of the bar as the practical unit in the mks system is expedient. In this system it will be defined as 10^5 newtons/meter². Finally, it should be noted that for complete consistency in applying the mks system to chemical work, the mole should be replaced by the kilomole.

Before the concept of absolute temperature was developed, temperature scales were set up by choosing two reference temperatures, assigning numbers to them, and using mercury thermometers, or, later, gas thermometers, to interpolate or extrapolate to other temperatures. Thus the centigrade scale uses the freezing and boiling points of water at 1 atm pressure as reference temperatures, and defines these points as 0° and 100° respectively. These two-point scales are not suitable for thermodynamic work, and it was early realized that a more fundamental temperature, known as the *absolute*, or *Kelvin*,[*] temperature, could be obtained by adding about 273 to the centigrade temperature. When the development of the second law put the concept of absolute temperature on a sound basis, the suggestion was made by Kelvin[7] that only one point be used to define the temperature scale. This was not practical at the time, since the absolute temperature could not be measured to the same degree of accuracy as the centigrade temperature. This situation changed with improved measuring techniques, and the suggestion was revived by Giauque[8] in 1939. The step was finally taken in 1954, when the General Conference on Weights and Measures specified that the triple point of

---

[*] The term *Kelvin* is preferable to *absolute* for this scale, since the latter may refer to other absolute scales, such as the *Rankine*, or absolute Fahrenheit, scale.

water should be, by definition, 273.16° K[9]. This defines the size of the degree to about 1 part in 30,000, whereas the difference between the freezing and melting points of water can be measured to about 1 part in 100,000. The new definition, therefore, entails a slight loss of precision.

The term *centigrade degree* will be used for the unit of temperature on the centigrade and Kelvin scales, while *degrees centigrade* will indicate a point on the centigrade scale.

Finally, the units of entropy follow from those of energy and temperature. Occasionally the term *entropy unit* (abbreviated eu) is used for the calorie per centigrade degree (or in engineering works, for the British thermal unit per Fahrenheit degree), but this practice will not be followed in this book.

3–9. Miscellaneous Topics

To facilitate remembering which of the main functions has a minimum or maximum value at equilibrium under given conditions, one can derive the equilibrium equations in the following manner: Assuming that any volume change is slow enough so that dW can, with reasonable accuracy, be replaced by $-p\ dV$, we find from the first and second laws that

$$dU = dQ + dW \leqslant T\ dS - p\ dV$$

The equality sign, which gives Eq. (2–9), applies to reversible processes; for a natural, or irreversible, change the inequality applies. If the entropy and volume are constant, the right side is zero, and so

$$dU \leqslant 0$$

This means that U decreases during every natural change under these conditions and must have a minimum value at equilibrium.

Similarly Eqs. (2–10), (3–4), and (3–5) become, for natural changes,

$$dH \leqslant T\ dS + V\ dp$$

$$dA \leqslant -S\ dT - p\ dV$$

$$dG \leqslant -S\ dT + V\ dp$$

and these can be treated like the inequality for dU. For example, at constant T and V, the right side of the second inequality becomes zero, and so A must have a minimum value at equilibrium.

Innumerable mnemonics have been devised for the principal thermodynamic relations. In general their use is not advisable, but two simple ones are presented here. The following diagram will serve for Eqs. (2–9), (2–10), and (3–1) through (3–5):

$$
\begin{array}{ccc}
U & p\,V & H \\
T & & -T \\
S & & S \\
A & -p\,V & G
\end{array}
$$

Thus by going around the diagram clockwise, we find $U + pV = H$, and similar equations. Going counterclockwise from one corner, ignoring the next corner, and supplying d's in an obvious manner leads to Eqs. (2–9), (2–10), (3–4), and (3–5). For the Maxwell relations, Eqs. (3–14) through (3–17), write

$$
T\,S \quad p\,V
$$

the letters appearing in the same order as in the expression for dU. Place below each side a pair which has as its first member either T or S, as its second either p or V; for example

$$
\begin{array}{cc}
T\,S & p\,V \\
T\,p & T\,p
\end{array}
$$

Now interpret each of these arrays as a derivative by placing the letter common to the upper and lower pairs outside the parentheses to indicate that this variable is held constant, and prefixing a negative sign if the common letter does not appear in the same position in the upper and lower pairs. Thus the array above becomes, after the equal sign is supplied,

$$
\left(\frac{\partial S}{\partial p}\right)_T = -\left(\frac{\partial V}{\partial T}\right)_p
$$

which is Eq. (3–17). There are four possible lower pairs, corresponding to the four Maxwell equations. This is not a purely mnemonic device, since it has a sound mathematical basis in the Jacobian method, which is discussed in Chapter 11.

The following procedure is generally preferable to the use of menmonic diagrams. First the equation $dU = T\,dS - p\,dV$ is firmly committed to memory, as are the definitions of H, A, and G in terms of U, pV, and TS. Then the Legendre transformations, replacing $T\,dS$ by $-S\,dT$ and $-p\,dV$ by $V\,dp$, are performed first separately to obtain dA and dH, and then together to derive dG. Finally, applying the relations for exact differentials to these yields the Maxwell equations. All these steps can be done mentally, and with a little practice they will be found easier than setting up mnemonic diagrams.

It is often desirable to transform a thermodynamic derivative into an expression involving other derivatives which are more familiar or more accessible experimentally. Without a systematic procedure for doing this, one can become lost in a labyrinth of transformations without ever arriving at the desired one. Several such procedures have been devised. A very elementary, though rather tedious, one by Tobolsky[10] is presented here; other more elegant and general methods are described in Chapter 10.

Suppose that it is desired to express $(\partial S/\partial H)_G$ in terms of derivatives whose independent variables are p and T; that is, derivatives with respect to T at constant p or vice versa. Write

$$dS = X \, dH + Y \, dG \qquad (3\text{--}21)$$

In this equation X is, of course, the quantity desired. Now all differentials must be expressed in terms of dp and dT. Thus

$$dS = \left(\frac{\partial S}{\partial T}\right)_p dT + \left(\frac{\partial S}{\partial p}\right)_T dp$$

The first of these derivatives is C_p/T (see Problem 3, Chapter 2); the second can be transformed by Maxwell's relation Eq. (3–17) into

$-(\partial V/\partial T)_p = -V\alpha$, where $\alpha = \dfrac{1}{V}\left(\dfrac{\partial V}{\partial T}\right)_p$ is the coefficient of (cubical) ex-

pansion. Then substituting the above expression, together with Eqs. (3–5) and (2–10), into Eq. (3–21), we get

$$-V\alpha \, dp + \frac{C_p}{T} dT = -TV\alpha X \, dp + C_p X \, dT + VX \, dp - SY \, dT + VY \, dp$$

Equating the coefficients of dp and dT separately gives the pair of simultaneous equations

$$(T\alpha - 1)X - Y = \alpha$$

$$C_p X - SY = \frac{C_p}{T}$$

which can be solved to obtain

$$X = \frac{(C_p/T) - \alpha S}{(T\alpha - 1)\, S + C_p}$$

The student should verify the dimensional consistency of this equation; both sides have the dimensions of $1/T$.

This method is easily adapted to the expression of any thermodynamic derivative in terms of others whose independent variables are any two of p, V, S, and T.

PROBLEMS

(1) Show that the condition for equilibrium at constant pressure and entropy is that the enthalpy must have a minimum value.

(2) Derive the following analogues of the Gibbs-Helmholtz equation:

(a)
$$\Delta A = \Delta U + T \left(\frac{\partial \Delta A}{\partial T} \right)_V$$

(b)
$$\Delta H = \Delta U + p \left(\frac{\partial \Delta H}{\partial p} \right)_S$$

(c)
$$\Delta U = \Delta A + S \left(\frac{\partial \Delta U}{\partial S} \right)_V$$

(3) Show that $\left(\dfrac{\partial S}{\partial V} \right)_T = \dfrac{\alpha}{\kappa}$. (Use Maxwell's equations and Eq. (1–13); κ is the compressibility, $-\dfrac{1}{V}\left(\dfrac{\partial V}{\partial p} \right)_T$.)

(4) Evaluate the following by Tobolsky's method:

(a)
$$\left(\frac{\partial H}{\partial V} \right)_U \quad \text{with independent variables } p \text{ and } S;$$

(b)
$$\left(\frac{\partial A}{\partial p} \right)_S \quad \text{with independent variables } T \text{ and } V.$$

(5) Show that when a homogeneous system does work by an adiabatic expansion, the temperature falls, remains constant, or rises according as the coefficient

of expansion is positive, zero, or negative. Hint: Evaluate $\left(\dfrac{\partial T}{\partial V}\right)_S$ in terms of α, κ, and C_v, by Tobolsky's method or otherwise.

(6) Show that

(a)
$$\left(\frac{\partial U}{\partial V}\right)_T = T\left(\frac{\partial p}{\partial T}\right)_V - p$$

(b)
$$\left(\frac{\partial A}{\partial V}\right)_S = S\left(\frac{\partial p}{\partial S}\right)_V - p$$

(Use Eqs. (1–11) and (3–6) through (3–17).)

(7) By combining results of Problems 3 and 6 above and Problem 4, Chapter 2, show that

$$C_p - C_v = \frac{TV\alpha^2}{\kappa}$$

(8) Work done on a rubber band in stretching it is given by $\tau\,dl$, where τ is the tension and l the length. Neglecting p-V terms, set up the expression for dU. Then by Legendre transformations derive expressions for the differentials of functions analogous to H, A, and G, and find the analogues of the Maxwell equations.

(a) Show that $C_l\ (= (\partial U/\partial T)_l)$ and $(\partial l/\partial\tau)_T$ are positive.

(b) Show that

$$\left(\frac{\partial T}{\partial l}\right)_S = -\frac{\left(\dfrac{\partial l}{\partial T}\right)_\tau}{\left(\dfrac{\partial S}{\partial T}\right)_l\left(\dfrac{\partial l}{\partial\tau}\right)_T}$$

Experimentally, stretched rubber shortens when heated at constant tension. Show from this that rubber becomes warmer when stretched adiabatically. (This effect can be felt if a rubber band is stretched while it is held loosely between the lips.)

REFERENCES

1. Larmor, J., *Proc. Roy. Soc.* (*London*), Series A, **81**, xlvii (1908).
2. Hill, T. L., "Statistical Mechanics," p. 149, New York, N.Y., McGraw-Hill Book Co., Inc., 1956.
3. Lewis, G. N., *J. Am. Chem. Soc.*, **35**, 1 (1913).
4. Lewis, G. N., and Randall, M., "Thermodynamics and the Free Energy of Chemical Substances," Chapter 14, New York, N.Y., McGraw-Hill Book Co., Inc., 1923.
5. Partington, J. R., "An Advanced Treatise on Physical Chemistry," Vol. 1, London, Longmans, Green, & Co., 1949.
6. Zemansky, M. W., "Heat and Thermodynamics," p. 220, New York, N.Y.,

McGraw-Hill Book Co., Inc., 1957; also *Am. J. Phys.* **25**, 349 (1957).

7. Joule, J. P., and Thomson, W., *Phil. Trans. Roy. Soc. (London)*, **144**, 351 (1854).
8. Giauque, W. F., *Nature*, **143**, 623 (1939).
9. "Temperature: Its Measurement and Control in Science and Industry," Vol. 2, p. 125, New York, N.Y., Reinhold Publishing Corp., 1955.
10. Tobolsky, A. V., *J. Chem. Phys.*, **10**, 644 (1942); see also Carroll, B., and Lehrmann, A., *J. Chem. Ed.*, **24**, 389 (1947).

chapter 4

Gases and Vapors

4-1. Pressure-Volume Relations to Gases

THE EARLIEST STUDY of the properties of gases was that of Robert Boyle in 1660. Boyle's experiments led him to the conclusion that for any given sample of a gas the product of pressure and volume is constant. The conditions of this work assured reasonably constant temperature; without this condition, the conclusion is not even approximately correct. More exact measurements show deviation from Boyle's law, negligible at low pressures but increasing with increasing pressure. On this basis we can assume that the pressure-volume product for a gas can be expressed as a power series in the pressure. Thus

$$pV = \alpha + Bp + Cp^2 + \ldots \tag{4-1}$$

In this equation, which is known as the *virial equation*, α, B, and C are functions of temperature and mass of gas. In actual practice, no more than three or four terms are used. For a few gases, especially helium, all terms except α are very small at pressures of a few bars or less. A gas for which all the coefficients in the virial equation (except α) are zero is called an ideal gas; as the name suggests, this is only an idealization never completely attained in practice. The magnitude of the other coefficients B, C, ..., is a measure of the deviation of the gas from ideality.

For reasons to be discussed later, this equation is not applicable near the critical point. An alternative form

$$pV = \alpha + \frac{\beta}{V} + \frac{\gamma}{V^2} \ldots \tag{4-2}$$

does not have this disadvantage. Eq. (4–1) is generally better for calculating volume from known pressure, while Eq. (4–2) is more convenient for calculating pressure from known volume. Relations between the first few coefficients of Eq. (4–1) and those of Eq. (4–2) are easily worked out (see problem 1, p. 70).

4–2. Temperature Measurement and the Gas Thermometer

It was stated in Section 2–7 that Eq. (2–8) provides a definition of temperature. However, it is not obvious how temperature so defined can be measured. Practically, of course, measurements on an arbitrary scale, but corresponding satisfactorily to the intuitive concept of temperature, were made long before any thermodynamic definition of temperature had been devised. This can be done by steadily increasing the temperature of a bath (by continuously adding energy to it) and measuring some property of the bath or an object immersed in it. Any property which is found always to increase (or always to decrease) with increasing temperature can be made the basis of measurement. Examples are the bending of a bimetallic strip, the electrical resistance of platinum or of semiconductors, and the emf of a thermocouple.

The arbitrariness of temperatures not based on the thermodynamic definition can be made clear by considering the calibration of a mercury-in-glass thermometer. If such an instrument is constructed without marks, it is readily calibrated at the points 0° C and 100° C by the use of freezing and boiling water respectively. Since only these two points are defined, there is nothing better to do about the intermediate temperatures than to divide the linear distance between the 0° and 100° marks into 100 equal parts, and measure according to these. The scale so obtained is reasonably satisfactory for many purposes, but it depends on the liquid chosen (and to a lesser extent on the glass). Alcohol would yield a scale similar to, but not identical with that of mercury; water would fail to yield an unambiguous scale at all, since its volume first decreases and then increases as the temperature rises from 0° to 100°. Similar remarks apply to the other properties mentioned.

However, when the pressure of a gas confined in a constant volume is used to establish a temperature scale, it is found that the scale is practically independent of the choice of gas, provided one of the so-called "permanent" gases is used, and the pressure is kept reasonably low. To measure the temperature on this scale, we set

$$\theta = kp + k'$$

where θ is the temperature and k and k' are constants. Measuring the pressure at the two defined temperatures (0°C and 100°C) makes it possible to evaluate k and k'. It is found that k' is always about $-273.2°$. Thus if we define a new temperature scale by setting Θ equal to $\theta + 273.2°$, the relation of this new temperature to pressure becomes a simple proportionality: $\Theta = kp$. It is this that first suggested the idea of absolute temperature. The need to use a "permanent" gas can be eliminated by using the quantity α in Eq. (4–1) instead of the pressure; this is determined by measuring the volume at various pressures at a fixed temperature and extrapolating the product pV to zero pressure. The scale obtained by setting α proportional to temperature is called the *ideal gas temperature scale*. It will be shown in the next two sections that this scale is identical with the thermodynamic scale defined by Eq. (2–8).

4–3. The Joule–Thomson Experiment

Important information on the thermodynamic properties of real gases can be obtained by the porous plug experiment of Joule and Thomson. In this experiment a gas at pressure p_1, molar volume v_1, and temperature T_1 is forced through a porous plug, emerging with pressure reduced to p_2, and with molar volume v_2 and temperature T_2. The purpose of the plug is to assure that all work that might be done by the expansion is dissipated

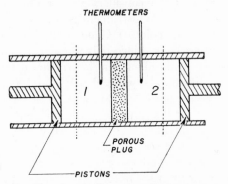

FIGURE 7. THE JOULE-THOMPSON EXPERIMENT.

by frictional forces instead. This experiment involves an open system, but a simple artifice permits us to treat a closed system instead. Consider the open subsystem consisting of the gas in the region bounded by the dotted lines in Figure 7. All significant property changes which occur in the gas are confined to this region. The experiment can in principle be carried out by using either of two methods to maintain the constant pressure: admitting gas continuously to the high-pressure side of the plug and withdrawing it from the low-pressure side, as is actually done in practice; or using movable pistons, as indicated in Figure 7. The choice cannot affect the behavior of the subsystem within the dotted lines, so long as the pistons do not invade this region. However, if pistons are used, the complete system, including all the gas in the apparatus, is closed. This permits us to use the first law in the form $\Delta U = Q + W$. The conditions are kept as nearly adiabatic as possible, so that we may set $Q = 0$.

If, during the period of observation, one mole of gas passes through the plug, and the molar energy changes from u_1 to u_2, then $\Delta U = u_2 - u_1$. The work done on the system by the left piston is $p_1 v_1$, while that done by the system on the right piston is $p_2 v_2$; therefore $W = p_1 v_1 - p_2 v_2$. These values lead to

$$u_2 - u_1 = p_1 v_1 - p_2 v_2$$

From this we find

$$u_2 + p_2 v_2 = u_1 + p_1 v_1$$

or

$$h_2 = h_1.$$

Generally, the temperature of the gas changes during expansion through the porous plug. If the temperature is measured on an arbitrary scale and designated by Θ to distinguish it from the thermodynamic temperature T, this experiment leads to an evaluation of $(\Theta_2 - \Theta_1)/(p_2 - p_1)$ at constant enthalpy. If the pressure difference is very small, or more exactly if the value for various difference is extrapolated to a difference of zero, we find the value of $(\partial \Theta/\partial p)_h$.

Values of $(\partial h/\partial \Theta)_p$ can also be found experimentally. Heat is added at a known rate to a constantly flowing stream of gas. This can be done, for example, by means of an electric heating coil with a wattmeter. The heater must offer so little resistance to the flow of gas that the pressures above and below it are practically equal. The temperature is measured above and below the heater. Since the mass rate of flow can also be measured, this permits calculation of $(h_2 - h_1)/(\Theta_2 - \Theta_1)$ at constant pressure and thence of $(\partial h/\partial \Theta)_p$.

These two quantities can be combined by Eq. (1–13) to give

$$\left(\frac{\partial h}{\partial p}\right)_\Theta = - \left(\frac{\partial h}{\partial \Theta}\right)_p \left(\frac{\partial \Theta}{\partial p}\right)_h$$

Now when Θ is constant, so is the thermodynamic temperature, T, and so $(\partial h/\partial p)_\Theta = (\partial h/\partial p)_T$.

These quantities have been determined experimentally in the manner described above for many gases, and the results are always qualitatively the same; $(\partial h/\partial \Theta)_p$ and $(\partial \Theta/\partial p)_h$ are almost constant at low pressure and show no sign of tending toward infinity as the pressure is reduced toward zero. It follows that $(\partial h/\partial p)_T$ behaves similarly, and we can adopt as a postulate, based on these observations, that *when the pressure of a gas is reduced toward zero at constant temperature, $(\partial h/\partial p)_T$ approaches a finite limit*. As a corollary of this, h itself must also approach a finite limit, and similarly H.

4–4. Identity of the Ideal Gas and Thermodynamic Temperature Scales

In order to use these results, we must derive an expression for $(\partial h/\partial p)_T$ in terms of T, p, and the virial coefficients. Eq. (1–11), with f, x, y, and z replaced by H, p, S, and T respectively, becomes

$$\left(\frac{\partial H}{\partial p}\right)_T = \left(\frac{\partial H}{\partial p}\right)_S + \left(\frac{\partial H}{\partial S}\right)_p \left(\frac{\partial S}{\partial p}\right)_T$$

The expression on the right is transformed by the use of Eqs. (3–8), (3–9), and (3–17) into

$$\left(\frac{\partial H}{\partial p}\right)_T = V - T \left(\frac{\partial V}{\partial T}\right)_p \qquad (4\text{–}3)$$

This relation, being based only on fundamental thermodynamic laws, is generally valid and is not restricted to gaseous systems. Applying it to a gaseous system of constant mass gives

$$\left(\frac{\partial H}{\partial p}\right)_{T,m} = \left[\frac{\alpha}{p} + B + Cp + \ldots\right] - T\left[\left(\frac{\partial \alpha}{\partial T}\right)_m \frac{1}{p} + \left(\frac{\partial B}{\partial T}\right)_m + \left(\frac{\partial C}{\partial T}\right)_m p + \ldots\right]$$

$$= \left[\alpha - T\left(\frac{\partial \alpha}{\partial T}\right)_m\right]\frac{1}{p} + \left[B - T\left(\frac{\partial B}{\partial T}\right)_m\right] + \left[C - T\left(\frac{\partial C}{\partial T}\right)_m\right]p + \ldots \qquad (4\text{–}4)$$

Obviously this can yield a finite limit as p approaches zero only if the coefficient of $1/p$ vanishes; that is,

$$\alpha - T \left(\frac{\partial \alpha}{\partial T} \right)_m = 0$$

In integrating this equation we must remember that since the derivative is taken at constant m, the constant of integration may involve m. The equation may be rewritten

$$\frac{d\alpha}{\alpha} = \frac{dT}{T}$$

and this integrates to

$$\ln \alpha = \ln T + \ln r(m)$$

or $\alpha = r(m)T$. Since both the thermodynamic temperature and the ideal gas temperature are proportional to α, they can differ at most in the size of the degree. But since the defined temperature of the fixed point (the triple point of water) is the same in both, even this possible difference is eliminated, and the two scales are identical. The ideal gas thermometer is the fundamental method of temperature measurement, and it is ultimately by calibration against it that the practical types of thermometer derive their validity.

In view of this, the experiments described in Section 3 may be used to determine $(\partial T/\partial p)_H$, known as the *Joule-Thomson coefficient*, and $(\partial H/\partial T)_p$, the heat capacity at constant pressure.

4–5. The Gas Constant R

The quantity $r(m)$ is easily evaluated on the basis of two reasonable assumptions about gases, both borne out by experience: (1) that the volume is an extensive property, and (2) Avogadro's law, that equal volumes of different gases at equal temperatures and pressures contain the same number of molecules, or, in other words, equimolar portions of different gases at the same temperature and pressure have equal volumes.

The first of these is strictly true of systems in which surface effects are negligible; this certainly includes all ordinary gaseous systems. It follows that $r(m)$, B, C, ... are all directly proportional to the mass. Mass may be measured in ordinary mass units, or in moles; the latter choice proves more convenient. With this choice we may divide the virial equation by n, the number of moles, to obtain

$$pv = RT + bp + cp^2 + \ldots \tag{4-5}$$

where $v = V/n$ is the molar volume, $R = r(m)/n$, $b = B/n$, $c = C/n$, $\ldots$, and all these quantities are independent of the mass of the system.

The second of the above assumptions is only approximate at ordinary pressures, but approaches exactitude as the pressure is lowered. We may express this by stating that for equimolar quantities of different gases at the same temperature, the product pV is approximately the same at ordinary pressures, and approaches exactly the same limit as the pressure is reduced toward zero. But according to the virial equation this limit is RT, and so R must be the same for all gases. It is called the *molar gas constant*.

Since pV is in units of (pressure times volume) per mole, or energy units per mole, R is in energy units per (mole·degree). The value of R in several useful units is given below:

8.314×10^7	ergs/(mole·degree)
8.314	joules/(mole·degree)
8314	joules/(kilomole·degree)
0.08314	liter·bars/(mole·degree)
0.08205	liter·atm/(mole·degree)
82.05	ml·atm/(mole·degree)
62,360	ml·mm of Hg/(mole·degree)
1.987	cal/(mole·degree)

Notice that if the energy and pressure units recommended in this book are used, only one set of significant figures (8314) is needed.

4–6. Thermodynamic Properties of Ideal Gases

The ideal gas may be regarded either as an approximate description of a real gas, valid whenever all higher terms of the virial equation are negligible compared to RT, or as the limit which a real gas approaches as the pressure is reduced toward zero. Its equation of state is $pv = RT$, or, for n moles, $pV = nRT$. Actually, because of its simplicity and the wide range of conditions over which it is a reasonably accurate approximation, the ideal gas equation is of great practical importance.

Substituting the ideal gas equation into Eq. (4–3) gives

$$\left(\frac{\partial H}{\partial p}\right)_T = V - T\left[\frac{\partial(nRT/p)}{\partial T}\right]_p = V - \frac{nRT}{p} = 0$$

It follows that the enthalpy of an ideal gas is independent of the pressure, and therefore also of the volume; it is dependent on temperature and mass only. Since pV $(= nRT)$ is also independent of pressure, and $U = H - pV$, the energy is also a function of temperature and mass only. Since both energy and enthalpy are extensive properties, their molar values are independent of mass and depend on temperature alone.

The heat capacity at constant pressure, C_p, is given in general by $(\partial H/\partial T)_p$; for an ideal gas this becomes simply dH/dT. Similarly C_v for an ideal gas is merely dU/dT. Now

$$H = U + pV = U + nRT$$

and differentiation gives

$$C_p = C_v + nR$$

With molar quantities

$$h = u + RT$$

and

$$c_p = c_v + R \qquad (4\text{-}6)$$

Entropy changes in an ideal gas can be derived from the fundamental equations for the first and second laws. Since the energy of an ideal gas depends only on temperature (assuming mass constant), $(\partial U/\partial V)_T = 0$, and

$$dU = \left(\frac{\partial U}{\partial V}\right)_T dV + \left(\frac{\partial U}{\partial T}\right)_V dT = C_v \, dT$$

Then

$$dQ = dU - dW = C_v \, dT + p \, dV,$$

and

$$dS = C_v\frac{dT}{T} + \frac{p}{T} \, dV = C_v \, dT + nR\frac{dV}{V} \qquad (4\text{-}7)$$

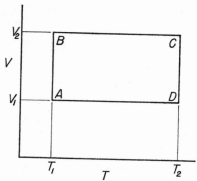

FIGURE 8. PATHS OF INTEGRATION FOR EQ. 4-7.

To find the entropy change from an initial state T_1, V_1 to a final state T_2, V_2, it is necessary to integrate this expression and evaluate the rather simple line integral which results. Since the entropy change cannot depend on the path of integration, we can choose a path consisting of a constant-temperature portion from T_1, V_1 to T_1, V_2, along which $dT = 0$, and a constant-volume portion from T_1, V_2 to T_2, V_2, along which $dV = 0$ (ABC in Figure 8). This gives

$$S(T_2, V_2) - S(T_1, V_1) = nR \ln \frac{V_2}{V_1} + \int_{T_1}^{T_2} C_v \frac{dT}{T} \qquad (4\text{-}8)$$

Since nR is independent of temperature and C_v of volume, the path ADC would give exactly the same expression. If C_v is practically constant between T_1 and T_2, the entropy change may be approximated by

$$S(T_2, V_2) - S(T_1, V_1) = C_v \ln \frac{T_2}{T_1} + nR \ln \frac{V_2}{V_1} \qquad (4\text{-}8a)$$

Still another form may be obtained by substituting in this equation $V_2/V_1 = p_1 T_2/p_2 T_1$ and using Eq. (4-6). This gives

$$S(T_2, V_2) - S(T_1, V_1) = C_p \ln \frac{T_2}{T_1} + nR \ln \frac{p_1}{p_2} \qquad (4\text{-}8b)$$

If we deal with molar quantities at constant temperature, Eq. (4-8b) becomes

$$s(v_2) - s(v_1) = R \ln \frac{p_1}{p_2} = -R \ln \frac{p_2}{p_1} \qquad (4\text{-}9)$$

Now let p_u represent a unit pressure, such as one bar or one atmosphere, and s' the entropy of the gas at this unit pressure. Then Eq. (4-9) leads to

$$s = s' - R \ln \frac{p}{p_u} \qquad (4\text{-}10)$$

This equation is often written

$$s = s' - R \ln p \qquad (4\text{-}11)$$

but this form is not dimensionally correct. We can take the logarithm of a ratio of two pressures, since this is a pure number, but the logarithm of a pressure* is meaningless. Notice that s', which is called the *standard*

---

* See the discussion of this point by Boggs and Copley.[1] The notation here is essentially that of Guggenheim and Prue.[2]

molar entropy, depends on the choice of the standard unit pressure, p_u; it is a function of temperature but not of pressure. The standard molar entropy corresponding to a particular unit pressure may be used even when the pressure is expressed in different units, provided p_u is also expressed in these units. For example, if s' is known for a unit pressure of 1 atm and we wish to find the entropy at 1500 millibars, we note that $p_u = 1$ atm $= 1013$ mb, so that

$$s(1500 \text{ mb}) = s' - R \ln \frac{1500 \text{ mb}}{1013 \text{ mb}} = s' - R \ln \frac{1500}{1013}$$

The Gibbs free energy can be derived either from Eq. (4–10) or directly from Eq. (3–13). From the latter we have

$$dg = v \, dp = \frac{RT}{p} \, dp$$

Then if g' is the Gibbs free energy at the unit pressure p_u, which is called the *standard molar Gibbs free energy*, integration gives

$$g = g' + RT \ln \frac{p}{p_u} \tag{4–12}$$

The standard molar Gibbs free energy, g', is, like the standard molar entropy, a function of temperature and not of pressure, though its value depends on the choice of the unit pressure. This equation is often written in a dimensionally inconsistent form analogous to Eq. (4–11).

As a final example of the application of thermodynamics to the ideal gas, the equation for a reversible adiabatic expansion (or compression) will be derived. For such a process $dS = dQ/T = 0$, so that the entropy does not change. Therefore, Eq. (4–8a) gives (for 1 mole)

$$c_v \ln \frac{T_2}{T_1} = -R \ln \frac{v_2}{v_1} = R \ln \frac{v_1}{v_2}$$

Since $R = c_p - c_v$, this can be rewritten

$$\ln \frac{T_2}{T_1} = \frac{c_p - c_v}{c_v} \ln \frac{v_1}{v_2} = (\gamma - 1) \ln \frac{v_1}{v_2}$$

where γ is the ratio of c_p to c_v. This may also be written

$$\frac{T_2}{T_1} = \left(\frac{v_1}{v_2}\right)^{\gamma-1}$$

Finally, since $T_2/T_1 = p_2 v_2/p_1 v_1$,

$$\frac{p_2}{p_1} = \left(\frac{v_1}{v_2}\right)^{\gamma} \tag{4-13}$$

Shanks[3] has shown that this equation can be derived without the use of thermodynamic considerations.

4–7. The Thermodynamics of Nonideal Gases

For ideal gases the equation $g = g' + RT \ln (p/p_u)$ is the starting point for the derivations of many relations, which take relatively simple form because of the simplicity of this equation. For real gases this expression does not hold, or does so only approximately, but it has been found useful to preserve its form, and those of relations derived from it, by an artifice suggested by G. N. Lewis. A dimensionless function a, called the *activity*, is defined by the equation

$$dg = RT \, d(\ln a) \tag{4-14}$$

(Unfortunately, this widely used symbol for activity is the same as the symbol used in this book for the molar Helmholtz free energy. However, the uses of the two functions are so different that no confusion should arise.) In integrated form this is

$$g = g' + RT \ln a \tag{4-15}$$

To evaluate the constant of integration, g', we note, by comparing Eqs. (4–12) and (4–15), that for an ideal gas $a = p/p_u$. Since all gases approach ideal behavior as the pressure is reduced, we require that, for real gases, a and p/p_u should be equal at low pressures. Expressed more rigorously, this requirement is that

$$\lim_{p \to 0} \frac{a p_u}{p} = 1 \tag{4-16}$$

Now if we add $RT \ln (p_u/p) = - RT \ln (p/p_u)$ to both sides of Eq. (4–15), we get

$$g - RT \ln \frac{p}{p_u} = g' + RT \ln \frac{a p_u}{p}$$

If the pressure is allowed to approach zero, the second term on the right also approaches zero, by Eq. (4–16); this leads to

$$g' = \lim_{p \to 0} \left(g - RT \ln \frac{p}{p_u} \right) \tag{4–17}$$

Thus if values of g at various pressures are known, the quantity on the right may be plotted against p and extrapolated to $p = 0$ to determine g'.

The quantity ap_u appearing in Eq. (4–16) is called the *fugacity* and is represented by the letter f; this term, like *activity*, was introduced by G. N. Lewis. It should be noted that for a gas the fugacity and the activity are numerically equal, differing only in dimensions. Activity is, by definition, dimensionless, while fugacity has the dimensions of pressure. The use of two functions so closely related is unnecessary and may be confusing; however, since both are widely used, they will be retained in this book.

Fugacity may be calculated directly from p–v data. First we note that

$$\ln \frac{f}{p_u} = \frac{g - g'}{RT}$$

Remembering that p_u is constant and that $(\partial g/\partial p)_T = v$, we get

$$\left[\frac{\partial (\ln f)}{\partial p} \right]_T = \left[\frac{\partial}{\partial p} \left(\frac{g - g'}{RT} \right) \right]_T = \frac{v}{RT} \tag{4–18}$$

(Note that although $\ln f$ is dimensionally inconsistent, $d(\ln f) = df/f$ is a ratio of two similar quantities and so is a pure number.) We then have, at constant temperature,

$$d\left(\ln \frac{f}{p} \right) = d(\ln f) - d(\ln p) = \left(\frac{v}{RT} - \frac{1}{p} \right) dp$$

Now when $p = 0$, $\ln f/p = 0$. Using these as the lower limits of integration, we get

$$\ln \frac{f}{p} = - \frac{1}{RT} \int_0^p \left(\frac{RT}{p} - v \right) dp \tag{4–19}$$

(The dimensionless ratio f/p should not be confused with the activity, f/p_u.) It is helpful to remember that the integrand of Eq. (4–19) is the amount by which the volume of an ideal gas would exceed that of the real gas. This equation may be integrated graphically with empirical data, or analytically by the use of empirical equations of state. Very accurate data are needed, since at low pressures the integrand is a small difference between two large quantities.

Since $(\partial g/\partial T)_p = -s$, differentiation of Eq. (4–15) gives

$$s = s' - R \ln a - RT \left[\frac{\partial (\ln a)}{\partial T} \right]_p \qquad (4-20)$$

where $s' \equiv -dg'/dT$ is the standard molar entropy. For ideal gases $a = p/p_u$, and this reduces to Eq. (4–10). For real gases $R \ln p/p_u$ may be added to both sides to give

$$s + R \ln \frac{p}{p_u} = s' - R \ln \frac{ap_u}{p} - RT \left[\frac{\partial \left(\ln \frac{ap_u}{p} \right)}{\partial T} \right]_p$$

since $[\partial(\ln p_u/p)/\partial T]_p = 0$. Further rearrangement of this equation leads to

$$s' - R \ln \frac{f}{p} - RT \left[\frac{\partial}{\partial T} \left(\ln \frac{f}{p} \right) \right]_p = s + R \ln \frac{p}{p_u}$$

If we now assume** that, as p approaches zero,

$$\lim \left[\frac{\partial}{\partial T} \left(\ln \frac{f}{p} \right) \right]_p = \left[\frac{\partial}{\partial T} \left(\lim \ln \frac{f}{p} \right) \right]_p$$

then this limit clearly is zero, since $\lim \ln (f/p) = 0$, and the equation becomes

$$s' = \lim_{p \to 0} \left(s + R \ln \frac{p}{p_u} \right) \qquad (4-21)$$

It is often necessary to calculate the standard molar entropy, s', of a gas from the experimentally determined molar entropy, s_1, at the unit pressure, p_u. Maxwell's equation $(\partial s/\partial p)_T = -(\partial v/\partial T)_p$ can be integrated to give

$$s = s_1 - \int_{p_u}^p \left(\frac{\partial v}{\partial T} \right)_p dp$$

** To justify this assumption mathematically, it would be sufficient to show that the derivative on the left approaches its limit uniformly in a neighborhood of T.

We substitute this into Eq. (4–21), using the expression $\int_{p_u}^{p} \frac{dp}{p}$ for $\ln p/p_u$,

and the result is

$$
s' = \lim_{p \to 0} \left[s_1 - \int_{p_u}^{p} \left(\frac{\partial v}{\partial T} \right)_p dp + R \int_{p_u}^{p} \frac{dp}{p} \right]
$$

$$
= s_1 + \lim_{p \to 0} \int_{p}^{p_u} \left[\left(\frac{\partial v}{\partial T} \right)_p - \frac{R}{p} \right] dp
$$

This last integral depends on p not because it appears in the integrand, but because it is one of the limits of integration. To find the limit of the integral as p approaches zero, we replace p in the lower limit by zero. We then have

$$
s' = s_1 + \int_{0}^{p_u} \left[\left(\frac{\partial v}{\partial T} \right)_p - \frac{R}{p} \right] dp \tag{4–22}
$$

Like the expression for f/p, this expression may be evaluated either from experimental data or from empirical equations of state. It differs, however, in requiring data on the temperature dependence of v, whereas f/p can be evaluated from data at a single temperature.

Finally, since $h = g + Ts$, Eqs. (4–15) and (4–20) can be combined to give

$$
h = h' - RT^2 \left[\frac{\partial (\ln a)}{\partial T} \right]_p \tag{4–23}
$$

where h' is defined as $g' + Ts'$. From this definition and Eqs. (4–17) and (4–21) we find

$$
h' = \lim_{p \to 0} \left(g - RT \ln \frac{p}{p_u} \right) + T \lim_{p \to 0} \left(s + R \ln \frac{p}{p_u} \right) = \lim_{p \to 0} (g + Ts) = \lim_{p \to 0} h
$$

That is, the standard enthalpy is the limiting value of the enthalpy as the pressure is reduced toward zero.

4–8. Standard States

From Eqs. (4–10) and (4–12), it is easily seen that when an ideal gas is at unit pressure, its molar entropy and Gibbs free energy are s' and g', respectively; further its enthalpy, which is constant at constant temperature, is h'. Since all these quantities have then their standard values, the state of unit pressure is called a *standard state* for an ideal gas. For a real gas $g = g'$ when the fugacity is one unit, so that this can be used as a standard state where only Gibbs free energy values are involved. However, Eqs. (4–20) and (4–23) show that, unless $[\partial(\ln f)/\partial T]_p = 0$, $s \neq s'$ and $h \neq h'$. There is, therefore, no standard state for a real gas. If desired, however, the standard state concept can be retained by devising fictitious states. To do this, we imagine a reversible, isothermal process whereby a gas can be made ideal at unit pressure. This is accomplished by expanding the gas to so low a pressure that it may be considered ideal, then compressing it to unit pressure, requiring it to follow not its own equation of state but that of an ideal gas during the compression. This is, of course, impossible, and the state to which it would lead is a purely fictitious one. Now by using Eqs. (4–12) and (4–16) we can easily show that in the fictitious ideal state at unit pressure the Gibbs free energy has its standard value; similar statements apply to the enthalpy and entropy. For this reason the standard values of these properties are sometimes referred to as the values in the ideal gas state.

Standard states, when they are physically realizable, are undoubtedly of value in visualizing the meaning of the standard values of the thermodynamic functions. However, when it is necessary first to visualize a fictitious state, which is often obviously unrealizable, the value of the standard state concept is very dubious. In this book no use will be made of fictitious standard states; instead, the standard quantities such as g' will be regarded as constants to be evaluated by a simple, straightforward mathematical treatment of experimental measurements. This procedure has an operational significance which is lacking in the use of fictitious standard states.

4–9. Fugacities of Liquids and Solids

Fugacities for condensed phases are defined by applying Eq. (4–15) to these phases, using the same value of g' as for the corresponding gas at the same temperature. When a liquid evaporates reversibly, the temperature and pressure remaining constant, the Gibbs free energy does not change (see Section 3–3). It then follows from Eq. (4–15) that the fugacity of the liquid and that of the vapor are equal. Now if the ideal gas law is used as an approximation for the vapor, the fugacity will be set equal to the pressure. Therefore the fugacity of a liquid is, to this degree of approximation, equal to its vapor pressure. More generally, the fugacity of a liquid bears the same relation to its vapor pressure as the fugacity of the vapor does to its pressure. Similar remarks apply to the fugacity of a solid.

The fugacity is generally valuable in treating equilibria within gaseous phases, and between gaseous and condensed phases. For equilibria within and between condensed phases it is rather inconvenient and is best replaced by other functions, which will be described in Chapter 7.

4–10. Experimental *p-v-T* Data and Equations of State for Real Gases

The solid lines in Figure 9 show the typical behavior of real gases at various temperatures. For a temperature well above the critical temperature the gas is nearly ideal, and the curve approximates to the hyperbola predicted by Boyle's law. The curve for the critical temperature shows an inflection point at the critical pressure and volume. At lower

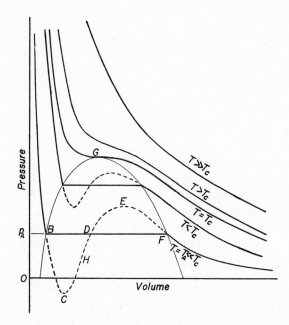

FIGURE 9. TYPICAL PRESSURE-VOLUME BEHAVIOR OF REAL GASES AT VARIOUS TEMPERATURES. The dashed lines show the predictions of the van der Waals Equation. This drawing is only schematic; on a scale drawing of any reasonable size many of the features shown here would be obscured.

temperatures there is a discontinuity in volume corresponding to the change from gaseous to liquid state.

When empirical or semiempirical equations of state are fitted to these data, the discontinuity is usually replaced by an S-shaped portion such as *BCDEF*. The portions *BC* and *EF* may be interpreted in terms of metastable states, *BC* representing superheated liquid and *EF* supercooled vapor. Some equations, such as that of van der Waals, show a region of negative pressure for the superheated liquid. This would correspond to a state in which a liquid is metastable under tension; such states have actually been observed in a few liquids. The portion *CDE*, however, cannot represent any physically realizable state, since it violates the condition that $(\partial v/\partial p)_T$ must be negative in any stable or metastable state (Section 3–6).

4–11. The Principle of Corresponding States

Suppose that the equation of state of a gas can be expressed in the form

$$p = f(v,T)$$

Now let us substitute the constant value T_A (Figure 9) for T and p_A for p; then the equation $p_A = f(v,T_A)$, when solved for v, will give three roots, represented by B, D, and F in the figure. Then Rolle's theorem shows that there must be a point between B and D, and another between D and F, at which

$$f_v(v,T_A) = 0$$

where the subscript v signifies differentiation with respect to v at constant T. These are, of course, the points C and E, at which the tangent to the curve is horizontal. Now a second application of Rolle's theorem shows that the second derivative must vanish somewhere between C and E; this will be at the point H, where the curve changes from concave upward to concave downward. Thus there are six points at which one of the functions $f(v,T_A) - p_A$, $f_v(v,T_A)$, and $f_{vv}(v,T_A)$ vanishes. Now as the temperature is raised, the S-shaped portion *BCDEF* becomes smaller, merging into the single point G at the critical temperature. It follows that at the critical point $f(v_c,T_c) - p_c$, $f_v(v_c,T_c)$, and $f_{vv}(v_c,T_c)$ are all zero.

Now many equations of state are of the type

$$p = \psi(v,T,R,a,b) \tag{4–24}$$

where a and b are dimensional constants characteristic of the particular gas; any other constants appearing in the equation are dimensionless numerical constants which are the same for all gases. At the critical point we have

$$\psi(v_c, T_c, R, a, b) = p_c \qquad (a)$$

$$\psi_v(v_c, T_c, R, a, b) = 0 \qquad (b) \quad (4\text{-}25)$$

$$\psi_{vv}(v_c, T_c, R, a, b) = 0 \qquad (c)$$

If R, a, and b are regarded as unknowns, and this set of equations can be solved for them, we have these quantities expressed as functions of p_c, v_c, and T_c. Dimensional considerations show that the expression for R must be of the form

$$R = \frac{\alpha p_c v_c}{T_c} \qquad (4\text{-}26)$$

where α is a pure number, since no other combination of the quantities on the right has the dimensions of R. Substituting these expressions for R, a, and b into Eq. (4-24) gives an expression for p in terms of v, T, v_c, and T_c. Dividing by p_c gives the ratio p/p_c, which we designate by π, as a function of the same quantities; that is,

$$\pi = \chi(v, T, p_c, v_c, T_c)$$

Since π is dimensionless, only dimensionless combinations of the other quantities can enter into the function on the right. This eliminates p_c, which can enter into no dimensionless combinations with the others. Moreover, the only dimensionless combinations of the others are the ratios v/v_c and T/T_c, designated by ϕ and θ, respectively. Thus the equation of state has been reduced to the form

$$\pi = \xi(\phi, \theta) \qquad (4\text{-}27)$$

in which all explicit reference to properties of individual gases has been eliminated; implicitly, of course, the critical constants of individual gases are involved. The ratios π, ϕ, and θ are referred to as *reduced* properties. Generally, if two gases obeying the original equation of state (Eq. (4-24)) have the same values of any two of the reduced properties, they have the same value of the third one also; they are then said to be in *corresponding states*. The only exception not involving metastable states is that a liquid and the vapor in equilibrium with it have the same reduced temperature and reduced pressure but different reduced volumes, so that if π and θ happen to fall exactly on a liquid-vapor equilibrium value, ϕ is not uniquely determined.

The extent to which the idea of corresponding states applies to real

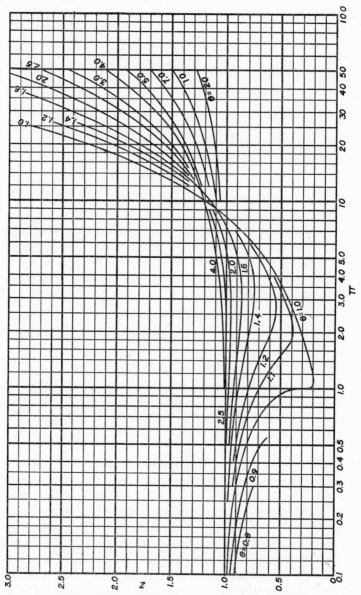

FIGURE 10. COMPRESSIBILITY FACTOR (z) AS A FUNCTION OF REDUCED PRESSURE (π) AT VARIOUS REDUCED TEMPERATURES (θ). For reduced temperatures of five or more, these data may be extended to lower reduced pressures by setting $z - 1$ proportional to the reduced pressure. More detailed graphs, and references to original sources of data, are given by Dodge, B. F., "Chemical Engineering Thermodynamics," pp. 160-162, New York, N. Y., McGraw-Hill Book Co., Inc., 1944.

gases and liquids varies with different substances. For chemically similar compounds divergences of no more than a few per cent are common. The accuracy of the idea has been held by some to indicate that an equation of state should contain only two constants peculiar to each individual substance; others hold that its lack of wider applicability and greater accuracy shows that more constants are needed. Clearly the answer depends on the accuracy desired.

For gases following the corresponding-state concept, it furnishes a convenient means of presenting many thermodynamic data. For example, the *compressibility factor*, z, is defined as pv/RT; we therefore have

$$z = \frac{pv}{RT} = \frac{\pi p_c \phi v_c}{R\theta T_c} = \frac{\pi\phi}{\alpha\theta} \tag{4-28}$$

so that z is the same for all gases in corresponding states. By Eqs. (4-27) any one of the reduced variables can be eliminated, and z can thus be regarded as a function of the other two. Commonly, z is plotted against π and θ, as in Figure 10. Such a graph can be used for any gas for which the critical pressure and temperature are known, with accuracy determined by the closeness with which the gas follows the principle of corresponding states. Similarly we can rearrange Eq. (4-19) to read

$$\ln \frac{f}{p} = \int_0^p \left(\frac{v}{RT} - \frac{1}{p} \right) dp$$

In this, z/p is substituted for v/RT, and the variable of integration is changed from p to π by the substitution $dp/p = d\pi/\pi$, the upper limit changing to π also. This gives

$$\ln \frac{f}{p} = \int_0^p (z-1)\frac{dp}{p} = \int_0^\pi (z-1)\frac{d\pi}{\pi} \tag{4-29}$$

which shows that the fugacity coefficient, f/p, is also a function of the reduced variables and is the same for all gases in corresponding states. Thus a graph of f/p against π and θ gives on a single graph fugacity data for a vast number of gases, with no auxiliary information needed to use it except the critical pressure and temperature. Newton[4] has shown that such graphs are remarkably accurate (usually within 2 per cent) for reduced pressures below about 50 and reduced temperatures above about 0.7. Only for a few gases of very low critical temperature (for example, hydrogen)

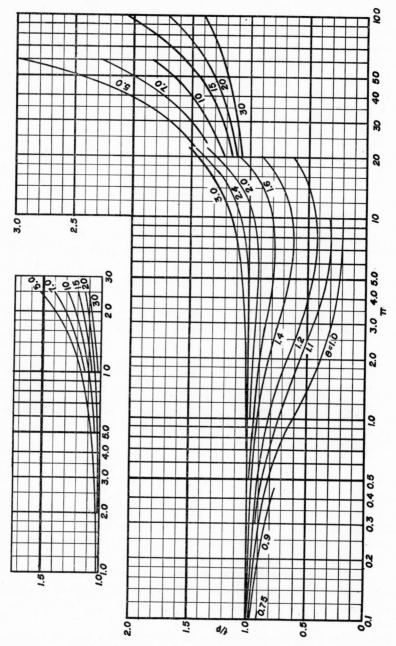

FIGURE 11. FUGACITY COEFFICIENT AS A FUNCTION OF REDUCED PRESSURE AT VARIOUS REDUCED TEMPERATURES. (Redrawn from the data of Newton.[4])

was this accuracy not attained. A graph of this type is given in Figure 11.

Finally, it should be pointed out that the usefulness of the principle of corresponding states in no way depends on our knowing what form the equation of state (Eq. (4–24)) or the reduced equation of state (Eq. (4–27)) takes. We can plot experimental values of z or f/p against reduced temperature and pressure without knowing the equation of state. The reasoning in this section merely gives some insight into why data plotted in this manner are valid for a wide variety of gases.

4–12. The van der Waals Equation

One of the earliest attempts to improve on the ideal gas law was announced by van der Waals in 1873. He concluded on the basis of ingenious but not entirely convincing reasoning that the effect of intermolecular attractions on a gas is the same as increasing the pressure by an amount which is inversely proportional to the square of the molar volume, and that the molar volume must be decreased by a constant amount, characteristic of each gas, to account for the space from which any one molecule is excluded by the presence of the others. The result is the well-known equation

$$\left(p + \frac{a}{v^2}\right)(v - b) = RT \tag{4-30}$$

where a and b are constants characteristic of each gas. Van der Waals' equation is of the type of Eq. (4–24), and yields a principle of corresponding states. It gives isothermal curves similar to those shown in Figure 9, with S-shaped curves in the condensation region and an inflection point representing the critical state. In these respects it is a great qualitative improvement over the ideal gas law. Quantitatively, the improvement is often not enough to justify the extra cumbersomeness, so that the ideal gas law is more widely used in applications. The heuristic value of the van der Waals equation may have exceeded its practical value, as it has inspired a vast amount of work on the equations of state of real gases.

Some of the thermodynamic properties of van der Waals gases will be derived here, not for their rather limited practical value, but as an exercise illustrating the methods developed in this chapter. Some properties cannot be derived from equations of state alone; among these are the standard energy, entropy, and heat capacities. The reason for this will be made clear by the ststistical treatment in Chapter 6.

The fugacity is calculated from Eq. (4–19). When the van der Waals equation is multiplied out, it is found to be a general cubic equation in v. Because of the cumbersomeness of the solution of this type of equation, it is not practical to solve for v and substitute the value into the integrand of Eq. (4–19). Instead the integral of $v\,dp$ is transformed into an integral in dv. If the van der Waals equation is written in the form

$$p = \frac{RT}{v - b} - \frac{a}{v^2} \tag{4–31}$$

differentiation gives

$$\left(\frac{\partial p}{\partial v}\right)_T = -\frac{RT}{(v - b)^2} + \frac{2a}{v^3} \tag{4–32}$$

Then we have

$$\int v\,dp = \int v\left(\frac{\partial p}{\partial v}\right)_T dv = \int\left[-\frac{RTv}{(v - b)^2} + \frac{2a}{v^2}\right] dv$$

$$= \int\left[-\frac{RT}{v - b} - \frac{bRT}{(v - b)^2} + \frac{2a}{v^3}\right] dv$$

$$= -RT \ln (v - b) + \frac{bRT}{v - b} - \frac{2a}{v}$$

The remaining portion of the integrand on Eq. (4–19) (dp/p) need not be transformed, since it is easily integrated to $\ln p$. These integrals are now substituted into Eq. (4–19), and the limits are inserted. At the lower limit, where $p \to 0$, $v \to \infty$ and $pv \to RT$. This gives

$$\ln\frac{f}{p} = \left[-\ln p(v - b) + \frac{b}{v - b} - \frac{2a}{RTv}\right]_{\substack{p\,=\,0 \\ v\,=\,\infty}}^{p,v}$$

$$= \ln\frac{RT}{p(v - b)} + \frac{b}{v - b} - \frac{2a}{RTv}$$

so that adding $\ln (p/p_u)$ to both sides gives

$$\ln\frac{f}{p_u} = \ln\frac{RT}{p_u(v - b)} + \frac{b}{v - b} - \frac{2a}{RTv} \tag{4–33}$$

The enthalpy can be regarded as a function of either pressure or volume at constant temperature; the latter choice proves more convenient. From Eqs. (2–10) and (3–16) we readily derive

$$\left(\frac{\partial h}{\partial v}\right)_T = T\left(\frac{\partial s}{\partial v}\right)_T + v\left(\frac{\partial p}{\partial v}\right)_T = T\left(\frac{\partial p}{\partial T}\right)_V + v\left(\frac{\partial p}{\partial v}\right)_T$$

The derivatives on the right can be taken from Eqs. (4–31) and (4–32). Substitution gives

$$\left(\frac{\partial h}{\partial v}\right)_T = \frac{RT}{v-b} - \frac{RTv}{(v-b)^2} + \frac{2a}{v^2} = -\frac{RTb}{(v-b)^2} + \frac{2a}{v^2} \qquad (4\text{--}34)$$

In integrating this equation, we can make use of the fact that as $p \to 0$, $v \to \infty$ and $h \to h'$. Using these as the lower limits of integration, we get

$$h = h' + \int_\infty^v \left[-\frac{RTb}{(v-b)^2} + \frac{2a}{v^2} \right] dv = h' + \frac{RTb}{v-b} - \frac{2a}{v} \qquad (4\text{--}35)$$

The Gibbs free energy follows immediately from the activity, here designated f/p_u to avoid confusion with the van der Waals a. Using Eq. (4–33), we find

$$g = g' + RT \ln \frac{f}{p_u} = g' + RT \ln \frac{RT}{p_u(v-b)} + \frac{RTb}{v-b} - \frac{2a}{v} \qquad (4\text{--}36)$$

The entropy is derived from Eqs. (4–35) and (4–36), with the help of the relation $s = (h - g)/T$. This gives

$$s = s' - R \ln \frac{RT}{p_u(v-b)} \qquad (4\text{--}37)$$

The van der Waals equation can easily be expressed as a virial equation in powers of $1/v$, as follows: First it is written in the form

$$pv = \frac{RTv}{v-b} - \frac{a}{v} = \frac{RT}{1 - \dfrac{b}{v}} - \frac{a}{v}$$

Since $b < v$, $1/[1 - (b/v)]$ can be expressed as a convergent geometric series, $1 + (b/v) + (b/v^2) + \ldots$ Substituting this into the equation above, we get

$$pv = RT + \frac{RTb - a}{v} + \frac{RTb^2}{v^2} + \ldots \tag{4-38}$$

As for the accuracy with which this equation represents the behavior of real gases, the first term is, of course, correct. The second can be derived by treating molecules as incompressible spheres and so is a reasonable, though not very accurate, approximation. The remaining terms bear no relation to the actual virial coefficients.

The temperature at which the coefficient of $1/v$ vanishes is called the *Boyle temperature*. At this temperature Boyle's law holds exceptionally well, because all deviations from it are second-order effects and so are small at low pressures (that is, at low values of $1/v$). Clearly the Boyle temperature of a van der Waals gas is given by

$$T_B = \frac{a}{Rb} \tag{4-39}$$

The Joule-Thomson coefficient $(\partial T/\partial p)_h$ can be derived as follows: From Eqs. (1-13) and (1-12) (in that order) we have

$$\left(\frac{\partial T}{\partial p}\right)_h = -\frac{\left(\frac{\partial h}{\partial p}\right)_T}{\left(\frac{\partial h}{\partial T}\right)_p} = -\frac{\left(\frac{\partial h}{\partial v}\right)_T}{c_p \left(\frac{\partial p}{\partial v}\right)_T}$$

The derivatives in the last expression can be taken from Eqs. (4-32) and (4-34). This gives

$$\left(\frac{\partial T}{\partial p}\right)_h = -\frac{1}{c_p} \left[\frac{\dfrac{RTb}{(v-b)^2} - \dfrac{2a}{v^2}}{\dfrac{RT}{(v-b)^2} - \dfrac{2a}{v^3}}\right] = -\frac{1}{c_p} \left[\frac{RTbv^3 - 2av(v-b)^2}{RTv^3 - 2a(v-b)^2}\right]$$

It is sometimes of interest to find the limiting value of the Joule-Thomson coefficient as the pressure approaches zero, or in other words, a low-pressure approximation to this coefficient. Now at low pressures, v is very large, and so all powers of v except the highest may be neglected. In the numerator of the above fraction the coefficient of v^3 is $RTb - 2a$, while in the denominator it is RT. Therefore the desired low-pressure approximation is given by

$$\left(\frac{\partial T}{\partial p}\right)_h \approx -\frac{1}{c_p}\frac{RTb - 2a}{RT} = \frac{1}{c_p}\left(\frac{2a}{RT} - b\right) \tag{4-40}$$

This equation shows that the Joule-Thomson coefficient at low pressures is negative at high temperatures and positive at low temperatures; qualitatively, real gases show this same behavior. The temperature at which the Joule-Thomson coefficient is zero is called the *inversion temperature*; for a van der Waals gas it is given by

$$T_i = \frac{2a}{Rb} \tag{4-41}$$

For real gases Eqs. (4-39) and (4-41) are only rough approximations, as is the relation $T_i = 2T_B$, which is readily derived from them.

The inversion temperature is important in connection with the liquefaction of gases. There are two main processes for this. In both, the gas is first compressed and cooled as much as practical. It is then allowed to expand, and in this step it is cooled further. Repeated application of these steps eventually liquefies part of the gas. In the Claude process the expanding gas does work against a piston or turbine, the expansion being made as near adiabatic and reversible as possible. This process will cool any gas. In the Linde process the expansion is through a throttling valve; this is the same process as the expansion in the Joule-Thomson experiment, and it results in cooling only if the gas is below its inversion temperature at the start of the expansion. At naturally occurring temperatures all gases except hydrogen and helium are below their inversion temperatures and can be liquefied by the Linde process. The Linde method cannot be used for hydrogen and helium unless they are first cooled below their inversion temperatures ($-80°$ and $-243°C$, respectively) by some auxiliary method.

The Claude process is much the more efficient thermodynamically, but it is more troublesome mechanically than the Linde process. A frequent compromise is to use the Claude process for the first part of the cooling and the Linde process for the actual liquefaction. In this way each is used in the range for which its advantage is greatest.

Finally, to convert the van der Waals equation to a reduced form, we start with Eqs. (4–25(b))and (4–25(c)). These become

$$-\frac{RT_c}{(v_c - b)^2} + \frac{2a}{v_c{}^3} = 0$$

and

$$\frac{2RT_c}{(v_c - b)^3} - \frac{6a}{v_c{}^4} = 0$$

Transposing the second member of each of these to the right and dividing the first by the second gives

$$\frac{v_c - b}{2} = \frac{v_c}{3}$$

so that $b = v_c/3$. Substituting this into either of the equations above leads to $a = 9RT_cv_c/8$. With these values of a and b the van der Waals equation at the critical point takes the form

$$p_c = \frac{RT_c}{v_c - \dfrac{v_c}{3}} - \frac{9RT_cv_c}{8v_c{}^2}$$

from which we find

$$R = \frac{8p_cv_c}{3T_c}$$

This permits elimination of R from the expression for a and leads to the value $a = 3p_cv_c{}^2$. Substituting these values of a, b, and R into the van der Waals equation and dividing by p_cv_c converts it to the reduced form

$$\left(\pi + \frac{3}{\phi^2}\right)\left(\phi - \frac{1}{3}\right) = \frac{8}{3}\theta$$

4–13. The Clapeyron Equation

Consider a change which meets the following conditions: (1) It takes place reversibly at constant temperature and pressure, and (2) at each temperature there is only one pressure at which it can occur reversibly. A phase change of a single substance is a typical example of this type of change. It also includes many chemical reactions, such as

$$CaCO_3 \rightarrow CaO + CO_2$$

and

$$NH_2CO_2NH_4 \rightarrow CO_2 + 2NH_3$$

It is convenient to use here the *degree of advancement*, a term introduced by De Donder[5] and designated by ξ, to indicate how far the reaction has proceeded. For the second reaction above, ξ is defined so that when it increases by $d\xi$, $d\xi$ moles of carbon dioxide and $2d\xi$ moles of ammonia are formed, while $d\xi$ moles of ammonium carbamate decompose. In general, if a product Z_i appears in the reaction equation with stoichiometric coefficient z_i, then the formation of dn_{Z_i} moles of Z_i means that the degree of advancement increases by

$$d\xi = \frac{dn_{Z_i}}{z_i}$$

A similar equation, but with negative sign, applies to reactants. Thus $d\xi$ is positive whenever the reaction proceeds forward.

When a change of the type considered here proceeds to a small extent $d\xi$, the changes in entropy and volume are given by

$$dS = (s_2 - s_1)\, d\xi \quad \text{and} \quad dV = (v_2 - v_1)\, d\xi$$

where s_2 is the entropy of that quantity of product formed when the degree of advancement increases by unity. For the decomposition of ammonium carbamate, s_2 is the entropy of a mixture of 1 mole of carbon dioxide and two moles of ammonia. From this we find

$$\left(\frac{\partial S}{\partial V}\right)_T = \frac{s_2 - s_1}{v_2 - v_1}$$

We now substitute this into the third of Maxwell's equations (Eq. (3–16)), noting that since p depends on T only, the derivative of p with respect to T is a total derivative. This gives

$$\frac{dp}{dT} = \frac{s_2 - s_1}{v_2 - v_1} = \frac{\Delta s}{\Delta v} \tag{4–42}$$

Since T and p are constant during the process, $\Delta h = T\,\Delta s$. Substituting this in Eq. (4–42) leads to *Clapeyron's equation*,

$$\frac{dp}{dT} = \frac{\Delta h}{T\,\Delta v} \tag{4–43}$$

Alternatively, we may derive this equation by noting that the condition for equilibrium at constant temperature and pressure requires that

$$g_1 = g_2$$

If we change to a slightly different set of equilibrium conditions, this equation must still hold, and so

$$dg_1 = dg_2$$

Since equilibrium is maintained during this small change of conditions, Eq. (3–5) can be applied, leading to

$$-s_1\, dT + v_1\, dp = -s_2\, dT + v_2\, dp$$

This is easily rearranged to give Eq. (4–42).

Although Clapeyron's equation as written involves molar enthalpy and volume changes, this is not essential. The enthalpy and volume changes may refer to any amount of the material undergoing the transformation, since it is only their ratio that is needed. Moreover, if the change is reversed, both Δh and Δv are changed in sign, and their ratio is unaffected.

When Clapeyron's equation is applied to the vaporization of a liquid, Δh is the heat of vaporization and p the vapor pressure. Since vapor pressures have been measured for more substances than have heats of vaporization, one of its most practical uses is the determination of the latter quantities. It should be pointed out that the units in which Δh is obtained are the units of pressure multiplied by those of volume; if p is in atmospheres and Δv in liters, Δh will be in liter·atmospheres, while if bars and liters are used, Δh will be in decijoules. When applied to the melting of a solid or the transition between two solid phases, the Clapeyron equation is usually turned upside down and used to find dT/dp, the variation of melting point or transition point with pressure.

PROBLEMS

(1) Solve Eq. (4–2) for p; by squaring and cubing the resulting series find expressions for p^2 and p^3, retaining terms through the one in $1/V^3$. Substitute these into Eq. (4–1), and by equating coefficients of like powers of V derive expressions for β, γ, and δ in terms of B, C, D, and RT.

(2) Standard entropies listed in tables are usually based on $p_u = 1$ atm. How would they need to be changed if values based on $p_u = 1$ bar were desired?

(3) Convert the following equations of state to reduced form:

(a) Berthelot's original equation $\left(p + \dfrac{a}{Tv^2}\right)(v - b) = RT$.

(b) $\left(p + \dfrac{a}{v^n}\right)(v - b) = RT$, where n is a constant.

(c) Deiterici's equation $p(v - b) = RTe^{-a/RTv}$.

Part (c) can be greatly simplified by first showing that in Eqs. (4–25(b)) and (4–25(c)) the derivatives of ψ may be replaced by derivatives of $\ln \psi$.

(4) Show that if p is given by Eq. (4–1), Eq. (4–25(b)) cannot be satisfied, so that Eq. (4–1) cannot represent a gas at its critical point. *Note*: Use the fact that $(\partial p / \partial v)_T = 1/(\partial v / \partial p)_T$.

(5) Berthelot's modified equation,

$$pv = RT \left[1 + \frac{9}{128} \frac{\pi}{\theta} \left(1 - \frac{6}{\theta^2} \right) \right]$$

is often used at low pressures, at which it is very satisfactory.

(a) Show that this equation cannot hold at the critical point. (See Problem 4.)

(b) Show that for a Berthelot gas

$$s' = s_1 + \frac{27 R p_u}{32 p_c \theta^3}$$

(c) Derive general expressions for s and $\ln (f/p)$ for a Berthelot gas. (In differentiating do not forget that π and θ are functions of p and T, respectively.)

(6) Derive expressions for the thermodynamic properties of a gas obeying Berthelot's original equation

$$\left(p + \frac{a}{Tv^2} \right) (v - b) = RT$$

The treatment of the van der Waals gas in the text may be used as a model if desired.

(7) Into Clapeyron's equation introduce the approximations of neglecting the volume of the liquid and approximating the volume of the vapor by the ideal gas law. The resulting equation is often called the *Clausius-Clapeyron* equation. Combine this with Trouton's empirical rule that the molar entropy of vaporization of most liquids at 1 atm pressure is about 21 cal/mole·degree, and by inserting numerical values derive a simple rule for correcting boiling points for minor variations in atmospheric pressure.

(8) The equation of state of Redlich and Kwong[6] is

$$p = \frac{RT}{v - b} - \frac{a}{T^{\frac{1}{2}} v(v + b)}$$

where a and b are constants. Show that this leads to $b = 0.261 v_c$. (The entire transformation to a reduced equation can be carried out, but it is rather tedious.)

(9) The following properties of carbon dioxide at 10°C were calculated from the compilation of Sweigert, Weber, and Allen.[7]

p/bars	v/lit·mole	s/joules/mole·degree
0.200	117.5	—
0.500	46.92	—
1.000	23.38	211.67
5.000	4.556	197.64
10.00	—	191.07
20.00	—	183.68
30.00	—	178.69
40.00	—	174.68

In this pressure range the enthalpy is given by

$$h = \left(31.48 - 0.068 \, \frac{p}{1 \text{ bar}}\right) \text{ kilojoules/mole.}$$

(a) Determine the value of R.

(b) Find h', s', and g' for CO_2 at this temperature, based on $p_u = 1$ bar. (Do not be disturbed by the negative value of g'; this results from the arbitrary choice of a zero point from which to measure h.)

(c) Calculate g, f, and f/p at 30 bars. Compare the last with the value read from Figure 11. The critical pressure is 73.9 bars, the critical temperature 31.1°C.

(d) Calculate the Joule-Thomson coefficient $(\partial T/\partial p)_h$. The heat capacity at constant pressure is 37.13 joules/mole·degree.

REFERENCES

1. Boggs, J. E., *J. Chem. Ed.*, **35**, 30 (1958); Copley, G. N., *ibid.*, p. 366.
2. Guggenheim, E. A., and Prue, J. E., "Physicochemical Calculations," Chap. 1, New York, N.Y., Interscience Publishers, Inc., 1955. Also Guggenheim, E. A., *J. Chem. Ed.*, **35**, 606 (1958).
3. Shanks, D., *Am. J. Phys.*, **24**, 352 (1956).
4. Newton, R. H., *Ind. Eng. Chem.*, **27**, 302 (1935).
5. DeDonder, Th., and Van Rysselberghe, P., "The Thermodynamic Theory of Affinity," Stanford University Press, Stanford, Calif., 1936.
6. Redlich, O., and Kwong, J. M. S., *Chem. Rev.*, **44**, 233 (1949).
7. Sweigert, R. L., Weber, P., and Allen, R. L., *Ind. Eng. Chem.*, **38**, 185 (1946).

chapter 5

Thermochemistry

The term *thermochemistry* generally refers to the determination of the heat gained or lost by systems undergoing chemical reaction. Since reactions are usually carried out at constant volume or constant pressure, this means evaluating the change in energy or enthalpy accompanying the reaction. In this chapter some attention is also given to the more general problem of determining the change in any thermodynamic property when a reaction occurs. Since there is no thermodynamic distinction between chemical and physical changes, the methods discussed here apply equally well to both.

5-1. Thermodynamic Property Changes in a Reaction: Hess's Law

Suppose that a reaction, chemical or physical, is symbolized as

$$\sum_i y_i Y_i \rightarrow \sum_i z_i Z_i$$

where the y's and z's are stoichiometric coefficients, the Y's are reactants, and the Z's products. Then the enthalpy change of this reaction is defined as

$$\Delta h \equiv \sum_i z_i h_{Z_i} - \sum_i y_i h_{Y_i} \tag{5-1}$$

If this is to have any meaning, the states of the reactants and products must be specified. This is usually done with the letters s, l, and g for solid, liquid, and gas respectively, plus thermodynamic information such as temperature and pressure when necessary. A few examples will help to make this clear. For the reaction

$$H_2O \ (l, 25° \ C) \rightarrow H_2O \ (g, saturated, 25° \ C)$$

the enthalpy change is

$$\Delta h = h_{H_2O} \ (g, saturated, 25° \ C) - h_{H_2O} \ (l, 25° \ C)$$

or, in other words, the heat of vaporization at 25°. For

$$Fe_2O_3 \ (s) + 3H_2 \ (g) \rightarrow 2Fe \ (s) + 3H_2O \ (g),$$

$$\Delta h = 2h_{Fe} \ (s) + 3h_{H_2O} \ (g) - h_{Fe_2O_3} \ (s) - 3h_{H_2} \ (g)$$

Of course, the temperatures of reactants and products must be specified before this is definite. Pressure is less important; the enthalpies of condensed phases vary little with pressure because of their low volume, while for gases the variation is slight unless they are far from ideal or the pressure is very high. However, for exact work, knowledge of the pressure is needed. The Δh values calculated by these equations give the enthalpy change when one *unit of reaction* occurs; that is, when for each reactant the number of moles reacting is equal to its stoichiometric coefficient. If, instead, ξ units of reaction occur, where ξ is the degree of advancement introduced in Section 4–13, the total enthalpy change is

$$\Delta H = \xi \Delta h \tag{5-2}$$

If the reaction is written with different coefficients, the unit of reaction and the enthalpy change will be correspondingly different, though of course the total enthalpy change for a given amount of material reacting will not be affected. Thus the unit of reaction and Δh for

$$H_2 \ (g) + Cl_2 \ (g) \rightarrow 2HCl \ (g)$$

are twice as great as those for

$$\tfrac{1}{2}H_2 \ (g) + \tfrac{1}{2}Cl_2 \ (g) \rightarrow HCl \ (g)$$

It does not matter whether the reaction actually occurs as a single step or a series of steps. For example, Δh for the reaction

$$2C\ (s) + O_2\ (g) \rightarrow 2CO\ (g) \tag{I}$$

is $2h_{CO\ (g)} - h_{O_2\ (g)} - 2\,h_{C\ (s)}$. If it is carried out in two steps

$$C(s) + O_2\ (g) \rightarrow CO_2\ (g) \tag{II}$$

and

$$C\ (s) + CO_2\ (g) \rightarrow 2CO\ (g) \tag{III}$$

The enthalpy changes for these steps are

$$\Delta h_{II} = h_{CO_2\ (g)} - h_{C\ (s)} - h_{O_2\ (g)}$$

and

$$\Delta h_{III} = 2h_{CO\ (g)} - h_{C\ (s)} - h_{CO_2\ (g)}$$

The over-all enthalpy change for the two steps is the sum of Δh_{II} and Δh_{III}; on adding these equations we find

$$\Delta h_{II} + \Delta h_{III} = \Delta h_I$$

Since at constant pressure Δh is equal to the heat absorbed, this result can be restated as follows: The heat of reaction at constant pressure is the same regardless of whether the reaction is carried out directly or through intermediate steps. In this form — except for the constant-pressure stipulation — it was first stated by Hess in 1840 and is known as *Hess's law*.

Throughout this section enthalpy has been used as an illustration, but the definitions and equations apply equally well to any thermodynamic property. They do not apply to heat and work, which are not properties, unless some stipulation such as constant volume or constant pressure is imposed. Hess's law, stated in terms of heat, is not correct without such a stipulation; stated in terms of Δh or Δu, it not only is correct but is obviously extensible to other properties also.

The unmodified phrase "heat of reaction" is generally used for Δh and so implies a constant-pressure reaction. The heat of reaction at constant volume is Δu. Note that this means that heats of reaction are positive for endothermic reactions, negative for exothermic ones. However, in some books, especially older ones, the signs are reversed, so that the values listed for heats of reaction are $-\Delta h$ or $-\Delta u$. One should be wary of this point in using thermochemical data from reference works. It is generally understood that heats of reaction are based on having the initial and final temperatures of the reacting system the same, unless otherwise specified.

Usually the heats of reaction recorded in reference works are the *standard heats of reaction,* defined by

$$\Delta h^0 \equiv \sum_i z_i h^0_{Z_i} - \sum_i y_i h^0_{Y_i} \qquad (5\text{-}3)$$

The superscript zero here indicates the standard value of the enthalpy. For liquids and solids this is generally defined as the enthalpy in the stable state at unit pressure (usually 1 atm) and whatever temperature is involved (the *standard state*). For gases the standard enthalpies are those defined in Section 4–8. Similar remarks apply to standard changes in other thermodynamic properties.

5–2. Determination of the Energy Change in a Reaction; the Constant-Volume Calorimeter

Consider a closed container for carrying out a reaction without change of volume. Such a device must have some means of starting the reaction (for example, an electrically heated wire), and it must be strong enough to withstand the high pressure developed in some reactions, such as that of hydrogen and oxygen. If it is to be useful for thermodynamic measurements, it must be provided with a thermometer (not usually of the liquid-in-glass type) and means of keeping down to a negligible amount the heat exchange between the container and its surroundings. The latter can be accomplished by surrounding the container with a vacuum jacket to minimize conduction, silvering it to reduce radiation, and varying the temperature of the surrounding medium so that it is always nearly equal

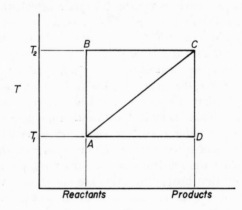

FIGURE 12. DIAGRAM FOR CLARIFYING DERIVATION OF CALORIMETRIC EQUATIONS.

to that of the container. Such an apparatus is called a *constant-volume calorimeter* or, more colloquially, a *bomb*.

Now if we regard the bomb and its contents as the system, we see that for a reaction carried out as described above, both Q and W are zero, and so $\Delta U = 0$. (This is based on the assumption that the energy added by the starting device is negligible; if it is not, a correction can be made for it.) In Figure 12, this change is indicated by AC. What we mean by the heat of reaction at constant volume is Q or ΔU for the process AD, in which the reactants are at the same temperature. By Hess's law,

$$Q_{AD} + Q_{DC} = Q_{AC} = 0$$

or

$$\Delta U_{AD} + \Delta U_{DC} = 0$$

Notice that the inclusion of the bomb itself in the system does not affect ΔU_{AD}, since the bomb has the same energy at the beginning and end of this change; it does change ΔU_{DC} and ΔU_{AC}, however. Now Q_{DC} is easily determined. First the system is brought to the state D; that is, bomb plus products at temperature T_1. Then energy is added in measured quantity (by an electric heater with a wattmeter, for example) until the temperature T_2 is reached; the energy input is Q_{DC}. More commonly, it is calculated by the equation

$$Q_{DC} = \int_{T_1}^{T_2} C_v^P \, dT$$

the superscript P indicating that this is the heat capacity of bomb plus products. It then follows that

$$\Delta U_{AD} = - \int_{T_1}^{T_2} C_v^P \, dT \tag{5–4}$$

Similarly, by considering the process ABC, we find that

$$\Delta U_{AB} + \Delta U_{BC} = 0, \text{ and } \Delta U_{AB} = \int_{T_1}^{T_2} C_v^R \, dT$$

the superscript R indicating that the heat capacity of the bomb plus reactants must be used. Therefore,

$$\Delta U_{BC} = - \int_{T_1}^{T_2} C_v^R \, dT \tag{5–5}$$

That is, we find the heat of reaction at the original temperature by using the heat capacity of the bomb plus products, and at the final temperature by using the heat capacity of the bomb plus reactants.

Although the bomb calorimeter is simple in principle, accurate experimental work with it requires a well-developed technique and many corrections for side effects. These are best discussed in a book devoted to this subject[1]; only a few of them will be mentioned here. If water is one of the products, some water is added to the bomb initially. This assures that the gas in the bomb is saturated with water vapor, and so any additional water formed must condense. Without this precaution an unknown portion of the water formed might remain as vapor; since the energy of water vapor is much higher than that of liquid water at the same temperature, this would cause a serious degree of uncertainty in the results. Even with water initially added, there may be slightly more water vapor present at the end of the reaction than at the beginning because of the temperature difference. If oxygen is used, it is usually contaminated with nitrogen, some of which may react to form nitric acid; the amount of this must be determined and a correction for its heat of formation applied. Reaction is sometimes incomplete. In combustion reactions, for example, some soot may be found at the end; the amount of this must be determined and a correction applied for the heat it would have released in burning. Since reactions are usually carried out at high pressure, the energies and enthalpies of gases may be considerably different from their standard values, and this necessitates a correction if standard heats of reaction are desired.

5–3. Determination of Enthalpy Change; the Constant-Pressure Calorimeter

If the calorimeter described in Section 2 is modified so that the reaction occurs at constant pressure instead of constant volume, the adiabatic nature of the process assures that ΔH (instead of ΔU as in the constant-volume case) is zero. We then have, referring to Figure 12,

$$\Delta H_{AD} + \Delta H_{DC} = 0 \quad \text{and} \quad \Delta H_{DC} = \int_{T_1}^{T_2} C_p^P \, dT$$

so that

$$\Delta H_{AD} = - \int_{T_1}^{T_2} C_p^P \, dT \tag{5–6}$$

As before, if we use the heat capacity of the calorimeter plus reactants, we find the heat of reaction at the final temperature; if we use the heat capacity of the calorimeter plus products, we get the heat of reaction at the initial temperature.

The constant-pressure calorimeter is generally used when all the reactants and products are in condensed phases; constancy of pressure is achieved accurately enough by operating at atmospheric pressure. Where gases are involved, the constant-volume calorimeter is more convenient. Since this gives Δu values, it is desirable to have a method for converting these to Δh's. The difference between Δh and Δu is usually much smaller than either, and so it does not have to be known with a high degree of accuracy. This makes it possible to simplify the problem greatly with two approximations: The volume of the condensed phases is neglected, and the gases are treated as ideal. Then we have for condensed reactants and products $u = h$; and for gaseous reactants and products,

$$h = u + pv = u + RT$$

Using these values in Eq. (5–1) leads to

$$\Delta h = \Delta u + \Delta nRT \tag{5-7}$$

where Δn is the increase in the number of moles of gas when one unit of reaction occurs. For example, the equation

$$N_2 + 3H_2 \rightarrow 2NH_3$$

in which all three are gases, indicates that three moles of hydrogen and one mole of nitrogen — a total of 4 moles — react to form 2 moles of ammonia. Therefore $\Delta n = 2 - 4 = -2$, and $\Delta h = \Delta u - 2RT$. For

$$H_2\ (g) + S\ (s) \rightarrow H_2S\ (g)$$

the sulfur, being a solid, has a negligible volume, and so $\Delta n = 1 - 1 = 0$, and $\Delta h = \Delta u$.

5–4. The Kirchhoff Equations

If the equation for the heat of reaction,

$$\Delta h = \sum_i z_i h_{Z_i} - \sum_i y_i h_{Y_i}$$

is differentiated with respect to T at constant pressure, the result is

$$\left(\frac{\partial \Delta h}{\partial T}\right)_p = \sum_i z_i c_{pZ_i} - \sum_i y_i c_{pY_i} \equiv \Delta c_p \tag{5-8}$$

the last quantity being defined in analogy to Δh. This equation, first published by Kirchhoff in 1858, permits the calculation of a heat of reaction at one temperature if it is known at another temperature, and the necessary heat capacities are available. Thus integration of this equation gives

$$h(T_2) = h(T_1) + \int_{T_1}^{T_2} \Delta c_p \, dT \qquad (5\text{--}9)$$

The integration may be carried out analytically if the heat capacities are known as functions of temperature, in the form of empirical equations or relations derived from statistical thermodynamics. If the heat capacities are known only in the form of tabulated experimental results, graphical integration can be used. In many cases sufficient accuracy can be attained by using a constant value for Δc_p; Eq. (5–9) then becomes

$$\Delta h(T_2) = \Delta h(T_1) + \Delta c_p(T_2 - T_1) \qquad (5\text{--}9a)$$

Equations of the Kirchhoff type are easily derived for other thermodynamic changes accompanying a reaction. For energy changes the derivation is exactly analogous to that for enthalpy changes, leading to the result

$$\Delta u(T_2) = \Delta u(T_1) + \int_{T_1}^{T_2} \Delta c_v \, dT \qquad (5\text{--}10)$$

For entropy changes we make use of the fact that $(\partial s/\partial T)_p = c_p/T$. Differentiation of

$$\Delta s = \sum_i z_i s_{Z_i} - \sum_i y_i s_{Y_i}$$

gives

$$\left(\frac{\partial \Delta s}{\partial T}\right)_p = \sum_i z_i \frac{c_{pZ_i}}{T} - \sum_i y_i \frac{c_{pY_i}}{T} = \frac{\Delta c_p}{T}$$

and integration of this leads to

$$s(T_2) = s(T_1) + \int_{T_1}^{T_2} \frac{\Delta c_p}{T} \, dT \qquad (5\text{--}11)$$

If Δc_p is practically constant, this becomes

$$s(T_2) = s(T_1) + \Delta c_p \ln \frac{T_2}{T_1} \qquad (5\text{--}11a)$$

Analogous equations can be derived for the entropy change at constant volume.

For Gibbs free energy changes two procedures are available. If we know Δg and Δh for a reaction at one temperature, we can use the equation $\Delta g = (\Delta h - \Delta g)/T$ to obtain Δs at this temperature. Then Δs and Δh are both evaluated at some other temperature by Eqs. (5–9) and (5–11). Finally they are combined to give Δg at the new temperature.

Alternatively, we may use Eq. (3–20) in the form

$$\left[\frac{\partial(\Delta g/T)}{\partial T} \right]_p = -\frac{\Delta h}{T^2}$$

Integration of this gives

$$\frac{g(T_2)}{T_2} = \frac{g(T_1)}{T_1} - \int_{T_1}^{T_2} \frac{\Delta h}{T^2} \, dT \tag{5–12}$$

Since Δh is usually found as a function of T by integrating Δc_p, this equation really involves a double integration, which is tedious to carry out graphically. For this reason the first method is preferable when no formula is available expressing Δc_p as a function of T. When such a formula is available, the second method is quite satisfactory.

5–5. Heats of Formation and Combustion

The term *heat of formation* generally designates the enthalpy change when a compound is formed from its elements with the final temperature and pressure being the same as the original. It will be denoted by Δh_f. For example, the heat of formation of water is the enthalpy change accompanying the reaction

$$H_2 + \tfrac{1}{2}O_2 \rightarrow H_2O$$

and so is equal to

$$h_{H_2O} - h_{H_2} - \tfrac{1}{2}h_{O_2}$$

Of course, it is necessary to specify the states of the reactants and products. Usually the standard heat of formation — that is, the standard heat of the reaction by which 1 mole of the compound is formed from its elements — is the value recorded in tables.

According to this definition, elements in their standard states have standard heats of formation of zero; in other states, their standard heats of formation will be different from zero (usually positive). Thus for bromine at 25°C the standard state is the liquid, and saturated bromine vapor at this temperature has a positive heat of formation equal to the heat of vaporization. Similarly, since the standard form of hydrogen is molecular, the atomic form has a positive heat of formation.

The use of heats of formation is equivalent to choosing the standard states of the elements as zero points from which to measure enthalpy. Since changes in enthalpy are not affected by any consistent choice of zero points, heats of reaction can be calculated by using heats of formation instead of enthalpies. Thus for the reaction

$$C_2H_5OH \rightarrow C_2H_4 + H_2O$$

we have

$$\Delta h = h_{H_2O} + h_{C_2H_4} - h_{C_2H_5OH} = \Delta h_{fH_2O} + \Delta h_{fC_2H_4} - \Delta h_{fC_2H_5OH}$$

Of course, standard heats of reaction are obtained if standard heats of formation are used.

The use of heats of formation is quite straightforward; their direct determination, however, is not always easy. The formation of water from its elements is easily carried out in a calorimeter, and so direct measurement is practical. On the other hand, the synthesis of ethanol from carbon, hydrogen, and oxygen is no simple matter, and the reactions involved are not suitable for calorimetric measurements. However, the combustion of ethanol to water and carbon dioxide in a calorimeter offers no serious problem; once the heat of this reaction is known, the heat of formation of ethanol is easily calculated. Thus for the reaction

$$C_2H_5OH\ (l) + 3O_2\ (g) \rightarrow 2CO_2\ (g) + 3H_2O\ (l)$$

Δh^0 is found to be $- 322.699$ kcal. The heats of formation of gaseous carbon dioxide and liquid water are $- 94.052$ kcal and $- 68.317$ kcal, respectively. We then have $- 322.699$ kcal $= 2(- 94.052)$ kcal $+ 3(- 68.317)$ kcal $- \Delta h^0$,
from which we find

$$\Delta h^0_{fC_2H_5OH} = -66.356 \text{ kcal}$$

Heats of combustion are, in a sense, negatives of enthalpy values, referred to combustion products as the zero points. Heats of reaction can often be calculated by using heats of combustion with signs changed exactly as if they were heats of formation. However, this procedure appears to offer more opportunities for mistakes than the use of heats of formation. For this reason it is advisable to use heats of combustion only to calculate heats of formation, and to make all further calculations from the latter.

5–6. Heats of Solution

When reactions involving dissolved substances are considered, it is often necessary to include information on the heat required for the process of solution. A thorough discussion of this topic requires concepts that will be introduced in Chapter 7; only the simplest case will be treated here.

If a substance is dissolved in varying amounts of solvent, and the heat absorbed or given off in each case is measured, it will be found that this heat approaches a definite limit as the amount of solvent increases. It is this limit that will be called the *heat of solution* in this chapter. In other words, the heat of solution is the heat absorbed when 1 mole of a substance dissolves in so much solvent that further dilution has only a negligible thermal effect.

Water is the commonest solvent, and so for aqueous solutions we use a special notation: The process of dissolving a mole of solid X in so much water that the heat of solution has practically its limiting value will be designated by

$$X\ (s) + aq \rightarrow X\ (aq)$$

5–7. Heats of Formation of Ions

Since many chemical reactions take place between ions in solution, it is desirable to be able to calculate the heats of these reactions from heats of formation. By analogy with the heats of formation of compounds, we might attempt to define the heats of formation of aqueous sodium and sulfate ions, for example, as the heats of the reactions

$$Na\ (s) + aq \rightarrow Na^+\ (aq) + \epsilon \qquad (5\text{–}13)$$

and

$$S\ (s) + 2O_2\ (g) + aq + 2\epsilon \rightarrow SO_4^=\ (aq)$$

where ϵ is an electron. However, neither of these reactions can be carried out without other reactions occurring simultaneously. It is true that the energy change for the reaction

$$Na\ (g) \rightarrow Na^+\ (g) + \epsilon$$

can be determined spectroscopically, and this, when combined with the heat of sublimation of sodium, would give a value for the reaction

$$Na\ (s) \rightarrow Na^+\ (g) + \epsilon$$

This, however, differs from Eq. (5–13) by the heat of solution of the sodium ion, and it is this that we cannot measure.

Certain reactions involving combinations of ions can, of course, be studied calorimetrically. Among these are the following:

$$Na\ (s) + \tfrac{1}{2}Cl_2\ (g) + aq \rightarrow Na^+\ (aq) + Cl^-\ (aq)$$

and

$$Zn\ (s) + 2Ag^+\ (aq) \rightarrow Zn^{++}\ (aq) + 2Ag\ (s)$$

for which the heats of reaction are

$$\Delta h_{f_{Na^+}} + \Delta h_{f_{C}} -$$

and

$$\Delta h_{f_{Zn^{++}}} - 2\Delta h_{f_{Ag^+}}$$

Note that these represent electrically neutral combinations of ions. This is true in general; we can measure combinations of heats of formation of ions only when the corresponding combination of ions is electrically neutral.

In particular, the following combinations can be measured:

$$\Delta h_{f_{Na^+}} - \Delta h_{f_{H^+}}$$

$$\Delta h_{f_{Mg^{++}}} - 2\Delta h_{f_{H^+}}$$

$$\Delta h_{f_{Cl^-}} + \Delta h_{f_{H^+}}$$

$$\Delta h_{f_{SO_4^=}} + 2\Delta h_{f_{H^+}}$$

It is these combinations that will be listed as the heats of formation of the ions on the left. In general, what we will mean by the heat of formation of an ion will be the heat of the reaction by which (1) 1 mole of the ion is formed from its elements, and (2) hydrogen gas is used up and hydrogen ion formed, or vice versa, as needed to balance the reaction electrically. This is equivalent to assigning the value zero to the heat of formation of hydrogen ion itself.

When heats of formation defined in this way are applied to electrically balanced ionic reactions, the heat of formation of hydrogen ion cancels out, so that no error can result from assigning the value zero to it; thus the correct values are obtained for the heats of reaction.

Of course, it is now generally recognized that under all conditions ordinarily encountered in chemical work the species H^+ is nonexistent; the realistic representation of the acid ion in aqueous solution is H_3O^+. This need cause no difficulty, however, for the reactions

$$\tfrac{1}{2}H_2 \ (g) + aq \rightarrow H^+ \ (aq) + \epsilon$$

and

$$\tfrac{3}{2}H_2 \ (g) + \tfrac{1}{2}O_2 \ (g) + aq \rightarrow H_3O^+ \ (aq) + \epsilon$$

differ only in that a mole of water which is formed from hydrogen and oxygen in the second equation is included in the symbol aq in the first. Therefore the heat of formation of the hydronium ion differs from that of the hydrogen ion by the heat of formation of water, which is $-$ 68.317 kcal/mole. Since the value zero is assigned to the heat of formation of H^+, the heat of formation of H_3O^+ is $-$ 68.317 kcal/mole. With both values available, we can base calculations on either. Ions such as that of magnesium, which is represented more accurately by $Mg(H_2O)_6^{++}$ than by Mg^{++}, can be treated similarly if desired.

5–8. Calculations Based on Hess's Law

Calculations from Hess's law of heats of reaction and other thermodynamic changes associated with a reaction are simple in principle. In practice, confusion can arise when a large number of reactions is involved; this can be avoided by arranging the work according to some consistent plan. Usually, the equations for the reactions are written with the Δh for each to the right. Then inspection of the set of equations will generally show that if they are to combine to give the equation for the desired reaction, some or all of them must be multiplied by suitable coefficients, and some of them may need to be reversed. Whenever an equation is multiplied through by any number, its Δh must be multiplied by the same number; if the equation is reversed, the sign of Δh is changed. The equations are now added, and terms which appear on both sides of the reaction arrow are canceled out; this should yield the desired equation. The corresponding Δh's are also added, giving Δh for the desired reaction.

This can be made clearer by an example. The heat of formation of anhydrous magnesium chloride is to be calculated from the heats of the following reactions:

$$\Delta h/\text{kcal}$$

(a) $\text{Mg } (s) + 2\text{H}^+ (aq) \rightarrow \text{Mg}^{++} (aq) + \text{H}_2 (g)$ -110.41

(b) $\text{MgCl}_2 (s) + aq \rightarrow \text{Mg}^{++} (aq) + 2\text{Cl}^- (aq)$ -37.06

(c) $\frac{1}{2}\text{H}_2 (g) + \frac{1}{2}\text{Cl}_2 (g) \rightarrow \text{HCl} (g)$ -22.063

(d) $\text{HCl} (g) + aq \rightarrow \text{H}^+ (aq) + \text{Cl}^- (aq)$ -17.96

Since the desired reaction is

$$\text{Mg } (s) + \text{Cl}_2 (g) \rightarrow \text{MgCl}_2 (s)$$

it is clear that we must reverse reaction (b) so as to bring MgCl_2 to the right side, and double (c) and (d) to cancel out the unwanted extraneous substances. This gives

(a') $\text{Mg } (s) + 2\text{H}^+ (aq) \rightarrow \text{Mg}^{++} (aq) + \text{H}_2 (g)$ -110.41

(b') $\text{Mg}^{++} (aq) + 2\text{Cl}^- (aq) \rightarrow \text{MgCl}_2 (s) + aq$ $+37.06$

(c') $\text{H}_2 (g) + \text{Cl}_2 (g) \rightarrow 2\text{HCl} (g)$ -44.13

(d') $2\text{HCl} (g) + aq \rightarrow 2\text{H}^+ (aq) + 2\text{Cl}^- (aq)$ -35.92

When we add these equations, along with the corresponding Δh's, we find that all the extraneous substances cancel out as planned, and we are left with

$$\text{Mg } (s) + \text{Cl}_2 (g) \rightarrow \text{MgCl}_2 (s) \qquad \Delta h = -153.40 \text{ kcal}$$

5–9. Applications to Theoretical Chemistry: Bond Energies, Electron Affinities, and Crystal Energies

The energy change when a molecule is formed from isolated atoms of the elements composing it is important in the theory of chemical bonding. For diatomic molecules the negative of this quantity is called the *bond energy*. For example, the bond energy in HCl is $-\Delta u$ for the reaction

$$\text{H } (g) + \text{Cl } (g) \rightarrow \text{HCl } (g)$$

For polyatomic molecules containing several bonds of one kind, the bond energy is generally defined as the negative of the average energy change per bond when the compound is formed as isolated molecules from isolated atoms. Thus for water, ammonia, and methane the bond energies are $\frac{1}{2}$, $\frac{1}{3}$, and $\frac{1}{4}$, respectively, of the $-\Delta u$ values for the reactions

$$2H \ (g) + O \ (g) \rightarrow H_2O \ (g)$$

$$3H \ (g) + N \ (g) \rightarrow NH_3 \ (g)$$

$$4H \ (g) + C \ (g) \rightarrow CH_4 \ (g)$$

It should be noted that the O–H bond energy as here defined is *not* the same as $-\Delta u$ for the reaction

$$H \ (g) + OH \ (g) \rightarrow H_2O \ (g)$$

The latter quantity, which is also important, is often called the *bond dissociation energy*. The energy changes used in defining bond energies and bond dissociation energies should be calculated for the reactions at 0°K, but the correction to this temperature is usually less than the uncertainty in experimental values. It can be seen from the theory of gases to be developed in the next chapter that for the formation of HCl from H and Cl Δc_v is about $-\frac{1}{2}R$, so that the correction for Δu from T to 0°K is only about $\frac{1}{2}RT$, or about 300 cal/mole at room temperature. The difference between Δu and Δh is usually of the same order of magnitude and can often be neglected.

The determination of bond energies is not always easy, and many of the values are in dispute. The methods, which include spectroscopic, electron impact, and thermochemical techniques, are extensively discussed by Gaydon[2]; only the last will be considered here. For HCl we combine the reactions

$$H \ (g) \rightarrow \tfrac{1}{2}H_2 \ (g) \qquad \qquad \Delta u = -51.61 \text{ kcal}$$

$$Cl \ (g) \rightarrow \tfrac{1}{2}Cl_2 \ (g) \qquad \qquad -28.54$$

$$\tfrac{1}{2}H_2 \ (g) + \tfrac{1}{2}Cl_2 \ (g) \rightarrow HCl \ (g) \qquad -22.06$$

The first two of these are determined spectroscopically, and the third by calorimetric measurement. Adding the three equations gives

$$H \ (g) + Cl \ (g) \rightarrow HCl \ (g) \qquad \Delta u = -102.21 \text{ kcal}$$

For ammonia $\Delta h_f = -11.0$ kcal, and $\Delta u_f = \Delta h_f - (-2RT) = -9.8$ kcal. The energy of dissociation of nitrogen is controversial, values from

120 to 393 kcal/mole having been reported. Gaydon recommends 225.1 kcal/mole, and this value will be used. We now have

$$N \ (g) \rightarrow \tfrac{1}{2}N_2 \ (g) \qquad \Delta u = -112.6 \ \text{kcal}$$

$$3H \ (g) \rightarrow \tfrac{3}{2}H_2 \ (g) \qquad -154.8$$

$$\tfrac{1}{2}N_2 \ (g) + \tfrac{3}{2}H_2 \ (g) \rightarrow NH_3 \ (g) \qquad -9.8$$

Adding gives

$$N \ (g) + 3H \ (g) \rightarrow NH_3 \ (g) \qquad \Delta u = -277.2 \ \text{kcal}$$

so that the energy of the N–H bond is one third of this, or 92.4 kcal. A further extension of the idea can be made if this same energy is assigned to the N-H bonds in hydrazine. The energy of formation of hydrazine is about +24.9 kcal/mole from N_2 and H_2. If this is combined with the values for the dissociation energies of hydrogen and nitrogen, the energy of formation of hydrazine from atoms is found to be -406.6 kcal/mole. Therefore the energy of the N-N bond must be $406.6 - 4(92.4) = 37$ kcal.

For carbon compounds another controversial figure is involved — the heat of sublimation of graphite. This is a very difficult quantity to determine experimentally, and at least four different values have had their supporters. Most recent publications favor either 141 kcal[3] or 170 kcal[2,4]; the latter will be used here.

Two methods are used to arrive at the heat of sublimation of graphite. One is to measure the rate of evaporation and use this, together with the kinetic theory of gases, to calculate the vapor pressure. This is then used in Clapeyron's equation to determine the heat of sublimation. Several complications are involved. The other method is to combine the dissociation energy of carbon monoxide, which is obtainable from spectroscopic observations or electron impact data, with the heat of formation of this compound and the dissociation energy of oxygen. Thus we have

$$CO \ (g) \rightarrow C \ (g) + O \ (g) \qquad \Delta u = 256.1 \ \text{kcal}$$

$$O \ (g) \rightarrow \tfrac{1}{2}O_2 \ (g) \qquad -58.6$$

$$C \ (s) + \tfrac{1}{2}O_2 \ (g) \rightarrow CO \ (g) \qquad -27.2$$

and the sum is

$$C \ (s) \rightarrow C \ (g) \qquad \Delta u = 170.3 \ \text{kcal}$$

However, some values as low as 160 kcal have been reported for the dissociation energy of carbon monoxide.

If we accept the value calculated above for the heat of sublimation of carbon, we find the C–H bond energy in methane to be 98.2 kcal. If this value is assumed to hold in other hydrocarbons also, the C–C bond energy works out to be 77.7 kcal in ethane and slightly more in other hydrocarbons; 80.5 kcal is the commonly used value. It is noteworthy that the C–C bond energy in diamond is 85 kcal. This follows from the fact that complete dissociation of diamond requires the breaking of two bonds per atom. Since the heat of sublimation is only about one half kcal less than that of graphite, the bond energy is one half of 170 kcal, or 85 kcal.

The energy of bonds between two given atoms is not quite independent of the rest of the molecule. However, since the variation is rather small, bond energies can be used to estimate roughly the heats of formation of many compounds. The method is illustrated by the following example.

Dimethyl ether contains six C–H bonds and two C–O bonds. Using a value of 98.2 kcal for the energy of each C–H bond and 79 kcal for each C–O bond, we find the total bond energy for the compound to be 747 kcal/mole; that is, Δu for the formation of 1 mole of dimethyl ether from carbon, hydrogen, and oxygen *atoms* is -747 kcal. The formation of atoms from these elements in their standard states requires energy in the following amounts:

$$2C\ (s) \rightarrow 2C\ (g) \qquad \Delta u = 2 \times 170 \quad = 340 \text{ kcal}$$

$$3H_2\ (g) \rightarrow 6H\ (g) \qquad 3 \times 103.2 = 310$$

$$\tfrac{1}{2}O_2\ (g) \rightarrow O\ (g) \qquad \tfrac{1}{2} \times 117.2 = \quad 59$$

Adding these to the equation

$$6H\ (g) + 2C\ (g) + O\ (g) \rightarrow (CH_3)_2O\ (g) \qquad \Delta u = -747$$

gives

$$2C\ (s) + 3H_2\ (g) + \tfrac{1}{2}O_2\ (g) \rightarrow (CH_3)_2O\ (g) \qquad \Delta u = -38 \text{ kcal}$$

Since $\Delta n = -5/2$, this gives approximately $\Delta h = -40$ kcal; the experimental value is -46 kcal. Although the agreement does not appear very good, it should be recognized that the calculated quantity is a small difference between two large quantities. The error — 6 kcal — is about 13 per cent of 46 kcal, but less than 1 per cent of 747 kcal.

In some cases calculated bond energies for compounds are seriously in error, the experimental bond energy being much larger than the calculated. This provides evidence that in such cases the simple valence-bond model does not adequately represent the actual manner of bonding. The discrepancy between the calculated and experimental bond energies is called the *resonance energy*. The best known example is benzene, for which the resonance energy is 39 kcal/mole.

Another application of thermochemistry to theoretical chemistry is the calculation of electron affinities from the Born-Haber cycle. In this method sodium chloride (for example) is regarded as being made by the following scheme:

(a) $\qquad$ Na $(s) \rightarrow$ Na (g) $\qquad$ $\Delta u = 25.4$ kcal

(b) $\qquad$ Na $(g) \rightarrow$ Na$^+$ $(g) + \epsilon$ $\qquad$ 117.9

(c) $\qquad$ $\frac{1}{2}$Cl$_2$ $(g) \rightarrow$ Cl (g) $\qquad$ 28.8

(d) $\qquad$ Cl $(g) + \epsilon \rightarrow$ Cl$^-$ (g) $\qquad$ $-EA$

(e) $\quad$ Na$^+$ $(g) +$ Cl$^-$ $(g) \rightarrow$ NaCl (s) $\qquad$ -183.1

Adding these and using the experimental value of Δu_f for NaCl, we get

(f) $\quad$ Na $(s) + \frac{1}{2}$Cl$_2$ $(g) \rightarrow$ NaCl (s) $\qquad$ $\Delta u = -97.9$ kcal

For reaction (a) Δu can be determined by thermodynamic methods (see Problem 7). The energy changes for (b) and (c) are measured spectroscopically. The energy involved in (e) is identified with the electrostatic work performed in bringing isolated ions to their positions in the crystal lattice, corrected for a small effect of the repulsive forces. Reaction (f) can be studied calorimetrically.

The term *electron affinity* is applied to $-\Delta u$, at $0°K$, for reaction (d). From the data given above, Δu for this reaction is seen to be -86.3 kcal. A small temperature correction then leads to the value 85.8 for the electron affinity of chlorine.

When this was first done, there was no other way of measuring electron affinities. The constancy of the electron affinity of an element as determined from several of its salts provided some confidence both in the electron affinity values and in the method of calculating crystal energies. Electron affinities have now been measured independently and show reasonable agreement with the values determined by the Born-Haber cycle.

5-10. The Problems of Entropy Determination

The calorimetric methods described in Section 5-2 are satisfactory for the determination of energy and enthalpy changes in chemical reactions. The determination of changes in the other thermodynamic properties — entropy and the free energy functions — can be considered together, since any can be calculated from any other if energy or enthalpy data are available.

If the equilibrium constant of a reaction can be measured, the Gibbs free energy change, and thence the entropy change, can be calculated by methods which will be discussed in Chapter 8. This does not solve the problem of determining entropies of reaction, however, for two reasons. In the first place, there are many reactions for which no experimental determination of the equilibrium constant is possible (most combustion reactions, for example). Secondly, one of the most important applications of thermodynamics in chemistry is the prediction of equilibrium constants of reactions which have not been carried out. If this could be done only by measuring the equilibrium constant first, the whole procedure would be rather futile.

If we try to determine entropy calorimetrically, we can apply Hess's law (in generalized form) to the process represented in Figure 12 to obtain

$$\Delta S_{AC} = \Delta S_{AD} + \Delta S_{DC}$$

However, applying the second law to the adiabatic process AC, we get

$$\Delta S_{AC} \geqslant 0$$

from which

$$\Delta S_{AD} + \Delta S_{DC} \geqslant 0$$

Now ΔS_{DC} can be calculated by integrating C_v^P/T (or C_p^P/T for a constant-pressure calorimeter) with respect to T, but then we have only

$$\Delta S_{AD} \geqslant -\int_{T_1}^{T_2} \frac{C_v^P}{T}\, dT$$

Therefore all we can find calorimetrically is a lower limit to the entropy change. This results from the fact that although the first law is a law of conservation expressed by the equality $\Delta U = Q + W$, the second law is a law of steady increase expressed by the inequality $T\, dS \geqslant dQ$.

The problem of determining entropies of reaction can be profitably viewed from another angle. Suppose that an engineer, in setting up tables for the thermodynamic properties of liquid water and steam, chose the entropy of water at 1 atm and 0°C as the zero point for measuring the entropy of liquid water, and similarly the entropy of saturated water vapor at this same temperature for measuring the entropy of steam. Entropy changes calculated from these tables would be valid so long as no conversion of liquid water to steam, or vice versa, occurred. However, this choice of zero points would imply that vaporization of water at 0°C is accompanied by no entropy change. Of course, the actual entropy change for this process is a measurable quantity which cannot be chosen arbitrarily, and it is not zero. The choice of these two zero points would not be acceptable, then, if vaporization or condensation occurred.

Actually, engineers use entropy values for water and steam based on liquid water at 0°C as the zero point. With both vapor and liquid entropies referred to this one zero point, the tables are valid for the calculations required in the design of steam power plants, for example, where vaporization and condensation are important.

This can now be carried a step further. Let us suppose that thermodynamic calculations must be made on a system containing nitrogen, hydrogen, and ammonia. We set up entropy tables for mixtures of these gases by choosing the entropy of each gas at 0°C and 1 atm pressure as the zero point for the entropy of that gas. This will be valid as long as the reaction

$$N_2 + 3H_2 \rightleftharpoons 2NH_3$$

does not occur. If it does, the entropies of nitrogen and hydrogen can still be based on these zero points, but that of ammonia must be determined by measuring the entropy change of this reaction. To choose arbitrarily all three of the zero points implies choosing arbitrarily the entropy change of the reaction, and this cannot be done.

In general, arbitrary zero points can be chosen for the thermodynamic properties of any substances if none of them are converted into others during the process under consideration. Thus it was pointed out in Section 5–5 that the use of heats of formation implies choosing elements in their standard states as zero points for measuring enthalpies. This is valid in chemical work, where no conversion of elements into other elements occurs. It is not valid for nuclear processes; we cannot apply ordinary heats of formation to a reaction such as

$$_7N^{15}\ (g) + {_1}H^1\ (g) \rightarrow {_6}C^{12}\ (g) + {_2}He^4\ (g)$$

If we attempted to calculate the enthalpy change for this reaction from ordinary heats of formation, we would arrive at an absurdly small value, about 140 kilojoules/mole; the correct value is negative, and of several million times greater magnitude. If heats of formation were based on the formation of atoms or molecules from protons, neutrons, and electrons, they could be used for this reaction as well as for chemical reactions, but not for β-decay, in which conversion of a neutron into a proton and an electron occurs. Needless to say, such a scheme would be grossly impractical; it is mentioned here only to illustrate the principles involved in choosing zero points for thermodynamic functions.

In 1906 Nernst made the important suggestion that the entropy changes for all reactions at absolute zero are zero, or, more rigorously, that as the temperature approaches zero, the entropy change for every reaction approaches zero. This idea has on the whole proved valid, provided it is restricted to pure crystalline substances; a few exceptions are known. It is generally known as the *third law of thermodynamics* (or as the *Nernst heat theorem*, despite the facts that it concerns not heat but entropy, and is not a theorem but a postulate).

It is easily seen that the third law provides an answer to the problem of determining entropies of reaction. To show this, let us simplify the notation previously used for a reaction by writing R for all the reactants and P for all the products, with a superscript 0 to indicate a temperature of absolute zero. Then for the reaction

$$R \to P$$

we have

$$\Delta s = s_P - s_R = (s_P - s_P^0) - (s_R - s_R^0) + (s_P^0 - s_R^0)$$

$$= \Delta(s - s^0) + \Delta s^0 = \Delta(s - s^0)$$

the third law having been used in the last step. Now $s - s^0$ is an experimentally determinable quantity, and this equation states that we can use values of this quantity in calculating reaction entropies, provided the s^0's are chosen so that $\Delta s^0 = 0$. Except for this one restriction, there is nothing in either the theory or experimental content of thermodynamics to limit the choice of the s^0's. Consider, for example, the following choices,

$$s_i^0 = 0$$

$$s_{isp}^0 = 1 \text{ joule/g·deg}$$

both being applied to each substance i for which Nernst's postulate is valid. (The subscript sp here means *specific*; that is, referring to 1 g of material.) Clearly both of these lead to $\Delta s^0 = 0$, and so both are acceptable. The first choice was made by Planck and has been universally adopted. The second is unnecessarily cumbersome, offers no advantages, and is never actually used; it is mentioned here only to emphasize the fact that the choice $s^0{}_i = 0$ is based on convenience and not on necessity. The frequently held view that this sets up an "absolute" entropy scale is certainly questionable, and it has been abandoned by many thermodynamicists; it will not be used here. In any case, the entropies commonly used in calculating entropy changes of chemical reactions are certainly not absolute entropies.

The determination of entropies based on the choice $s^0{}_i = 0$ is simple in principle. Since $ds = c\ dT/T$, where c is the appropriate heat capacity, we have

$$s_i(T) = \int_0^T \frac{c_i}{T}\, dT$$

provided no phase changes occur below the temperature T. The appropriate heat capacity is usually c_p; for condensed phases the difference between c_p and c_v is usually so slight at low temperatures that either may be used. From $0°K$ to the lowest temperature for which experimental data are available (usually about $15°K$) the heat capacity is generally estimated by means of Debye's theory, according to which c_v at very low temperatures is proportional to the cube of the temperature. At higher temperatures graphical integration of experimental data is applied to either of the equivalent expressions:

$$s(T) - s(T') = \int_{T'}^T \frac{c}{T}\, dT = \int_{\ln\,(T'/1°)}^{\ln\,(T/1°)} c\, d(\ln T)$$

Note that the second expression cannot be carried graphically down to $0°K$, since this would require extending the $\ln\,(T/1°)$ axis to $-\infty$.

If phase changes occur, each such change contributes to the entropy the amount $\Delta h/T$ (or $\Delta u/T$ if the change occurs at constant volume), where T is the temperature at which the change occurs reversibly. At points of phase change the heat capacity changes discontinuously, so that the graph of c_p/T versus T has the appearance shown in Figure 13. Nevertheless, the entropy is equal to the area under the curve from $T = 0$ to the desired temperature, plus the contributions from any phase changes that take place in this range.

Finally, it is worth pointing out that the third law is often called the *principle of the unattainability of absolute zero*, and is stated as follows: *It is impossible for any process involving a finite number of steps to reduce the temperature of any system to absolute zero.* To prove that these two formulations of the third law are equivalent, we must show that $\Delta s^0 = 0$ implies the unattainability of absolute zero, and vice versa.

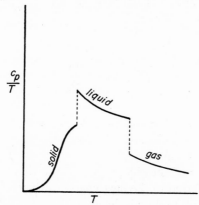

FIGURE 13. GRAPH OF C_p/T VERSUS T,
ILLUSTRATING GRAPHICAL DETERMINATION OF ENTROPY.

To prove the first part of this, let us assume that a system has been cooled to the temperature of the coldest of its surroundings, so that no further cooling by conduction to a colder body is possible. The most hopeful type of process to use for further cooling, then, would be an adiabatic one — the evaporation of a liquid, for example, or the demagnetization of a magnetized salt. If we denote properties in the initial and final states by subscripts 1 and 2, respectively, we have

$$S_1 \leqslant S_2$$

and so

$$S_1^0 + \int_0^{T_1} \frac{C_1}{T} \, dT \leqslant S_2^0 + \int_0^{T_2} \frac{C_2}{T} \, dT \qquad (5\text{--}14)$$

Now the third law states that $S_1^0 = S_2^0$, and so if T_2 is to be zero, we must have

$$\int_0^{T_1} \frac{C_1}{T} \, dT \leqslant 0$$

But this is impossible, since C_1 is positive for all temperatures except zero.

Similarly, to show that the unattainability of absolute zero implies that $\Delta S^0 = 0$, we rewrite Eq. (5-14), using an equality sign, which implies a reversible process:

$$\int_0^{T_1} \frac{C_1}{T} \, dT = \Delta S^0 + \int_0^{T_2} \frac{C_2}{T} \, dT$$

Now if ΔS^0 were positive, we could make the integral on the left equal to it by a suitable choice of T_1. But this would mean that

$$\int_0^{T_2} \frac{C_2}{T} \, dT = 0$$

which is possible only if $T_2 = 0$. But since T_2 is the final temperature achieved in the process, this would imply that absolute zero can be attained. This contradiction shows that ΔS^0 cannot be positive. Applying the same argument to the reverse of this process will show that it cannot be negative. It is, therefore, zero.

Further discussion of the significance of the third law and the exceptions to it will be deferred to the next chapter, where the statistical theory necessary for its understanding is developed.

PROBLEMS

(1) Into a calorimeter containing an electric heater 50.00 g of water (specific heat 4.18 joules/g·deg) is introduced, the heater is turned on, and a steady input of 10.00 w is maintained for 1 min. This results in a temperature rise of 1.824.° Calculate the heat capacity of the calorimeter.

(2) Exactly 100 ml of a 0.1000-M solution of NaOH is introduced at a temperature below 25°C into a calorimeter with a heater. The apparatus and solution is heated carefully until the temperature is exactly 25°. At this time exactly 100 ml of a 0.1050-M solution of HCl, whose temperature has been previously adjusted to 25°, is added. This causes the temperature to increase by 0.5131°. The heater is then turned on, and an input of 5.000 w is maintained for exactly 1 min: the resulting increase in temperature is 1.152°. Calculate Δh for the reaction H^+ (aq) + OH^- (aq) → H_2O (l). Assume constancy of C_P throughout the temperature range involved.

(3) Hughes, Corrucini, and Gilbert[5] carried out the combustion of hydrazine and its hydrate in a bomb calorimeter, and reported the following Δu_{sp} values for the combustion of these compounds to nitrogen and liquid water:

N_2H_4 (l)	−4637.5 cal/g
$N_2H_4 \cdot H_2O$ (l)	−2935.2 cal/g

Calculate Δh_f for each of these compounds and Δh for the reaction

$$N_2H_4 \ (l) + H_2O \ (l) \rightarrow N_2H_4 \cdot H_2O \ (l)$$

(4) Giauque and Archibald[6] prepared two identical samples of $Mg(OH)_2$ slightly contaminated with KOH, each consisting of 85.526 millimoles of $Mg(OH)_2$ and 0.192 millimoles of KOH. When one of these samples was dissolved in 900 cc of 1.0000 N HCl, ΔH was found to be -2294.1 cal. The other sample was heated until all but 4.407 millimoles of the $Mg(OH)_2$ had been converted into MgO; the KOH, of course, remained unchanged. When this sample was dissolved in the same amount of HCl solution, ΔH was -3083.3 cal. It was estimated that the enthalpy of water in the resulting solution was 4 cal/mole less than that of pure water. Calculate Δh for the reaction

$$Mg(OH)_2 \ (s) \rightarrow MgO \ (s) + H_2O \ (l)$$

(5) Coughlin[7] found that when $CaO \cdot Al_2O_3$ (s) is dissolved in aqueous HCl, $\Delta h = -102.42$ kcal. Find Δh for the reaction

$$CaO \ (s) + Al_2O_3(s) \rightarrow CaO \cdot Al_2O_3 \ (s)$$

using heats of formation from Appendix 2.

(6) Find Δh, Δs and Δg as functions of temperature for the reaction

$$CH_4 \ (g) + 2O_2 \ (g) \rightarrow CO_2 \ (g) + 2H_2O \ (g)$$

Heats of formation and entropies may be found in Appendix 2, and heat capacities are given by the equation

$$c_p = A + BT + CT^2$$

with the constants given by

$A \Big/ \dfrac{\text{cal}}{\text{mole} \cdot \text{deg}}$		$B \Big/ \dfrac{\text{cal}}{\text{mole} \cdot \text{deg}^2}$	$C \Big/ \dfrac{\text{cal}}{\text{mole} \cdot \text{deg}^3}$
CH_4	3.381	0.0018044	-43.00×10^{-7}
O_2	6.148	0.003102	-9.23×10^{-7}
CO_2	6.214	0.010396	-35.45×10^{-7}
H_2O	7.256	0.002298	2.83×10^{-7}

(7) The vapor pressure of sodium (liquid) is given by the empirical equation

$$\ln \frac{P}{1 \text{ millibar}} = -\frac{12440°}{T} + 17.69$$

which is valid from 180° to 883°C. Assuming that this equation is most accurate at the midpoint of its range, estimate Δh and Δu for the sublimation of sodium at 18°C. The heat of fusion of sodium at its normal melting point of 98°C is 729 cal/mole. The heat capacities of solid and liquid sodium are 6.95 and 7.36 cal/mole·deg respectively; that of the vapor can be taken as $\frac{3}{2}R$. (The answer does not agree perfectly with the value used in Section 5-9; the two sets of data were taken from different sources.)

(8) Giauque and Stephenson[8] measured the following properties of sulfur dioxide:

$T/°K$	$c_p / \dfrac{cal}{mole \cdot deg}$	$T/°K$	$c_p / \dfrac{cal}{mole \cdot deg}$
15 (solid)	0.83	110	11.97
20	1.66	120	12.40
25	2.74	130	12.83
30	3.79	140	13.31
35	4.85	150	13.82
40	5.78	160	14.33
45	6.61	170	14.85
50	7.36	180	15.42
55	8.02	190	16.02
60	8.62	200 (liq)	20.97
70	9.57	220	20.86
80	10.32	240	20.76
90	10.93	260	20.66
100	11.49		

The latent heat of fusion is 1769 cal/mole at the normal melting point of 197.64°K, and the heat of vaporization 5960 cal/mole at 263.08°K, which is the boiling point at 1 atm pressure.

(a) Calculate the entropy of gaseous sulfur dioxide at its boiling point and 1 atm pressure.

(b) Calculate the standard entropy of gaseous sulfur dioxide at its boiling point, using the Berthelot equation. The critical temperature is 430.60°K and the critical pressure 77.79 atm.

REFERENCES

1. Rossini, F. D., Ed., "Experimental Thermochemistry," New York, N.Y., Interscience Publishers, Inc., 1956.
2. Gaydon, A. G., "Dissociation Energies," New York, N.Y., Dover Publications, Inc., 1950.
3. Steacie, E. W. R., "Atomic and Free Radical Reactions," Vol. 1, Chap. 3, New York, N.Y., Reinhold Publishing Corp., 1954.
4. Brewer, L., Gilles, P., and Jenkins, F. A., J. Chem. Phys., **16**, 797 (1948); Hagstrum, H. D., J. Chem. Phys., **23**, 1178 (1955); Morrison, J. D., J. Chem. Phys., **28**, 9 (1958).
5. Hughes, A. M., Corrucini, R. J., and Gilbert, E. C., J. Am. Chem. Soc., **61**, 2639 (1939).
6. Giauque, W. F., and Archibald, R. C., J. Am. Chem. Soc., **59**, 566 (1937).
7. Coughlin, J. P., J. Am. Chem. Soc., **78**, 5479 (1956).
8. Giauque, W. F., and Stephenson, C. C., J. Am. Chem. Soc. **60**, 1389 (1938).

chapter 6

Statistical Thermodynamics

IN PREVIOUS CHAPTERS thermodynamics has been approached mostly from the large-scale properties of systems, such as their energy and temperature; this is the classical treatment of the subject. It was early realized, however, that a more fundamental and more satisfying method would begin with the positions and momenta of the individual particles — molecules, atoms, etc. — which make up the system, and apply the known laws of mechanics to them. Because of the enormous complexity of thermodynamic systems, which may contain, for example, 10^{24} particles, nothing more than a statistical treatment could be hoped for, but this is exactly what is needed to furnish a mechanical basis for thermodynamics. The development of this statistical approach was carried out largely by Maxwell, Gibbs, and Boltzmann in the latter half of the nineteenth century.

The theory at this stage afforded important insights into the nature of thermodynamics, but it also led to some results that were questionable or even erroneous, such as the Rayleigh-Jeans equation for radiation. Few of the results were quantitative. The introduction first of quantum theory and then of quantum mechanics necessitated a reformulation of statistical mechanics, which cleared up these difficulties but retained many points of analogy with the older theory. It is from the quantal viewpoint that some elementary aspects of statistical mechanics will be presented here. This approach is much simpler than that based on classical mechanics, provided the quantized energy levels are simply accepted as quantum mechanical results to be treated statistically.

6–1. General Principles and Definitions

A fundamental notion in statistical thermodynamics is that of an *ensemble* (or *assembly*) *of systems*. The systems considered in this chapter are closed, and mostly are macroscopic systems, similar to those considered in classical thermodynamics; for example, a mole of gas. An ensemble is a collection of many replicas of a single system, all alike in certain specified respects, though not necessarily in all respects. Throughout this chapter (though not in some more general treatments) the systems in an ensemble will be regarded as having the same number of molecules of each kind. For some purposes it is more convenient to regard a single thermodynamic system as an ensemble; in this case the individual molecules, atoms, or other constituents which make it up are treated as systems in the statistical thermodynamic sense. Both viewpoints will be used here, but most of the treatment involves macroscopic, rather than molecular, systems.

Thus if molecules of a gas are regarded as systems, a mole of the gas would constitute an ensemble; but if each system is a mole of gas, an ensemble would consist of many separate moles of the gas. If identical crystals of a solid, each weighing 1 μg, are the systems, a kilogram of the solid, containing 10^9 crystals, is an ensemble.

Sometimes it is convenient to stipulate that the systems in an ensemble are isolated, having identical fixed energies; such an ensemble is called a *microcanonical ensemble*, provided that it is in equilibrium. In other cases we prefer to have the systems in thermal contact, so that they can exchange energy, the total energy of the ensemble being constant; this type, when in equilibrium, is called a *canonical ensemble*. Other ensembles are important for many problems, but only these two will be used here.

The phrase *state of a system* is used here in the quantum mechanical, not the thermodynamic, sense; that is, each state can in principle, though not often in practice, be described by specifying the Schrödinger function for the system in that state; more briefly, the state may be specified by means of quantum numbers. Fortunately, it is sufficient for most purposes to know the energy corresponding to each possible state of the systems, and this information is often available from quantum mechanical calculations or spectroscopic observations.

As an example, consider a system consisting of three linear harmonic oscillators (or one three-dimensional harmonic oscillator). Quantum mechanics shows that the states of this system can be specified by three quantum numbers, n_1, n_2, and n_3, which must be nonnegative integers. The energy is given by $(n_1 + n_2 + n_3 + \frac{3}{2}h\nu)$, where h is Planck's constant and ν is the frequency. The state of lowest energy for this system has all three of the quantum numbers equal to zero; the energy is $\frac{3}{2}h\nu$. There are three states with energy $\frac{5}{2}h\nu$; in these the quantum numbers are: 0,0,1 (for n_1, n_2, and n_3, respectively); 0,1,0; and 1,0,0. Six states can be found with energy $\frac{7}{2}h\nu$; these are 0,0,2; 0,2,0; 2,0,0; 0,1,1; 1,0,1; and 1,1,0. In a similar manner ten states of energy $\frac{9}{2}h\nu$ can be worked out. When several states correspond to the same energy, the energy level and the corresponding set of states are said to be *degenerate*; the number of states corresponding to a given energy is called the *degeneracy* (or, more accurately, the *degree of degeneracy*) of that energy level.

Now suppose that some measurement can be made on an ensemble to determine the state of each of its systems at a given time. It would be found that a certain fraction, which will be designated by γ_1, of the systems are in state 1, γ_2 in state 2, etc. If the ensemble was in equilibrium, a repetition of the experiment would show the same number of systems (subject only to very slight fluctuations) in each state; that is, the same set of γ's should be obtained, even though the particular systems in a given state may not be the same ones as were in it previously. Each of the γ's may be interpreted as the probability that a given system will be found in the state corresponding to that γ. Clearly we must have

$$\sum_i \gamma_i = 1 \qquad (6\text{--}1)$$

If the ensemble was not originally in equilibrium, we cannot expect to find the same set of γ's on successive measurements. We can still interpret the γ's as probabilities, but these probabilities are now time-dependent.

When the ensemble is in equilibrium, another interpretation of the probability of a state is possible. Instead of observing all the systems of an ensemble simultaneously, we observe a single system repeatedly. For each state i we would find that a certain fraction of the observations showed the system in this state, and this fraction would be interpreted as γ_i. This immediately raises the question: Are these two interpretations of the γ's identical? It has generally been postulated that they are. A vast amount of effort has been expended on attempts to prove this; it is now regarded as fairly well established under rather general conditions. However, it will here be regarded as a postulate: *Probabilities of states can be determined either by observing simultaneously the states of all the systems in an ensemble or by observing the successive states of a single system, and at equilibrium the two methods give identical results.*

Another postulate is also needed: *The probability of a state is dependent only on the energy of a system in that state.* This is often stated in a different form: *States of equal energy have equal probabilities*. From this statement comes its common name, the *postulate of equal a priori probabilities*.

6–2. The Boltzmann H Theorem

In 1862 Boltzmann published the extremely long and tedious proof of a theorem which forms the basis of the interpretation of entropy in statistical mechanics. The quantal form of this theorem is much simpler, but requires a considerable background of quantum mechanics for its understanding. In either form its proof is beyond the scope of this book; it will here be merely stated, with examples which, it is hoped, will make it appear reasonable.

The theorem states that in any isolated ensemble the quantity

$$\sum_i \gamma_i \ln \gamma_i$$

steadily decreases as the ensemble tends toward equilibrium. Although minor (in macroscopic ensembles, negligible) fluctuations may carry it up or down, its general trend is always downward, and equilibrium of the ensemble is marked by a minimum value of this sum. Boltzmann designated this sum by H; it should not, of course, be confused with the enthalpy. Although the summation is normally taken over all states accessible to the systems of the ensemble, it is often convenient to include inaccessible states by assigning to them the probability zero. In this case terms of the form $0 \ln 0$ occur; these must be assigned the value zero, which is the limit of $\gamma \ln \gamma$ as γ approaches zero.

Now consider an ensemble which, by some unknown means, has been so restricted that its systems are all in the same state. The probability of this state is then 1, while that of all other states is zero; the sum

$$\sum_i \gamma_i \ln \gamma_i$$

is then zero. If the restriction is now removed, transitions will occur, taking many of the systems to different states. There will now be many γ's lying between zero and 1; their logarithms will be negative, and they will make negative contributions to H. Since there are no positive terms, H itself is negative. It has therefore decreased as the ensemble changed toward equilibrium.

Next consider an ensemble in which the systems are isolated so that they cannot exchange energy, each having the same energy. Then only states of this energy are available, and by the postulate of equal *a priori* probabilities each has the same probability. Suppose that the number of these is Ω; then each γ is equal to $1/\Omega$, and there are Ω identical terms in H. Therefore,

$$H = \Omega \frac{1}{\Omega} \ln \frac{1}{\Omega} = -\ln \Omega \qquad (6\text{--}2)$$

Again we assume that originally all the systems are confined to the same state, so that $H = 0$. When the restriction is removed, certain states become available immediately. There may be other states, however, which become available more slowly, because, for example, of the transition restrictions of quantum mechanics. Thus the number of available states increases steadily from 1 to its final value, Ω. If we now assume equal probabilities for all states available at any time (an admittedly crude assumption), it can be seen that H decreases steadily from 0 to $-\ln \Omega$.

6–3. The Entropy Postulate

These examples illustrate Boltzmann's theorem that the approach of an isolated ensemble to equilibrium is accompanied by a steady decrease in H. Thermodynamically, this process is accompanied by a steady increase in the entropy. Clearly a connection must exist between these two functions. We now postulate the form of this connection by adopting the following statistical definition of the entropy of a system:

$$s = -kH = -k \sum_i \gamma_i \ln \gamma_i \qquad (6\text{--}3)*$$

where k (called *Boltzmann's constant*) is a constant whose value will be determined later. The entropy of the entire ensemble of N systems will then be $-kNH$.

Having postulated a statistical definition of entropy, we must now determine whether it is consistent with the thermodynamic definition. We already know from the discussion above that the statistical entropy and the thermodynamic entropy share one important characteristic: both increase to a maximum when an isolated system comes to equilibrium. This does not prove the identity of the two, however; the function s^3, for example, also has this property. However, we can also show that the statistical entropy, like the thermodynamic entropy, is additive; this would not be true of s^3.

---

* In this chapter lower-case letters will be used for the thermodynamic properties of single systems when convenient.

To show this, consider two independent macroscopic systems, one designated by unprimed quantities, the other by primed quantities. We will deal with successive states of these systems rather than simultaneous states in an ensemble. States 1, 2, . . . of the unprimed system have probabilities γ_1, γ_2, . . . , while states $1'$, $2'$, . . . of the primed one have probabilities γ'_1, γ'_2, ... The corresponding entropies are

$$s = -k \sum_i \gamma_i \ln \gamma_i \quad \text{and} \quad s' = -k \sum_j \gamma'_j \ln \gamma'_j$$

Now the states of the composite system (made up of both these systems) are combinations of some state of the unprimed system with some state of the primed one. Since the systems are independent, the probabilities of these composite states are products of the probabilities of the single-system states; that is, they are of the form $\gamma_i \gamma'_j$. The entropy of the composite system is, therefore,

$$s'' = -k \sum_{i,\,j} \gamma_i \gamma'_j \ln (\gamma_i \gamma'_j)$$

$$= -k \sum_{i,\,j} \gamma_i \gamma'_j \ln \gamma_i - k \sum_{i,\,j} \gamma_i \gamma'_j \ln \gamma'_j$$

$$= -k \sum_j \gamma'_j \sum_i \gamma_i \ln \gamma_i - k \sum_i \gamma_i \sum_j \gamma'_j \ln \gamma'_j = s + s'$$

use being made of Eq. (6–1) and the definition of entropy in the last step. This leaves only two possible ways in which the statistical and thermodynamic entropies may differ. One of these is in the size of the unit; the value of the constant k can be adjusted to take care of this. The other is that Eq. (6–3) gives an actual entropy value and so implies the choice of a zero point. Since in Chapter 5 a zero point for entropy based on the third law was given, we must ask whether the two choices are equivalent. It will be shown later that whenever the rule $s_i^0 = 0$ applies, the statistical definition of entropy gives the same result. However, the statistical definition is more general, giving correct entropies even when $s_i^0 \neq 0$. Meanwhile, statistical and thermodynamic entropies will be treated as identical.

6–4. The Distribution of Systems in Equilibrium

The values of the γ's for a canonical ensemble will now be derived. A canonical ensemble, as defined in Section 6–1, is an ensemble that has reached equilibrium under the condition that systems are allowed to exchange energy, the energy of the ensemble being constant. This means that the average energy per system — averaged over the systems of the ensemble or over successive states of a single system — is constant. Therefore we must minimize H under two restricting conditions — Eq. (6–1), expressing the fact that probabilities must add up to 1, and

$$\sum_i \gamma_i \epsilon_i = \bar{u} \tag{6-4}$$

where ϵ_i is the energy of a system in state i, and $\bar{u}$ is the average energy per system.

To do this we apply Lagrange's method (Section 1–6). Setting the differential of H equal to zero gives

$$\sum_i (1 + \ln \gamma_i) \, d\gamma_i = 0 \tag{6-5}$$

The restricting conditions, in differential form, become

$$\sum_i d\gamma_i = 0 \tag{6-6}$$

and

$$\sum_i \epsilon_i \, d\gamma_i = 0 \tag{6-7}$$

Eq. (6–6) may be used to simplify Eq. (6–5) so that it takes the form

$$\sum_i \ln \gamma_i \, d\gamma_i = 0 \tag{6-8}$$

Now Eqs. (6–6) and (6–7) are multiplied by Lagrangean multipliers α and β, respectively, and added to Eq. (6–8). This gives

$$\sum_i (\ln \gamma_i + \alpha + \beta \epsilon_i) \, d\gamma_i = 0$$

At the minimum each of these factors must be zero, and so the equilibrium probabilities are given by

$$\ln \gamma_i + \alpha + \beta \epsilon_i = 0, \text{ or } \gamma_i = e^{-\alpha} e^{-\beta \epsilon_i} \tag{6-9}$$

Clearly states of very high energy must be very improbable, and this requires that β be positive. We can eliminate α by substituting Eq. (6–9) into Eq. (6–1); this gives

$$e^{-\alpha} \sum_i e^{-\beta \epsilon_i} = 1$$

or

$$e^{-\alpha} = \frac{1}{\sum_i e^{-\beta \epsilon_i}}$$

The sum in the denominator is usually called the *partition function*[**]; it will be denoted by Z. Eq. (6-9) now becomes

$$\gamma_i = \frac{e^{-\beta \epsilon_i}}{Z} \qquad (6\text{-}10)$$

Two features of this treatment may appear paradoxical. In the first place, we expect the most probable state to be one whose energy is approximately the average energy per system; that is, we do not expect the energy of a system (especially not a macroscopic system) to deviate widely from its average value. Yet according to Eq. (6-10), the most probable state is the state of lowest possible energy. In the second place, consider a microcanonical ensemble; that is, an ensemble of identical, isolated sysmens all having the same energy. The entropy of such a system is given by Eqs. (6-2) and (6-3) as $k \ln \Omega$; all the systems must be in states corresponding to their fixed energy. If now thermal contact is established among the systems so that they can exchange energy, many additional states become available. According to Eq. (6-10), some of these are of relatively high probability, and so an increase in entropy is to be expected. On thermodynamic grounds, however, the systems must be in thermal equilibrium originally, and so the establishment of thermal contact should cause no change. These apparent paradoxes will be discussed later; meanwhile it is desirable to develop further consequences of the distribution equation, Eq. (6-10).

6-5. Relation of the Partition Function to Thermodynamic Properties

Differentiating the logarithm of the partition function with respect to β, keeping the ϵ's constant, gives

$$\left[\frac{\partial (\ln Z)}{\partial \beta} \right]_\epsilon = \frac{- \sum_i \epsilon_i e^{-\beta \epsilon_i}}{Z} = - \sum_i \gamma_i \epsilon_i = -\bar{u} \qquad (6\text{-}11)$$

where Eqs. (6-10) and (6-4) have been used in the last two steps. The thermodynamic energy is to be identified with the average energy, $\bar{u}$; for this reason the bar will be omitted from the symbol for this quantity, except where a distinction is necessary.

[**] Boltzmann called it *Zustandssumme;* the English equivalent *sum-over-states* is occasionally used.

The entropy is found by substituting Eq. (6–10) into Eq. (6–3). This gives

$$s = -k \sum_i \gamma_i \ln \frac{e^{-\beta \epsilon_i}}{Z} = k\beta \sum_i \gamma_i \epsilon_i + k \sum_i \gamma_i \ln Z$$

or

$$s = k\beta u + k \ln Z \qquad (6\text{–}12)$$

Thus we now have statistical analogs of the thermodynamic quantities u and s. The statistical analog of the equation

$$du = T \, ds$$

which is Eq. (2–9) as applied to a constant-volume system, will now be derived. First it is necessary to consider how the energy levels, ϵ_i, are fixed by quantum mechanical theory. The Schrödinger equation, from which, in principle, the ϵ's can be calculated, involves the number of particles in the system, their masses, and the potential energy of the system as a function of its coordinates. The permissible solutions are restricted by boundary conditions, an example of which is the dimensions of a container in which a gas is enclosed. Now all processes here considered involve no change in the number of masses of the particles. Therefore the ϵ's change only when the potential energy or the boundary conditions change. But changing either potential energy or boundary conditions involves the performance of work on or by the system. It follows that a process involving no work is a process at constant ϵ's.

We now differentiate Eq. (6–12), keeping the ϵ's constant, so that Z is a function of β only. This gives

$$ds = k\beta \, du + ku \, d\beta + k \left[\frac{\partial (\ln Z)}{\partial \beta} \right] d\beta = k\beta \, du$$

since, by Eq. (6–11), the last two terms cancel each other. We thus have

$$du = \frac{1}{k\beta} \, ds \qquad (6\text{–}13)$$

Since this was derived for constant ϵ's, it applies to a change in which no work is done. The fact that the equilibrium distribution (Eq. (6–10)) has been assumed to hold implies that the change is also reversible. Eq. (6–13) must, therefore, be identical with the thermodynamic equation for a reversible process involving no work, namely, $du = T \, ds$. Comparison gives the important relation

$$T = \frac{1}{k\beta} \quad \text{or} \quad \beta = \frac{1}{kT} \qquad (6\text{–}14)$$

With the help of this relation, we can now abandon β, using instead the more familiar quantity T. This gives

$$Z = \sum_i e^{-\epsilon_i/kT} \tag{6-15}$$

$$u = -\left[\frac{\partial(\ln Z)}{\partial \beta}\right]_\epsilon = -\frac{\left[\dfrac{\partial(\ln Z)}{\partial T}\right]_\epsilon}{\dfrac{d\beta}{dT}} = kT^2\left[\frac{\partial(\ln Z)}{\partial T}\right]_\epsilon \tag{6-16}$$

$$s = \frac{u}{T} + k \ln Z \tag{6-17}$$

From the last the Helmholtz free energy is seen to be

$$a = u - Ts = -kT \ln Z \tag{6-18}$$

The pressure can be found by differentiating this equation. Thus

$$p = -\left(\frac{\partial a}{\partial v}\right)_T = kT\left[\frac{\partial(\ln Z)}{\partial v}\right]_T \tag{6-19}$$

6-6. The Einstein Crystal Model

In order to illustrate the use of these relations and to point out the answers to the apparent paradoxes mentioned at the end of Section 6-4, Einstein's crystal model will be discussed. This model does not correspond very well to any actual crystal, but it is historically important and serves well the purpose of illustration.

According to classical statistical mechanics, the molar heat capacity of an elemental solid should be $3R$, or about 6 cal/mole·degree. That many elemental solids do have approximately this molar heat capacity is the familiar law of Dulong and Petit. However, several exceptions, the most glaring of which is diamond, could not be explained on this theory. In 1907 Einstein proposed his model, which accounted for these discrepancies, but was still inadequate as a quantitative theory.

In Einstein's model a crystal is regarded as a collection of atoms each oscillating about a fixed position. The oscillations are assumed to be three-dimentional, harmonic, isotropic, and all of the same frequency. More abstractly, the model may be regarded as a collection of N three-dimensional oscillators, or, more conveniently, $3N$ one-dimensional oscillators, each of the same frequency, ν. Although such a collection of oscillators is usually treated as an ensemble, it will be regarded here as a single system. This point is important enough to be worth reiterating: *the system in this treatment is not an oscillator, but a collection of 3N oscillators, corresponding to a crystal of N atoms.* The ensemble, then, is a collection of many such crystals.

According to the original form of the quantum theory, used when this model was first proposed, the energy of a system of $3N$ harmonic oscillators of identical frequency is $rh\nu$, where r (the sum of the $3N$ quantum numbers for the individual oscillators) is a nonnegative integer. This value will be used, although later quantum mechanics assigned the value $(r + \frac{3}{2}N)h\nu$ to the energy of such a system; the effect of the extra term will be discussed in the next section.

In Section 6–4 it was pointed out that states of lowest energy have the highest probabilities. In this case, then, the most probable state is one of zero energy; next is one having energy $h\nu$. However, in the zero energy level only one state is possible, each of the quantum numbers being zero; the level of energy $h\nu$, on the other hand, is degenerate, $3N$ states of this energy being possible. This can be seen from the fact that any one of the $3N$ quantum numbers can be 1, the others being zero; or in other words, the single quantum of energy can be assigned to any one of the $3N$ oscillators, and each such assignment constitutes another state. Now if $h\nu$ is small compared to kT, the quantity $\exp(-h\nu/kT)$ is nearly 1, and the probability of each of the $3N$ states of energy $h\nu$ differs only trivially from that of the single state of energy zero. Thus the probability of finding the system in the energy level $h\nu$, as distinguished from any one of the $3N$ states in that energy level, is nearly $3N$ times as great as that of finding it in the zero energy level. Similarly, the degeneracy of the level of energy $2h\nu$ can be shown to be $3N(3N + 1)/2$, and its probability is correspondingly high.

This reasoning can be extended to determine the most probable energy level. The degeneracy Ω_r of the level r, of energy $rh\nu$, is the number of ways in which r quanta can be distributed among $3N$ oscillators. This is shown in Appendix 3 to be

$$\binom{3N + r - 1}{r}.$$

If the state i, of probability γ_i, is one of the Ω_r states in the energy level r, then the probability Γ_r of the rth level is given by

$$\Gamma_r = \Omega_r \gamma_i = \frac{\Omega_r e^{-rh\nu/kT}}{Z}$$

The ratio of probabilities for two adjacent levels is then

$$\frac{\Gamma_{r+1}}{\Gamma_r} = \frac{\Omega_{r+1} \, e^{-(r+1)h\nu/kT}}{\Omega_r e^{-rh\nu/kT}} = \frac{\binom{3N+r}{r+1}}{\binom{3N+r-1}{r}} \, e^{-h\nu/kT}$$

$$= \frac{3N+r}{r+1} \, e^{-h\nu/kT}$$

For small values of r, this is greater than 1, except at very low temperatures, and so the higher level is more probable. As r increases, $(3N+r)/(r+1)$ approaches 1; since the exponential factor is less than 1, the ratio of the two probabilities becomes less than 1. Clearly the lowest value of r that makes Γ_{r+1}/Γ_r less than 1 designates the most probable level. Writing y for $\exp(-h\nu/kT)$, we have, for the most probable level r_m,

$$\frac{3N+r_m}{r_m+1} \, y < 1$$

or

$$3Ny + r_m y < r_m + 1$$

from which

$$r_m(1-y) > 3Ny - 1$$

Finally we have

$$r_m > \frac{3Ny-1}{1-y} = \frac{3Ne^{-h\nu/kT}-1}{1-e^{-h\nu/kT}} \tag{6--20}$$

This shows that the most probable energy level for any system is the one having energy $r_m h\nu$, where r_m is the smallest integer satisfying this inequality. It is readily shown that in any reasonable circumstances the 1 in the numerator is negligible. For example, for crystals of one micromole (i.e., N equal to one millionth of Avogadro's number) and $h\nu/k$ equal to $100°$, the error produced by neglecting this term is only 1 ppm at $4°K$ and diminishes rapidly as the temperature increases. Moreover, we can neglect the difference between the fraction on the right and the smallest integer exceeding it, since this difference cannot be more than 1. Thus the most probable energy is

$$r_m h\nu = \frac{3Nh\nu e^{-h\nu/kT}}{1-e^{-h\nu/kT}} = \frac{3Nh\nu}{e^{h\nu/kT}-1} \tag{6--21}$$

Later it will be shown that this is precisely the average energy per system in the ensemble. This, then, is the answer to the first of the apparent paradoxes. Individual states are, indeed, more probable at the lowest energy levels, but the vastly greater number of states in the higher levels offsets this, so that the most probable level is that of average energy, as we would expect. The most probable level is not the lowest, but the one at which the decrease in the exponential term exp $(-\epsilon_i/kT)$ as we go to higher levels first offsets the increase in degeneracy.

Although this shows that the energy-level probability has a maximum at the average energy, it does not show how sharp the maximum is. In other words, we have shown that more systems are near the average energy than any other, but not that most systems are very near this energy. To show this, the entropy will be calculated both for the canonical ensemble, in which the systems are allowed to wander over various energy levels, and for the microcanonical ensemble, in which they are confined strictly to the same energy. If the results are practically equal, this will show that even when the systems are allowed to wander over states far removed from the average energy, no significant number of them take advantage of the opportunity.

To do this we must first determine the partition function. This has been defined as the sum of the quantity exp $(-\epsilon_i/kT)$ over all accessible states of the systems. However, when degenerate levels are involved, all states having the same energy will contribute identical terms to this sum, and these may as well be grouped into a single term $\Omega_r \exp(-\epsilon_r/kT)$, where the index r refers to the rth energy level, not the rth state. For the Einstein crystal we have shown that

$$\Omega_r = \binom{3N + r - 1}{r}$$

The energy levels are given by $\epsilon_r = rh\nu$, and so the partition function is

$$Z = \sum_r \binom{3N + r - 1}{r} e^{-rh\nu/kT} = \sum_r \binom{3N + r - 1}{r} y^r$$

where y is used, as before, for exp $(-h\nu/kT)$. The largest value of r that should be included in this summation is certainly finite, since no system can have more energy than the entire ensemble, and this is a fixed finite quantity. However, it is much easier to carry r to infinity and evaluate the resulting infinite series, and the error produced is utterly negligible. In fact, many of the terms in the finite sum are negligible, as is shown by the fact that the last term is proportional to the probability that one system will somehow acquire all the energy of the ensemble.

By the binomial theorem we have

$$(1 - y)^{-3N} = 1 + 3Ny + \frac{3N(3N + 1)}{2!} y^2 + \ldots$$

It is easily verified that the coefficient of y^r is

$$\frac{3N(3N + 1)(3N + 2) \ldots (3N + r - 1)}{r!}$$

If we multiply both numerator and denominator by $(3N - 1)!$, the numerator becomes $(3N + r - 1)!$, and the coefficient itself is seen to be equal to

$$\binom{3N + r - 1}{r}$$

This series is, therefore, identical with the one representing the partition function, and so

$$Z = (1 - y)^{-3N} \qquad (6\text{-}22)$$

From this we obtain the average energy per system by Eq. (6–16). First it is helpful to note that since $\ln y = - h\nu/kT$, $(\partial y/\partial T)_\nu = yh\nu/kT^2$. Then Eqs. (6–16) and (6–22) give

$$u = kT^2 \left[\frac{\partial(\ln Z)}{\partial T} \right]_\epsilon = -3NkT^2 \left[\frac{\partial \ln (1 - y)}{\partial T} \right]_\nu = -3NkT^2 \frac{-\left(\frac{\partial y}{\partial T} \right)_\nu}{1 - y}$$

$$= \frac{3Nyh\nu}{1 - y} = \frac{3Nh\nu}{e^{h\nu/kT} - 1} \qquad (6\text{-}23)$$

This is identical with the energy calculated for the most probable level (Eq. (6–21)).

To find the entropy per system in the canonical ensemble, we use Eq. (6–17), obtaining

$$s = \frac{u}{T} + k \ln Z = \frac{3Nh\nu/T}{e^{h\nu/kT} - 1} - 3Nk \ln (1 - e^{-h\nu/kT}) \qquad (6\text{-}24)$$

Next we consider a microcanonical ensemble of Einstein crystals, each being restricted to the average (and most probable) energy calculated above. The entropy is given by

$$s = k \ln \Omega_{r_m} = k \ln \binom{3N + r_m - 1}{r_m} \qquad (6\text{-}25)$$

with r_m equal to the previously determined most probable quantum number, $(3Ny - 1)/(1 - y)$. To evaluate the logarithm of a binomial coefficient, we use the approximate form of Stirling's formula, $\ln n! = n \ln n - n$. This gives

$$\ln \binom{a}{b} = a \ln a - b \ln b - (a - b) \ln (a - b)$$

Before applying this to Eq. (6-25), we can simplify several terms by dropping small quantities, as follows:

$$r_m = \frac{3Ny - 1}{1 - y} \approx \frac{3Ny}{1 - y}$$

$$3N + r_m - 1 = 3N + \frac{3Ny - 1}{1 - y} - 1 = \frac{3N + y - 2}{1 - y} \approx \frac{3N}{1 - y}$$

and

$$3N - 1 \approx 3N$$

We then have

$$s = k \ln \binom{3N + r_m - 1}{r_m}$$

$$= k \left[\frac{3N}{1 - y} \ln \frac{3N}{1 - y} - \frac{3Ny}{1 - y} \ln \frac{3Ny}{1 - y} - 3N \ln (3N) \right]$$

$$= k \left[\left(\frac{3N}{1 - y} - 3N - \frac{3Ny}{1 - y} \right) \ln (3N) + \left(\frac{3Ny}{1 - y} - \frac{3N}{1 - y} \right) \ln (1 - y) \right.$$

$$\left. - \frac{3Ny}{1 - y} \ln y \right]$$

$$= -3Nk \left[\ln (1 - y) + \frac{y}{1 - y} \ln y \right]$$

Substituting the value of y then gives

$$s = \frac{3Nh\nu/T}{e^{h\nu/kT} - 1} - 3Nk \ln (1 - e^{-h\nu/kT})$$

exactly as for the canonical ensemble.

It may appear surprising that the results are *exactly* the same for the two types of ensembles, since the canonical ensemble allows the systems access to more states and so in principle must result in higher entropy. It does in fact lead to higher entropy, but the difference is so trivial that it has been obscured in the calculation by the several approximations which have been introduced — the use of only a crude form of Stirling's formula, the dropping of small terms, and treating the partition function sum as an infinite series. It can readily be shown by a numerical calculation that for crystals of one micromole each at 300°K, the error introduced by these approximations is of the order of magnitude of one part in 10^{18}. This reconciles the apparently contradictory requirements of classical thermodynamics and statistical mechanics in regard to the entropy difference between a canonical ensemble and a microcanonical ensemble of the same energy. The entropy is greater for the canonical ensemble, as required statistically, but the difference is undetectably small, so that the entropies are experimentally identical, as required by classical thermodynamics.

The status of the second law itself is similar. In principle, deviations from the second law occur, but for macroscopic systems they are so small as to be far beyond the possibility of experimental detection. In smaller systems deviations are more important; for colloidal particles (of the order of a few thousand to a few million atoms) they are readily observable, Brownian motion being the most familiar example. On a still smaller scale — single atoms or small molecules — the law ceases to be applicable at all.

6–7. Change of Zero of Energy Scale

It is frequently desirable to know how thermodynamic functions will be affected by a change in the zero point from which energy is measured; that is, by a transformation $\epsilon'_i = \epsilon_i + \eta$, where η is a constant. For some of the thermodynamic functions only differences have any physical significance, and the values may well be changed by a mere change of the zero of the energy scale. This is not true of the probabilities associated with given states; the actual values of these are physically significant and so must be independent of the choice of energy scale. We can repeat the derivation of the equilibrium equation, Eq. (6–9), using ϵ_i', α', and β' instead of ϵ_i, α, and β, and arrive at an analogous expression for γ_i. Thus

$$\gamma_i = e^{-\alpha} e^{-\beta \epsilon_i} = e^{-\alpha'} e^{-\beta' \epsilon_i'}$$

Applying this to states i and j and dividing one equation by the other gives

$$\frac{\gamma_i}{\gamma_j} = e^{-\beta(\epsilon_i - \epsilon_j)} = e^{-\beta'(\epsilon'_i - \epsilon'_j)} = e^{-\beta' (\epsilon_i - \epsilon_j)}$$

since energy differences on the two scales are identical. From this we see that $\beta = \beta'$; that is, the value assigned to the temperature is unaffected by the change of scale. On the new scale the partition function becomes

$$Z' = \sum_i e^{-\epsilon'_i/kT} = \sum_i e^{-(\epsilon_i + \eta)/kT} = e^{-\eta/kT} \sum_i e^{-\epsilon_i/kT}$$

$$= e^{-\eta/kT} Z \qquad (6\text{–}26)$$

Now applying Eq. (6–18) gives

$$a' = -kT \ln Z' = -kT\left(-\frac{\eta}{kT} + \ln Z\right) = \eta + a \qquad (6\text{–}27)$$

and so the Helmholtz free energy is changed in exactly the same way as the energy scale itself. This also applies to the energy, as can be seen by using Eq. (6–16):

$$u' = kT^2 \left[\frac{\partial (\ln Z')}{\partial T}\right]_{\epsilon_i} = kT^2 \left[\frac{\partial}{\partial T}\left(-\frac{\eta}{kT} + \ln Z\right)\right]_{\epsilon_i} = \eta + u \quad (6\text{–}28)$$

From this we see that $u - a = u' - a'$, and so

$$s' = \frac{u' - a'}{T} = \frac{u - a}{T} = s \qquad (6\text{–}29)$$

and the entropy is unaffected.

This procedure may be used to determine the effect that inclusion of the quantum-mechanical zero point energy of the oscillators would have on an Einstein crystal. It would merely increase the energy, enthalpy, and free energies by $\frac{3}{2}Nh\nu$, without changing the entropy. In a similar manner one can include the binding energy of the atoms in a crystal. This amounts to referring energy measurements to separated atoms — that is, to the gaseous state — instead of the lowest-energy state of the crystal. This would be essential, for example, in treating the vapor pressure of a solid. In the application of statistical thermodynamics to thermochemistry, the energies of reactants and products must be referred to the same zero. For example, if the reaction is

$$A + B \rightarrow C$$

then

$$\Delta u = u_C - u_A - u_B = kT^2 \frac{\partial}{\partial T}\left(\ln \frac{z_C}{z_A z_B}\right) \tag{6–30}$$

provided the partition functions are for 1 mole of material and are referred to the same energy zero point. However, partition functions are usually based on energies measured from the lowest level for each compound. If we denote by primed quantities energies measured from the lowest level for each molecule, and by unprimed letters energies measured from a common zero-point for all molecules involved, we have

$$\epsilon_{iA} = \epsilon'_{iA} + \epsilon_{0A}$$

and so

$$z_A = z'_A e^{-\epsilon_{0A}/kT}$$

and

$$u_A = \epsilon_{0A} + kT^2 \frac{\partial}{\partial T}(\ln z'_A)$$

with similar equations for B and C. Therefore

$$\Delta u = \epsilon_{0_C} - \epsilon_{0_A} - \epsilon_{0_B} + kT^2 \frac{\partial}{\partial T}\left(\ln \frac{z'_C}{z'_A z'_B}\right)$$

The first three terms on the right represent the energy change of the reaction when all reactants and products are in their lowest states, or in other words, the energy of reaction at $0°K$. Finally, then, we have

$$\Delta u = \Delta u_0 + kT^2 \frac{\partial}{\partial T}\left(\ln \frac{z'_C}{z'_A z'_B}\right) \tag{6–31}$$

The determination of Δu_0 is outside the scope of statistical thermodynamics; in practice, experimental values must usually be used, though in principle quantum mechanical calculation is possible.

6–8. Factorization of the Partition Function

It often happens that the energy of a system can be expressed as the sum of two or more terms representing different types of energy, and that these different types of energy are independent of each other, at least to a first approximation. For example, the different types of energy may be the energies of several independent particles making up the system, or the rotational and translational energies of a diatomic molecule. This makes possible the factorization of the partition function into the product of several partition functions, one for each type of energy. To show this, let the energy levels be given by

$$\epsilon_{ij} = \epsilon_i^t + \epsilon_j^r$$

the superscripts t and r referring to translational and rotational energy, respectively. These two types of energy are independent, and any translational level may be combined with any rotational level. Since we must sum over all states in calculating the partition function, a double sum over i and j is needed. Therefore,

$$Z = \sum_{i,\,j} e^{-\epsilon_{ij}/kT} = \sum_{i,\,j} e^{-\epsilon_i^t/kT}\, e^{-\epsilon_j^r/kT}$$

$$= \sum_i e^{-\epsilon_i^t/kT} \sum_j e^{-\epsilon_j^r/kT} = Z_t Z_r \qquad (6\text{--}32)$$

To illustrate the use of this, we can determine the partition function of an Einstein crystal. The total energy is considered as the sum of $3N$ terms, each representing the energy of a single oscillator. Now the oscillators are identical and so have identical partition functions. Therefore Eq. (6–32) becomes the product of $3N$ identical terms, each representing the partition function for a single oscillator. The energy levels of a single oscillator are $rh\nu$ $(r = 0,\ 1,\ 2, \dots)$ and are nondegenerate. Thus the single-oscillator partition function is

$$1 + y + y^2 + \dots = \frac{1}{1 - y}$$

The partition function for the entire crystal is the $3N$th power of this, in agreement with Eq. (6–22), which was derived by a somewhat more complicated procedure.

6–9. The Ideal Monatomic Gas

An ideal monatomic gas will be regarded as a system of N identical atoms, with practically independent energy levels, and confined in a rectangular box of dimensions a, b, and c. The partition function of a single atom will be calculated first, and then that of the whole system will be taken as the Nth power of this. However, it will then be shown that the quantal method of counting states requires a simple modification of the result. From the corrected partition function the thermodynamic properties of the gas will be derived.

Quantum mechanical calculations show that the energy levels of a particle in a box of dimensions a, b, and c are given by

$$\epsilon_{rst} = \frac{h^2}{8m}\left(\frac{r^2}{a^2} + \frac{s^2}{b^2} + \frac{t^2}{c^2}\right)$$

where m is the mass and r, s, and t are the quantum numbers associated with motion along the directions of a, b, and c, respectively. Since this can be separated into three terms, each dependent on only one quantum number, the partition function can be factored into the product of three partition functions, one for motion along each of the three directions. The first of these is

$$z_a = \sum_{r=1}^{\infty} \exp\left(-\frac{h^2 r^2}{8mkTa^2}\right)$$

As in the case of the Einstein crystal, the summation is carried to infinity for mathematical convenience, the error being negligible. In practical

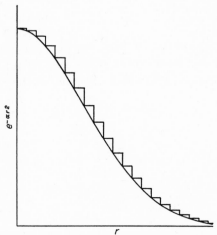

FIGURE 14. DIAGRAM ILLUSTRATING THE SUBSTITUTION OF $\displaystyle\int_0^{\infty} e^{-\alpha r^2}\,dr$ FOR $\displaystyle\sum_{r=1}^{\infty} e^{-\alpha r^2}$.

This is drawn for $\alpha = 0.01$; for $\alpha = 10^{-20}$ (a more realistic value in applications to gases) the error produced by the substitution is less than one part in 10^{10}.

cases, the important values of r extend to very high numbers, as will be shown later by a numerical calculation. This makes it possible to replace the sum in this expression by an integral; that is, to replace the area under the step-like line of Figure 14 by the area under the curve. We then have

$$z_a = \int_0^\infty \exp\left(-\frac{h^2 r^2}{8mkTa^2}\right) dr$$

This integral is of the type

$$\int_0^\infty e^{-\alpha x^2} \, dx = \tfrac{1}{2}\left(\frac{\pi}{\alpha}\right)^{\tfrac{1}{2}}$$

which is evaluated in Appendix 5. Applying this to z_a gives

$$z_a = \tfrac{1}{2}\left(\frac{8mkTa^2\pi}{h^2}\right)^{\tfrac{1}{2}} = \frac{(2\pi mkT)^{\tfrac{1}{2}}a}{h}$$

Analogous expressions are derivable for z_b and z_c, b or c appearing in place of a. The complete partition function for a single atom is then

$$z = z_a \, z_b \, z_c = \frac{(2\pi mkT)^{\tfrac{3}{2}}V}{h^3}$$

where $V = abc$ is the volume of the container. The next step in determining the partition function for the entire system of N atoms is to raise this to the Nth power, which leads to

$$Z' = \left[\frac{(2\pi mkT)^{3/2}\,V}{h^3}\right]^N$$

where the prime is used to indicate that this is not yet the correct partition function, since it has not been corrected for the difference in the classical and quantal methods of counting states.

This correction can be understood best after a discussion of what is meant by a "state" in quantum mechanics. In principle, all that can be stated about a quantum mechanical system is implicit in its Schrödinger function, ψ. This is a function of the coordinates needed to describe the system and, if nonstationary states are being considered, of the time. Certain operations permit the calculation of various properties of the system from ψ. Among the properties that can be calculated are the total energy, the average kinetic energy, the components of angular momentum, and the probability that the coordinates will lie in a prescribed range. An important feature of these calculations is that they all depend on ψ^2 or on ψ times one of its derivatives, and so they do not change if the sign of ψ is changed; ψ and $-\psi$ describe the same state.

Suppose that two particles, 1 and 2, are of different types. We will indicate that particle 1 is in state A by $\psi_A(1)$. If particle 2 is simultaneously in state B, as indicated by $\psi_B(2)$, the state of the whole system, consisting of both particles, is $\psi_A(1)\psi_B(2)$. To facilitate comparison of classical and quantum states, this symbol will also be used in classical systems to indicate that particles 1 and 2 are in states A and B, respectively.

Now consider two *identical* particles, with two states available to each. Possible system states are

$$\psi_A(1)\ \psi_A(2) \qquad \psi_A(1)\ \psi_B(2)$$

$$\psi_B(1)\ \psi_A(2) \qquad \psi_B(1)\ \psi_B(2)$$

a total of four. Classically, this would be the correct way to count states. Quantum mechanics, however, imposes an additional requirement: the Schrödinger function for the whole system must be either symmetric or antisymmetric. In this usage a symmetric function means a function that does not change when two identical particles are interchanged; an antisymmetric function changes in sign, but in no other way, when such an interchange occurs. Whether symmetric or antisymmetric functions are demanded depends on the type of particles; electrons, protons, neutrons, He^3 nuclei, and other particles composed of an odd number of elementary particles require antisymmetric functions; while for deuterons, He^4 nuclei, and others containing an even number of elementary particles, symmetric functions are needed. Of the four functions listed above, $\psi_A(1)\psi_A(2)$ and $\psi_B(1)\psi_B(2)$ are unaffected by the interchange of 1 and 2, and so are symmetric functions. The other two functions, $\psi_A(1)\psi_B(2)$ and $\psi_B(1)\psi_A(2)$, are changed each into the other by this interchange; these are neither symmetric nor antisymmetric. In this case we construct either the symmetric combination

$$2^{-\frac{1}{2}}\ [\psi_A(1)\ \psi_B(2) + \psi_B(1)\ \psi_A(2)]$$

or the antisymmetric one

$$2^{-\frac{1}{2}}\ [\psi_A(1)\ \psi_B(2) - \psi_B(1)\ \psi_A(2)]$$

and the appropriate one of these represents a possible state of the system.

(The purpose of the *normalization constant*, $2^{-\frac{1}{2}}$, need not concern us here.) We see, then, that the possible states in each case are:

Classical	Quantal, symmetric	Quantal, antisymmetric
$\psi_A(1)\,\psi_A(2)$	$\psi_A(1)\,\psi_A(2)$	
$\psi_B(1)\,\psi_B(2)$	$\psi_B(1)\,\psi_B(2)$	
$\psi_A(1)\,\psi_B(2)$	$2^{-\frac{1}{2}}\,[\psi_A(1)\,\psi_B(2)+\psi_B(1)\,\psi_A(2)]$	
$\psi_B(1)\,\psi_A(2)$		$2^{-\frac{1}{2}}\,[\psi_A(1)\,\psi_B(2)-\psi_B(1)\,\psi_A(2)]$

These total four for the classical method of counting, but only three for the symmetric, and one for the antisymmetric, quantal counts.

Two further consequences of the symmetry rule are easily deduced. Since interchange of particles either leaves ψ unchanged or changes only its sign, it does not lead to a new state. This situation is often described by saying that the particles are indistinguishable. Actually, more than mere indistinguishability is involved; even in classical physics it was recognized that identical particles cannot be distinguished, but it was not realized that interchange of them would not lead to a new state. Secondly, if a system of particles requires antisymmetric states, then no two of them can be in the same state, for if there were two in one state, interchange of these two would not affect the ψ-function for the system as a whole, and it would be symmetric with respect to this interchange. This rule, when applied to electrons, is the Pauli exclusion principle.

Thus if a system consists of N identical particles with antisymmetric ψ-functions, each of which has c particle-states available to it, we can specify a system-state merely by choosing, out of the c particle-states, N which are to be occupied by one particle each, the remaining $c - N$ being unoccupied. The number of system-states is, then, the number of groups of N objects which can be selected from a total of c. This is equal to the binomial coefficient $\begin{pmatrix} c \\ N \end{pmatrix}$. (See Appendix 3.)

For a system of N particles with symmetric ψ-functions, and c particle-states available to each, the number of system-states is the number of ways N indistinguishable particles can be placed in c states, with no limitation on the number in each state. Alternatively, this is the number of groups of N states (the ones to be occupied) which can be selected from a total of c with no limitation on the number of times each can be chosen (that is, each state to be occupied by more than one particle is chosen more than once). This is shown in Appendix 3 to be

$$\begin{pmatrix} c + N - 1 \\ N \end{pmatrix}$$

Classically, the number of system-states is found by assigning each of the N particles in turn to any one of the c states. This gives c^N system-states.

To summarize, the number of states by each method of counting is:

Classical $\qquad\qquad\qquad\qquad\qquad\qquad c^N$

Quantal, symmetric $\qquad\qquad\qquad \dbinom{c + N - 1}{N}$

Quantal, antisymmetric $\qquad\qquad\qquad \dbinom{c}{N}$

Now the method of constructing the provisional partition function Z' implies the classical count of the number of states. To show this let us consider again the system of two particles, each having two particle-states available. Then the partition function for a single particle is

$$e^{-\epsilon_A/kT} + e^{-\epsilon_B/kT}$$

and for the system of two particles

$$Z' = (e^{-\epsilon_A/kT} + e^{-\epsilon_A/kT})^2$$

$$= e^{-2\epsilon_A/kT} + 2e^{-(\epsilon_A + \epsilon_B)/kT} + e^{-2\epsilon_B/kT}$$

The system in the state $\psi_A(1)\psi_A(2)$ has energy $2\epsilon_A$; the first term corresponds to this. The states $\psi_A(1)\psi_B(2)$ and $\psi_B(1)\psi_A(2)$ each involve energy $\epsilon_A + \epsilon_B$; the second term corresponds to these (note the coefficient 2). Similarly the last term corresponds to the system-state $\psi_B(1)\psi_B(2)$. Thus there is one term for each state in the classical count.

In consequence, the provisional partition function Z', being based on the classical method of counting, is too large. If the classical count over-estimated the number of states in each energy level by the same ratio, the problem of correcting for it would be simple; we would merely divide by this ratio. Although this condition is not met, we can justify this method of correcting in another manner. It was shown for the Einstein crystal, and is true for other macroscopic systems, that we find the same results regardless of whether we allow the systems to wander over various energy levels, keeping only the average energy constant, or confine each system strictly to the average energy. This means that the important terms in the partition function all have practically the same exponential factor. To correct the partition function, therefore, we need merely reduce the number of states from the number appropriate to a classical system to that appropriate to a quantal system; this can be done by dividing by the ratio of the classical to the quantal count. The next step is to find, in practical terms, the value of this ratio.

In the symmetric case, the ratio is

$$\frac{c^N}{\left(\begin{matrix} c + N - 1 \\ N \end{matrix}\right)} = \frac{c^N}{\dfrac{c(c + 1)\,(c + 2)\,\ldots\,(c + N - 1)}{N\,!}}$$

$$= \frac{N\,!}{\left(1 + \dfrac{1}{c}\right)\left(1 + \dfrac{2}{c}\right)\ldots\left(1 + \dfrac{N - 1}{c}\right)}$$

Now for a typical case we might have $N = 10^{23}$, and c could be conservatively estimated at 10^{30}. Then none of the factors in the denominator differs from 1 by more than 10^{-7}, and we might be tempted to think that the entire denominator differs only trivially from 1. This would be too naïve, however, since the number of factors is very large — about 10^{23}. With these figures the actual value of the denominator exceeds $10^{10^{15}}$, and replacing it by 1 appears to be a rather crude approximation. Nevertheless, it is justified. The reason is that thermodynamic properties are calculated not directly from Z, but from $\ln Z$, and Z is such an enormous number that $\ln 10^{10^{15}}$ is negligible compared to $\ln Z$. (These statements will be justified by a numerical calculation later.) The ratio of the number of classical states to the number of symmetric quantal states reduces, in the approximation required, simply to $N!$. The argument for the antisymmetric case is similar and leads to the same result. Thus the conclusion of this long digression is that the partition function for an ideal monatomic gas is given by

$$Z = \frac{Z'}{N\,!} = \left[\frac{(2\pi m k T)^{3/2} V}{h^3}\right]^N \frac{1}{N\,!} \tag{6-33}$$

In calculating thermodynamic functions from this equation, it is helpful to write it as

$$\ln Z = \frac{3}{2} N \ln T + N \ln V + \text{constant}$$

although the terms on the right, taken individually, are dimensionally inconsistent. From this we easily find

$$U = kT^2 \left[\frac{\partial (\ln Z)}{\partial T} \right]_V = kT^2 \left(\frac{3}{2} N \right) \left(\frac{1}{T} \right) = \frac{3}{2} NkT \qquad (6\text{-}34)$$

Here the derivative is taken at constant V instead of constant ϵ_i for convenience; this is valid, since the derivation has shown that it is through V that the partition function depends on the ϵ's. For the pressure we have

$$p = kT \left[\frac{\partial (\ln Z)}{\partial V} \right]_T = \frac{NkT}{V} \qquad (6\text{-}35)$$

This gives us a means of evaluating k. Let N be equal to Avogadro's number, N_a, so that the amount of gas under consideration is 1 mole, and the volume is the molar volume, v. Then comparison of this equation with the ideal gas law gives

$$pv = N_a kT = RT$$

and so

$$k = \frac{R}{N_a} \qquad (6\text{-}36)$$

Because of this, k is often called the *molecular gas constant*, in analogy to the name *molar gas constant* for R. Its value is $(1.38047 \pm 0.00026) \times 10^{-16}$ erg/molecule·degree (the units are usually written erg/degree).

Using Stirling's formula for $\ln N!$, we find for the entropy,

$$S = \frac{U}{T} + k \ln Z = \frac{3}{2} Nk + Nk \ln \frac{(2\pi mkT)^{3/2} V}{h^3} - k(N \ln N - N)$$

$$= Nk \left\{ \frac{5}{2} + \ln \left[\frac{(2\pi mkT)^{3/2} V}{h^3 N} \right] \right\} \qquad (6\text{-}37)$$

Notice that if T and p are constant, any variation of N and V must be such that V/N is constant, by Eq. (6-35); this makes the term in braces in Eq. (6-37) constant, and so S is proportional to N. This expresses the fact that S is an extensive property. This would not be true without the factor $1/N!$ in the partition function. In the days of classical statistical mechanics this factor was introduced as an empirical correction needed to make the entropy extensive, but the reason for it was not understood until the development of quantum mechanics.

To justify the approximations in this treatment by a numerical example, we must find an expression for the number of system-states of a given energy. The equation for the energy of a particle in a box can be rewritten

$$\frac{r^2}{\left[\frac{a(8m\epsilon)^{\frac{1}{2}}}{h}\right]^2} + \frac{s^2}{\left[\frac{b(8m\epsilon)^{\frac{1}{2}}}{h}\right]^2} + \frac{t^2}{\left[\frac{c(8m\epsilon)^{\frac{1}{2}}}{h}\right]^2} = 1$$

which is the equation of an ellipsoid whose semiaxes are the quantities in brackets in the denominators. The number of system-states of energy no greater than ϵ is the number of points (r, s, t) with positive integral coordinates lying within this ellipsoid. Except near the surface, there is one of these in each unit of volume. Neglecting irregularities near the surface, then, the number of system-states is simply the volume of the positive octant of this ellipsoid. Now the volume of one octant of an ellipsoid is $\pi/6$ times the product of its semiaxes, and so the number of states is given by

$$\omega(\epsilon) = \frac{\pi}{6} \frac{abc(8m\epsilon)^{3/2}}{h^3} = \frac{4\pi V}{3h^3}(2m\epsilon)^{3/2} \tag{6-38}$$

Now consider the particular case in which

$T = 300°K$

$\epsilon = \frac{3}{2}kT = 1.5 \times 1.38 \times 10^{-16}$ erg/molecule

$N = 10^{23}$ molecules

$m = \frac{50}{6.02} \times 10^{-23}$ g (molecular weight = 50 g/mole)

$V = 5 \times 10^3$ cm³

Then substitution gives $\omega = 2.2 \times 10^{30}$. The value actually chosen as "a conservative estimate" was about half of this. To determine the quantity

$$D \equiv \left(1 + \frac{1}{c}\right)\left(1 + \frac{2}{c}\right)\cdots\left(1 + \frac{N-1}{c}\right)$$

we take its logarithm, and then expand each of the terms by the series for ln $(1 + x)$. After the terms are grouped, we have

$$\ln D = \frac{\sum\limits_{i=1}^{N-1} i}{c} + \frac{1}{2}\frac{\sum\limits_{i=1}^{N-1} i^2}{c^2} + \ldots \approx \frac{N^2}{2c} + \frac{N^3}{6c^2} + \ldots$$

When the values of N and c are substituted, only the first term is found to be important, and the value of ln D proves to be about 5×10^{15}, or $\log_{10} D \approx 2 \times 10^{15}$. Therefore D itself exceeds $10^{10^{15}}$, as stated previously. Substitution of these same values into the expression for the logarithm of Z gives ln $Z = 2.04 \times 10^{24}$, and so neglecting ln $10^{10^{15}}$ in comparison with this makes an error of less than one part in 10^8.

Since Eq. (6–37) was derived for ideal gases, it applies only approximately to real gases. However, the standard entropy, s', can be calculated exactly from this equation. Since every gas is practically ideal at low pressures, and exactly so in the limit of zero pressure, the extrapolation of $s + R \ln (p/p_u)$ to zero pressure can be carried out with either the true entropy or the entropy calculated for an ideal gas. For 1 mole Eq. (6–37) becomes

$$s = R \left\{ \frac{5}{2} + \ln \left[\frac{(2\pi mkT)^{3/2}v}{h^3 N_a} \right] \right\}$$

which is known as the *Sackur-Tetrode equation*. If we add $R \ln (p/p_u)$ to this, we get

$$s + R \ln \frac{p}{p_u} = R \left\{ \frac{5}{2} + \ln \left[\frac{(2\pi mkT)^{3/2}pv}{h^3 N_a p_u} \right] \right\}$$

When this is extrapolated to zero pressure, $pv \rightarrow RT$, and we have

$$s' = R \left\{ \frac{5}{2} + \ln \left[\frac{(2\pi mkT)^{3/2}RT}{h^3 N_a p_u} \right] \right\} \qquad (6\text{–}39)$$

Note that the units of the R inside the brackets must be chosen so that RT/p_u has the units of cubic centimeters. The R outside the braces, however, should be in the same units as are chosen for s'. Of the quantities that appear in this equation, only m and T are variable. If we substitute

$m = M/N_a$, where M is the molecular weight, and use standard numerical values for the other quantities, we find that

$$s' = R \left(\frac{3}{2} \ln M + \frac{5}{2} \ln T - K \right) \qquad (6\text{--}40)$$

where K is 1.1523 for unit pressure of 1 bar and 1.1646 for unit pressure of 1 atm. M and T here represent the numerical measure of molecular weight and temperature in the usual units, not the quantities themselves. For neon at 25°C, for example, $M = 20.183$ and $T = 298.15$; with these values the equation gives $s' = 146.22$ joules/mole·degree, in exact agreement with the value found from thermal measurements and the third law.

6-10. Diatomic Gases

The treatment of diatomic gases will be based on a commonly used approximation, which is valid except at high temperatures. This is the separation of the energy into independent terms, each dependent on only one of the several types of energy. Thus the energy will be expressed as $\epsilon_t + \epsilon_r + \epsilon_v + \epsilon_e$, referring to translational, rotational, vibrational, and electronic terms, respectively. As shown in Section 6-8, this makes it possible to express the partition function as a product of factors corresponding to each of these types of energy. Since the thermodynamic properties are calculated from the logarithm of the partition function, this results in expressing these properties as the sum of contributions from each type of energy. These will be treated separately.

Nothing needs to be done in regard to the translational terms and translational properties. These are exactly the same as for a monatomic gas, and the results of the preceding section can be used.

For rotation, the energy levels given by quantum mechanics are

$$\epsilon_J = \frac{J(J + 1)h^2}{8\pi^2 I} = \frac{[(J + \frac{1}{2})^2 - \frac{1}{4}] h^2}{8\pi^2 I} \qquad (6\text{--}41)$$

where J is a nonnegative integer and I is the moment of inertia of the molecule about its center of gravity. The moment of inertia is given by

$$I = \mu r^2 \qquad (6\text{--}42)$$

where r is the distance between the centers of the atoms and μ, the *reduced mass*, is given by

$$\frac{1}{\mu} = \frac{1}{m_1} + \frac{1}{m_2} \qquad (6\text{--}43)$$

The energy level J has a degeneracy of $2J + 1$. All these states are available only if the two atoms are different, either different elements or different isotopes of the same element. In this case the rotational partition function for one molecule is given by

$$z_r = \sum_{J=0}^{\infty} (2J + 1)e^{-\sigma [(J + \frac{1}{2})^2 - \frac{1}{4}]}$$

where σ has been written for $h^2/8\pi^2 IkT$. Substituting integration for summation and changing the variable to $x = J + \frac{1}{2}$ leads to

$$z_r = \int_0^{\infty} (2J + 1)e^{-\sigma [(J + \frac{1}{2})^2 - \frac{1}{4}]} \, dJ$$

$$= e^{\sigma/4} \int_{-\frac{1}{2}}^{\infty} 2xe^{-\sigma x^2} \, dx = e^{\sigma/4} \left[-\frac{e^{-\sigma x^2}}{\sigma} \right]_{-\frac{1}{2}}^{\infty} = \frac{1}{\sigma} \qquad (6\text{--}44)$$

From this we have, for the partition function of the entire system,

$$Z_r = z_r^N$$

and

$$\ln Z_r = -N \ln \sigma = N \ln \left(\frac{8\pi^2 IkT}{h^2} \right)$$

The molar rotational energy is, therefore,

$$u_r = kT^2 \left[\frac{\partial (\ln Z_r)}{\partial T} \right]_V = N_a kT^2 \frac{d(\ln T)}{dT} = RT \qquad (6\text{--}45)$$

Since the rotational partition function does not depend on volume, it makes no contribution to the pressure. The fact that rotation affects the energy of a gas without affecting its pressure is one of the reasons, mentioned in Section 4-12, why the energy of a gas cannot be calculated from its p-v-T equation. The molar rotational entropy is

$$s_r = \frac{u_r}{T} + k \ln Z_r = R \left[1 + \ln \left(\frac{8\pi^2 IkT}{h^2} \right) \right] \qquad (6\text{--}46)$$

If the two atoms in the molecule of gas are identical, only half the rotational energy levels are available. These may be either the even-numbered or the odd-numbered ones, depending on other factors. In either case the effect is to reduce the partition function for a single molecule by a factor of two. This does not affect the rotational energy, but it reduces the molar rotational entropy by $R \ln 2$.

For most diatomic gases the above treatment is sufficient for calculating the thermodynamic properties at or below room temperature, and in some cases to much higher temperatures. There are a few exceptions. The halogens require consideration of vibrational effects even at room temperature. Hydrogen remains a gas at such low temperatures that the substitution of integration for summation is not valid. At very low temperatures rotation is "frozen out"; that is, practically all molecules are in their lowest rotational energy level, and the gas behaves like a monatomic gas. Moreover, the distinction between even and odd rotational levels is important for hydrogen, as the equilibrium between ortho- and para-hydrogen (odd and even rotational levels respectively) depends on it. This will be discussed further in Section 6–17. For nitric oxide and oxygen the spin degeneracy of unpaired electrons must be considered.

The treatment of vibration is similar to that of the Einstein crystal, with the difference that a diatomic molecule is a one-dimensional oscillator instead of a three-dimensional one. This makes the partition function, in analogy with Eq. (6–22),

$$Z_v = (1 - y)^N$$

where $y = \exp{(- h\nu/kT)}$ as in Section 6–6. The energy is given by Eq. (6–23), modified to apply to only N oscillators,

$$U_v = \frac{N h\nu}{e^{h\nu/kT} - 1}$$

The vibrational entropy is

$$S_v = \frac{U_v}{T} - Nk \ln{(1 - y)}$$

For all diatomic gases $h\nu$ is higher than kT at room temperature; this means that vibrational contributions to the thermodynamic properties will be small. For the halogens it is sufficient that its inclusion is necessary, but for other diatomic gases it is negligible except at higher temperatures.

Electronic energy levels are usually so widely spaced that only the lowest level need be considered, the term $e^{-\epsilon/kT}$ being negligible for all higher levels. If we measure energy from the lowest level, so that $\epsilon_0 = 0$, the partition function becomes merely

$$Z_e = \omega_0{}^N$$

where ω_0 is the degeneracy of the lowest electronic level for a single molecule. This has no effect on the energy, but adds $R \ln \omega_0$ to the molar entropy. For oxygen, with two unpaired electrons with parallel spins, $\omega_0 = 3$, and the electronic contribution to the entropy is $R \ln 3$. The second electronic energy level becomes important only at temperatures near or above 2000°K. For nitric oxide, with one unpaired electron, $\omega_0 = 2$, but the situation is complicated by another doubly degenerate level only 2.47×10^{-14} erg above the lowest level. This leads to a partition function of

$$Z_e = (2 + 2e^{-179°/T})^N$$

and the entropy can be calculated from this.

6–11. Polyatomic Gases

The complete treatment of polyatomic gases is beyond the scope of this book, but a few qualitative remarks are in order. The effects of translation offer nothing new, being the same as for monatomic and diatomic gases. For linear molecules such as carbon dioxide, acetylene, and hydrogen cyanide, the treatment of rotation given for diatomic gases is applicable. For nonlinear molecules the effect of rotation is more complicated; it adds $\frac{3}{2}RT$ to the molar energy, and the rotational entropy depends on all three of the principal moments of inertia. There are several modes of vibration ($3n - 5$ for linear, $3n - 6$ for nonlinear molecules, where n is the number of atoms in the molecule), and some of these are likely to be important at relatively low temperatures. The analysis of these modes of vibration is an advanced problem in dynamics. Finally, the simplification which results from separating rotational and vibrational energies is often not available, since the two interact. Nevertheless, thermodynamic properties have been calculated for many polyatomic gases by methods identical in principle to those given here.

6–12. Determination of Rotational and Vibrational Constants of Molecules

The moment of inertia of a diatomic molecule can be calculated by Eqs. (6–42) and (6–43) if the interatomic distance is known. This distance can often be measured by electron diffraction of the gas, or X-ray diffraction in the solid state. Direct measurement of rotational energy levels, from which the moment of inertia can be calculated by Eq. (6–41), is now widely carried out by means of microwave spectra; similar results can be obtained from the fine structure which rotational transitions impose on the vibrational spectra in the near infrared region.

Vibrational frequencies of molecules are generally determined from infrared or Raman spectra.

6–13. Properties of Ideal Mixtures

Let us suppose that two gases are confined in the same container, and that no molecular interactions need be considered. The facts that molecules of gas 1 do not interact, nor do those of gas 2, mean that these two gases are ideal; the fact that molecules of gas 1 do not interact with those of gas 2 shows that they also form an *ideal mixture*.***

Since the two kinds of gas molecules in this ideal mixture do not interact, each gas may be regarded as a subsystem whose energy levels are unaffected by the presence of the other subsystem; moreover, the energy of the system is the sum of the energies of the subsystems. We can, therefore, factor the partition function into a product of partition functions for the subsystems. Thus

$$Z = Z_1 Z_2$$

and

$$\ln Z = \ln Z_1 + \ln Z_2$$

Now applying the expressions for u, s, a, and p (Eqs. (6–16) through (6–19)) to this sum, we find

$$u = u_1 + u_2 \qquad a = a_1 + a_2$$

$$s = s_1 + s_2 \qquad p = p_1 + p_2$$

That is, we assign to each gas the thermodynamic properties it would have if it were alone in the same volume and at the same temperature as the mixture; then the thermodynamic properties (other than temperature and volume) of the mixture are the sums of those of the individual gases. This reasoning is easily extended to mixtures of more than two gases.

This enables us to find the entropy change accompanying the constant-pressure mixing of gases by diffusion. Suppose that n_1, n_2, . . .

*** A more general definition of an ideal mixture will be given in Chapter 7.

moles of several ideal gases, all at the same temperature and pressure, are separated only by removable walls. Their volumes will be

$$V_1{}^i = \frac{n_1 RT}{p} \qquad V_2{}^i = \frac{n_2 RT}{p} \ldots$$

where the superscript i indicates that these are initial values, before mixing. When the walls are removed, the gases mix by diffusion, and each then occupies the entire volume. This volume is

$$V^f = (n_1 + n_2 + \ldots)\frac{RT}{p} = \frac{nRT}{p}$$

where n is the total number of moles. This process is irreversible and so must cause an increase in entropy. Actually, by Eq. (6-37) (or Eq. (4-8)), each gas undergoes an increase in entropy of

$$S_j^f - S_j^i = n_j R \ln \frac{V^f}{V_j^i} = n_j R \ln \frac{n}{n_j} = -n_j R \ln x_j$$

where $x_j \equiv n_j/n$ is the mole fraction of gas j. Now since the final entropy of the mixture is the sum of the quantities S_j^f, the entropy change accompanying the process is

$$\Delta S = -R \sum_j n_j \ln x_j \qquad (6\text{-}47)$$

The entropy change per mole of mixture formed is

$$\Delta s = -R \sum_j x_j \ln x_j \qquad (6\text{-}48)$$

This is usually called the *entropy of mixing*. Rushbrooke[†] has objected to this name on the grounds that the entropy change results from the increase in the volume of each gas rather than from mixing.

6-14. The Debye Crystal Model

In 1912 Debye, in one of the very early applications of quantum theory, proposed a crystal model which is far superior to Einstein's model in predicting the thermodynamic properties of solids. Debye's model has attracted a vast amount of attention. Serious objections have been raised to its logic, and several modified theories have been proposed.[1] Despite the apparent validity of some of these objections, none of the more ad-

† See p. 176 of Rushbrooke's book, listed in GENERAL REFERENCES.

vanced theories has been notably more successful than the simple Debye theory.

Debye's model, like Einstein's, pictures a crystal of N atoms as a collection of $3N$ harmonic oscillators. Debye's oscillators, however, are not single atoms, but vibrations of the entire crystal, essentially the same as sound waves. The number of oscillators at different frequencies is to be calculated by the classical theory of standing waves in a continuous elastic medium. This theory, however, provides no limit to the number of oscillators. Therefore the distribution of oscillators is cut off sharply at a frequency ν_m, chosen so as to make the total number of oscillators $3N$. The permitted energy levels of each oscillator are taken to be those predicted by quantum theory, $rh\nu$; later modification by quantum mechanics changed this to $(r + \frac{1}{2})h\nu$. The zero-point energy, $\frac{1}{2}h\nu$, will be ignored here; it can be added later if desired. (See Problem 8.)

If we have a system of ω_1 oscillators of frequency ν_1, ω_2 of frequency ν_2, etc., the partition function will be given by

$$Z = z_1^{\omega_1} z_2^{\omega_2} \ldots$$

where z_i is the partition function for a single oscillator of frequency ν_i. In logarithmic form this is

$$\ln Z = \sum_i \omega_i \ln z_i$$

In Debye's model — and in most others also — the number of oscillators is so large, and the possible frequencies so closely spaced, that the distribution can be approximated by a continuous function $\omega(\nu)$; that is, the number of oscillators with frequency between ν and $\nu + d\nu$ is $\omega(\nu)\, d\nu$. The summation is then replaced by integration, and we have

$$\ln Z = \int_0^{\nu_m} \omega(\nu) \ln z \, d\nu = - \int_0^{\nu_m} \omega(\nu) \ln(1 - y)\, d\nu \quad (6\text{-}49)$$

where $y = \exp(-h\nu/kT)$ as in Section 6-6, and the partition function for a single oscillator is $(1 - y)^{-1}$. Remembering that $\partial y/\partial T = yh\nu/kT^2$, we find that the energy is

$$U = -kT^2 \frac{\partial}{\partial T} \int_0^{\nu_m} \omega(\nu) \ln(1 - y)\, d\nu$$

$$= -kT^2 \int_0^{\nu_m} \omega(\nu) \frac{\partial}{\partial T}[\ln(1 - y)]\, d\nu$$

$$= kT^2 \int_0^{\nu_m} \omega(\nu) \frac{\partial y/\partial T}{1 - y}\, d\nu = \int_0^{\nu_m} \omega(\nu) \frac{h\nu y}{1 - y}\, d\nu \quad (6\text{-}50)$$

To proceed any further we need to know the distribution function $\omega(\nu)$; it is mainly in this function that Debye's model differs from later refinements. The derivation of $\omega(\nu)$ for the Debye crystal, which is given in Appendix 6, leads to

$$\omega\,(\nu)\,=\,4\pi V\left(\frac{2}{c_t{}^3}+\frac{1}{c_l{}^3}\right)\nu^2\,=\,K\nu^2 \tag{6-51}$$

where V is the volume of the crystal, c_t and c_l are the speeds of transverse and longitudinal waves in the crystal, and K is a constant.

The maximum frequency is given by

$$\int_0^{\nu_m}\omega\,(\nu)\,d\nu\,=\,\frac{1}{3}K\nu_m{}^3\,=\,3N \tag{6-52}$$

so that $K\,=\,9N/\nu_m{}^3$.

Substituting Eq. (6–51) into Eq. (6–50) gives

$$U\,=\,K\int_0^{\nu_m}\nu^2\,\frac{h\nu y}{1-y}\,d\nu\,=\,\frac{9Nh}{\nu_m{}^3}\int_0^{\nu_m}\frac{\nu^3\,d\nu}{e^{h\nu/kT}-1} \tag{6-53}$$

It is customary to define a *characteristic temperature*, Θ, equal to $h\nu_m/k$. Changing the variable of integration to $x\equiv h\nu/kT$ and then introducing the characteristic temperature leads to

$$U\,=\,\frac{9Nh}{\nu_m{}^3}\left(\frac{kT}{h}\right)^4\int_0^{h\nu_m/kT}\frac{x^3\,dx}{e^x-1}\,=\,\frac{9NkT^4}{\Theta^3}\int_0^{\Theta/T}\frac{x^3\,dx}{e^x-1} \tag{6-54}$$

Notice that Θ can be calculated by Eqs. (6–51) and (6–52) from the volume of the crystal and the speeds of the two types of waves. The speeds can be measured directly, or calculated from mechanical properties. Thus the energy can be calculated without the use of any thermal measurements. The agreement is generally satisfactory.

Two limiting cases of the Debye equation are of special interest. If the temperature is much higher than Θ, x is small throughout the range of integration, and $e^x - 1$ is approximately equal to x. Making this simplification in the denominator of Eq. (6–53), we find for the molar energy

$$u\,=\,\frac{9RT^4}{\Theta^3}\int_0^{\Theta/T}x^2\,dx\,=\,\frac{9RT}{\Theta^3}\frac{(\Theta/T)^3}{3}\,=\,3RT \tag{6-55}$$

so that $c_v\,=\,3R$ as demanded by the law of Dulong and Petit. The other limiting case is that of very low temperature, at which the upper limit of integration, Θ/T, is large. For large x the integrand is very small, because of the exponential term in the denominator. For this reason carrying the integration to infinity does not appreciably alter its value. Now

$$\int_0^\infty \frac{x^3\,dx}{e^x - 1}$$

is a standard integral, which can be evaluated by rather advanced methods (see Appendix 5); its value is $\pi^4/15$. Inserting this gives

$$u = \frac{3\pi^4 R}{5\Theta^3}\, T^4 \tag{6-56}$$

and

$$c_v = \frac{12\pi^4 R}{5\Theta^3}\, T^3 \tag{6-57}$$

This equation, unlike that derived from Einstein's model, agrees with the behavior of heat capacities at low temperatures. As was mentioned in Chapter 5, this equation is used practically in the determination of entropies by the third law.

The physical reason that Debye's model accounts for higher heat capacities at low temperatures than Einstein's is that it includes low-frequency oscillators. Since the energy quantum for an oscillator is proportional to the frequency, low-frequency oscillators can absorb energy in relatively small amounts and so absorb at low temperatures, where little energy is available. Under these circumstances high-frequency oscillators cannot acquire the large amount of energy needed if they are to absorb at all, and so remain largely "frozen" in their lowest state. At high temperatures the high-frequency oscillators are important. However, the exact distribution of these appears to be relatively unimportant, since even the simple Einstein model gives satisfactory results in this range. In the more refined models the distribution function differs from that of Debye chiefly in the high-frequency range, and so it is not surprising that these have not achieved significant improvement over the Debye theory in accuracy of calculated values.

6-15. Planck's Radiation Equation

Planck's equation for the distribution of radiant energy in equilibrium with matter was the first application of the idea of quantization of energy and so is regarded as the beginning of quantum theory. Its derivation is so similar to that of the equation for the energy of a Debye crystal that it is unnecessary to present it fully; instead, a few simple modifications of the Debye treatment will suffice. The first modification is that there is no limit to the number of photons and so to the number of modes of vibration. No equation analogous to Eq. (6–52) appears, and the integration is always carried to infinity. The second is that light waves are always transverse, and so the term $1/c_l{}^3$ must be omitted. Applying these modifications to Eqs. (6–51) and (6–53) gives for the energy density $\psi \equiv U/V$

$$\psi = \frac{8\pi h}{c^3} \int_0^\infty \frac{\nu^3 \, d\nu}{e^{h\nu/kT} - 1} \tag{6–58}$$

Planck's equation is the differential form of this expression

$$d\psi = \frac{8\pi h\nu^3 \, d\nu}{c^3 \left(e^{h\nu/kT} - 1\right)} \tag{6–59}$$

which gives the energy density of radiation in the frequency range $d\nu$. If the variable x is introduced as in the Debye treatment, Eq. (6–58) becomes

$$\psi = \frac{8\pi h}{c^3} \left(\frac{kT}{h}\right)^4 \int_0^\infty \frac{x^3 \, dx}{e^x - 1} = \frac{8\pi^5 k^4 T^4}{15 c^3 h^3} \tag{6–60}$$

This proportionality of the radiant energy density to the fourth power of the temperature is closely related to the Stefan-Boltzmann law, which states that the rate of radiant emission from a black body is proportional to the fourth power of the temperature. In fact, it can be shown that the radiant energy emitted per unit area per second is $c/4$ times the equilibrium energy density.

6–16. Statistical Thermodynamics and the Third Law

If we measure the energy of each system in an ensemble from its lowest state, so that $\epsilon_0 = 0$, the number of systems in the lowest energy level is given by

$$\frac{N\Omega_0}{Z} = \frac{N\Omega_0}{\Omega_0 + \Omega_1 e^{-\epsilon_1/kT} + \dots}$$

This approaches N as the temperature approaches zero; that is, all systems drop to the lowest energy level, provided equilibrium can be maintained. The ensemble then becomes essentially a microcanonical ensemble, and the entropy is given by

$$s^0 = k \ln \Omega_0$$

From this we see that the third law is equivalent to the assumption that $\Omega_0 = 1$, and that the equilibrium can be maintained, or attained, as the temperature approaches zero. Alternatively, s^0 may still be set equal to zero if the lowest state is degenerate, but the degeneracy is of a type that is not affected by a chemical reaction. An example of this is nuclear spin degeneracy. For a nucleus with spin number j (having an integral or half-integral value) the degeneracy is $2j + 1$, corresponding to the values $j, j - 1, \ldots, -j$ for the component of spin along a prescribed axis. This corresponds to an entropy at $0°K$ of $Nk \ln (2j + 1)$; since, however, these atoms will have this same nuclear spin entropy in any state of chemical combination, it makes no contribution to the entropy change of a reaction. For this reason it may or may not be included in entropy values as desired; it is usually omitted. Similarly, if an element consists of a mixture of two or more isotopes, an entropy of mixing persists even to absolute zero. However, since chemical reactions effect little or no change in isotopic ratios, this does not contribute to the entropy change of reactions and so may be omitted in dealing with chemical reactions. Of course, it must be included if entropy data are to be applied to a process for separating isotopes. To determine the value of this entropy of mixing, note that a total of N sites in the solid must be occupied by N_1 atoms of isotope 1, N_2 atoms of isotope 2, $\ldots$, where $N_1 + N_2 + \ldots = N$. The number of possible arrangements (see Appendix 3) is

$$\Omega = \frac{N!}{N_1!N_2!\ldots}$$

Using Stirling's approximation, we find for the entropy

$$S = k \ln \Omega = k(N \ln N - N_1 \ln N_1 - N_2 \ln N_2 - \ldots)$$

$$= -k [N_1 (\ln N_1 - \ln N) + N_2 (\ln N_2 - \ln N) + \ldots]$$

$$= -k [N_1 \ln x_1 + N_2 \ln x_2 + \ldots]$$

$$= -R (n_1 \ln x_1 + n_2 \ln x_2 + \ldots)$$

where the n's are mole numbers. This is the same as the entropy of mixing for ideal gases.

Electron spin degeneracy occurs with molecules having an odd number of electrons, such as NO, ClO_2, and a few others. Chemical reaction often removes this type of degeneracy, and so its contribution must be included in the entropy. For example, the reaction

$$2NO_2 \rightarrow N_2O_4$$

results in pairing the odd electrons of NO_2. Since the spin degeneracy of these unpaired electrons contributes $R \ln 2$ to the entropy of each mole of NO_2, ignoring it would cause us to overestimate the entropy change of this reaction by $2R \ln 2 = 2.76$ cal/mole·degree.

It sometimes happens that linear molecules whose ends are neither identical nor too unlike (for example, CO, NNO) can fit into a crystal pattern in either of two orientations. Thus if a crystal of carbon monoxide is so located that the C-O lines lie east and west, some of the molecules will have the O atom toward the west, others will have it toward the east. If each of the N molecules has this twofold choice of position, the number of configurations for the entire crystal is 2^N. If this positional degeneracy persists to 0°K, it results in an entropy of

$$S^0 = k \ln 2^N = kN \ln 2$$

or $R \ln 2$ for 1 mole. Actually, it is found that if the calorimetric entropy of CO is to agree with the statistically determined entropy, we must take $s^0 = 1.2$ cal/mole·degree. Since $R \ln 2$ is 1.38 cal/mole·degree, this indicates that the orientation is not quite random, a slight tendency toward an orderly arrangement existing. Similarly, a threefold positional degeneracy has been postulated[2] for triangular molecules ($OCCl_2$) and a fourfold degeneracy[3] for tetrahedral ones ($FClO_3$). Clearly this type of entropy is affected by chemical changes and must be included in entropies for chemical use.

A slightly different type of positional degeneracy occurs in ice. Each oxygen atom is surrounded by four others in a tetrahedral arrangement. Along each O-O line lies a hydrogen atom close to one oxygen, to which it is covalently bonded, and more distant from the other, to which it is joined by a weak hydrogen bond. Any one hydrogen atom may be covalently bonded to either of the oxygen atoms it lies between. However, of the four hydrogen atoms around any one oxygen atom, exactly two must be covalently bonded, in accordance with the formula H_2O. This leads to a rather complicated set of possible positions, but Pauling[4] has shown that for macroscopic crystals the positional degeneracy is $(3/2)^N$. This gives $s^0 = k \ln (3/2)^N = R \ln (3/2) = 0.805$ cal/mole·degree, in good agreement with the experimental value of 0.82 cal/mole·degree. Despite the good agreement, Bjerrum[5] has raised doubts about the validity of this interpretation. Several later writers[6] support Pauling's viewpoint.

Entropies listed in tables for use in chemical work include contributions from positional and electron spin degeneracy, but they usually omit entropy of mixing of isotopes and the contribution from nuclear spin degeneracy. Such values are satisfactory for calculating the entropy changes of chemical reactions, but are not good enough where isotope separation is involved. For this reason these entropy values will be referred to as *chemical entropies.*

Finally, we know practically nothing about any possible modes of degeneracy within the nucleus. Entropy changes in nuclear reactions cannot be determined experimentally, because their effects are overshadowed by the enormous energy changes. This lack of knowledge of nuclear entropy is one of the reasons why we cannot say whether the idea of an absolute entropy is valid or not.

6–17. Ortho- and Para-Hydrogen

Hydrogen is one of the few gases for which nuclear spins have an important bearing on the properties. The hydrogen nucleus has a spin quantum number of $\frac{1}{2}$, corresponding to an angular momentum of $\frac{1}{2}(h/2\pi)$. In a molecule these may be aligned in the same direction (parallel) or in opposite directions (antiparallel). This situation is best described by using two spin functions α and β, representing spins of $\frac{1}{2}$ and $-\frac{1}{2}$, respectively. Then, if the nuclei are designated by A and B, we have as possible spin states for the molecule

$$\text{Parallel:} \begin{cases} \alpha(A)\alpha(B) \\ 2^{-\frac{1}{2}}\,[\alpha(A)\beta(B) + \beta(A)\alpha(B)] \\ \beta(A)\beta(B) \end{cases}$$

$$\text{Antiparallel:} \; 2^{-\frac{1}{2}}\,[\alpha(A)\beta(B) - \beta(A)\alpha(B)]$$

Molecules with parallel spins (symmetric spin states) are referred to as *ortho-hydrogen*, those with antiparallel spins (antisymmetric spin functions) as *para-hydrogen*. At ordinary temperatures there is little tendency for one to change to the other, so little, in fact, that they can practically be regarded as two different substances. Free radicals, strongly inhomogeneous magnetic fields, and certain catalysts can hasten the change; in their absence, several years are required to establish equilibrium between the two forms.

The energy of the various spin states is practically the same and so can be ignored; the importance of spin lies in its effect on the symmetry and degeneracy characteristics of the wave function for the molecule. Hydrogen nuclei, being single protons, require antisymmetric wave functions. Translational and vibrational wave functions are symmetric, and so the rotation and spin functions must be of opposite symmetry character to preserve over-all antisymmetry. This means that ortho-hydrogen, having symmetric spin states, must have antisymmetric rotation states; para-hydrogen, having antisymmetric spin states, is confined to symmetric rotation states. Rotation states with even J are symmetric, those with odd J antisymmetric. Ortho-hydrogen therefore has only odd values of J, and the degeneracy of each energy level must be multiplied by three, since each of the $2J + 1$ rotation states can be combined with any of the three nuclear spin states. Para-hydrogen has only even values of J and no spin degeneracy. If we regard the two forms as separate substances, the rotational partition function (including spin effects) for each is

$$\text{Ortho: } 3 \sum_J (2J + 1)e^{-\sigma J(J + 1)} \qquad (J = 1, 3, 5, \ldots)$$

$$= 3z_{ro}$$

$$\text{Para: } \sum_J (2J + 1)e^{-\sigma J(J + 1)} \qquad (J = 0, 2, 4, \ldots)$$

$$= z_{re}$$

where z_{ro} and z_{re} have been used for the sums over the odd and even values of J, respectively. Clearly

$$z_{ro} + z_{re} = z_r \tag{6-61}$$

where z_r is the usual rotational partition function (not including spin effects) derived in Section 6–10. At high temperature we have

$$z_{re} = \sum_{J \text{ even}} (2J + 1)e^{-\sigma[(J + \frac{1}{2})^2 - \frac{1}{4}]}$$

$$= e^{\sigma/4} \sum_{r=1}^{\infty} (4r + 1)e^{-\sigma(2r + \frac{1}{2}^2)}$$

$$= 2e^{\sigma/4} \int_0^{\infty} (2r + \tfrac{1}{2})e^{-\sigma(2r + \frac{1}{2})^2} \, dr$$

$$= e^{\sigma/4} \int_{-\frac{1}{2}}^{\infty} xe^{-\sigma x^2} \, dx = \frac{1}{2\sigma} = \frac{z_r}{2}$$

by making the successive changes of variable $J = 2r$ and $x = 2r + \frac{1}{2}$. Eq. (6–61) then shows that $z_{ro} = \frac{1}{2}z_r$ also. To find the equilibrium ratio between the two forms, we must treat ortho-and para- hydrogen as two states (or rather groups of states) of a single substance, and its partition function per molecule is $z_{re} + 3z_{ro}$. Then the fraction of molecules in the Jth rotational level, where J is odd, is

$$\frac{3(2J + 1)e^{-\sigma J(J + 1)}}{z_{re} + 3z_{ro}}$$

The fraction of the molecules in all odd levels — that is, the fraction of ortho-hydrogen — is the sum of this quantity over all odd J. But this sum is simply

$$\frac{3z_{ro}}{z_{re} + 3z_{ro}}$$

By a similar argument the fraction of para-hydrogen is found to be

$$\frac{z_{re}}{z_{re} + 3z_{ro}}$$

These expressions are valid at any temperature, but they are most easily evaluated at high temperatures, where the approximation $z_{re} = z_{ro}$ is valid. This leads immediately to a ratio of $\frac{3}{4}$ ortho and $\frac{1}{4}$ para. At low temperatures the fact that the lowest rotational level ($J = 0$) is a para level becomes important; if equilibrium is maintained, the percentage of para increases as the temperature is lowered, reaching 100 per cent at absolute zero. At the temperature of liquid hydrogen the equilibrium mixture is practically pure para. Since this equilibrium can readily be attained by means of an activated carbon catalyst, the preparation of nearly pure para-hydrogen is relatively easy. Pure ortho-hydrogen, however, has not been obtained.

If hydrogen is cooled to near absolute zero in the presence of a catalyst to maintain ortho-para equilibrium, the entropy approaches zero as expected. However, if no catalyst is used, a large residual entropy, about 4.34 cal/mole·degree, is found. In this case the 3:1 ratio of ortho to para persists, and for each molecule there is a probability of $\frac{1}{4}$ that it will be para, $\frac{3}{4}$ that it will be ortho. The para molecules go to the nondegenerate $J = 0$ level, and so the probability that a molecule will reach this state is $\frac{1}{4}$. The ortho molecules go to their lowest level, corresponding to $J = 1$; this level is ninefold degenerate, since each of the three rotation states must be combined with one of the three symmetric nuclear spin states.

The probability that a molecule will reach any one of these nine states is, therefore, $\frac{1}{9} \times \frac{3}{4} = \frac{1}{12}$. Then in the fundamental definition of entropy (Eq. (6–3)) we have ten terms, one with $\gamma = \frac{1}{4}$ and nine with $\gamma = \frac{1}{12}$. The entropy for 1 mole is, therefore,

$$s^0 = -Nk \left(\tfrac{1}{4} \ln \tfrac{1}{4} + \tfrac{9}{12} \ln \tfrac{1}{12} \right) = R(\ln 4 + \tfrac{3}{4} \ln 3)$$

Numerically, this is 4.39 cal/mole·degree, in good agreement with the observed value.

PROBLEMS

(1) Derive the following alternate expression for the entropy:

$$S = k \left[\frac{\partial}{\partial T} (T \ln Z) \right]_V$$

(2) According to the Bohr correspondence principle, the classical behavior of a system can be determined by letting h approach zero in the expressions describing its quantal behavior. Applying this to the Einstein crystal, determine the classical energy and heat capacity, and show that the classical theory does not lead to an expression for the entropy.

(3) Show that for a set of n one-dimensional harmonic oscillators of the same frequency, the relative difference between the average energy, $\bar{u}$, and the most probable energy, u_m, defined as

$$\delta \equiv \frac{\bar{u} - u_m}{\bar{u}}$$

obeys the inequality

$$\frac{1}{n} \leqslant \delta < \frac{1}{ny}$$

(Use Eqs. (6–20) and (6–23), replacing $3N$ by n. Note that in this problem the 1 in the denominator of Eq. (6–20) is not negligible. Also note that "r is the smallest integer exceeding x" means $x + 1 \geqslant r > x$.) Interpret this result for the case in which $n = 1$. Also calculate the value of n necessary to assure that δ is less than 10^{-6} if the temperature is 100°K and the frequency is 2×10^{12} sec^{-1}.

(4) Derive an expression for the molar heat capacity of an Einstein crystal by differentiating Eq. (6–23), and show that it approaches $3R$ at high temperatures and zero at low temperatures. (It was to account for the heat capacities of solids that the Einstein and Debye models were devised.)

(5) Consider a system of N distinguishable particles, each of which may be in either of two particle states, of energy 0 and ϵ, respectively. Set up the partition function and derive expressions for the energy, entropy, and temperature in terms of the number n_1 of particles in the upper state. Show that as the energy

increases past the value $\frac{1}{2}N\epsilon$, the temperature approaches $+\infty$, changes discontinuously to $-\infty$, and takes negative values for higher energies. (This situation is realized experimentally in certain crystals in which the nuclear spins are so weakly coupled with other forms of energy in the crystal that they can be regarded as a sort of thermodynamic system. When such a system is subjected to a strong magnetic field, and the field is suddenly reversed, a negative temperature (of the system of nuclear spins, not of the crystal) results and may persist for several seconds. It should be noted that a system at negative temperature is hotter, not colder, than one at positive temperature, and that the temperature returns to positive values not by passing through zero but by an infinite discontinuity.[7])

(6) One of the factors affecting the intensity of a spectral line is the number of molecules in the initial state of the transition responsible for the line. For rotation of diatomic molecules show that the energy level having the largest number of molecules is the one with quantum number nearest

$$\sqrt{\frac{1}{2\sigma}} - \frac{1}{2}$$

Hint: Treat J as if it were a continuous variable.

(7) Infrared and microwave spectra of HI show that its first vibrational absorption band occurs at a frequency of 6.67×10^{13} sec^{-1} and its first rotation line (corresponding to the transition from $J = 0$ to $J = 1$) at 3.76×10^{11} sec^{-1}. Calculate the standard entropy of HI gas at 25°C.

(8) By multiplying the zero-point energy of a single oscillator by $\omega(\nu)\,d\nu$ and integrating, show that the zero-point energy of a Debye crystal is $\frac{9}{8}Nk\Theta$.

(9) Derive the following expressions for properties of a Debye crystal:

$$\ln Z = 3N \left(\frac{T}{\Theta}\right)^3 \int_0^{\Theta/T} \frac{x^3\,dx}{e^x - 1} - 3N \ln (1 - e^{-\Theta/T})$$

$$= \frac{U}{3kT} - 3N \ln (1 - e^{-\Theta/T})$$

$$S = \frac{4}{3}\frac{U}{T} - 3Nk \ln (1 - e^{-\Theta/T})$$

$$C_v = 36Nk \left(\frac{T}{\Theta}\right)^3 \int_0^{\Theta/T} \frac{x^3\,dx}{e^x - 1} - \frac{9Nk\Theta}{T(e^{\Theta/T} - 1)}$$

$$= 9Nk \left(\frac{T}{\Theta}\right) \int_0^{\Theta/T} \frac{x^4 e^x\,dx}{(e^x - 1)^2}$$

(The derivation of the expression for ln Z requires using integration by parts to transform

$$\int_0^{\Theta/T} x^2 \ln (1 - e^{-x}) \, dx.$$

The first expression for C_v can be obtained by using $(\partial U/\partial T)$ or $T(\partial S/\partial T)$; the second is shown to be equal to the first by integration by parts.)

(10) In some crystals, such as graphite, the atoms are bound into sheet-like structures, and vibrating membranes, rather than vibrating solids, provide the most realistic model for such crystals. At low temperatures the only vibrations which need be considered are those perpendicular to the plane of the membrane, since these are of much lower frequency than vibrations in the membrane plane. The total number of these perpendicular vibrations (for N atoms) is N, and their distribution equation (analogous to Eq. (6–51)) is

$$\omega(\nu) = 2\pi A \frac{\nu}{c^2}$$

where A is the area of the membrane. By carrying this model through a treatment analogous to that of the Debye model, show that the low-temperature heat capacity is

$$\frac{6RT^2}{\Theta^2} \int_0^\infty \frac{x^2 \, dx}{e^x - 1} = 14.4R \left(\frac{T}{\Theta}\right)^2$$

the value of the integral being 2.40. (This treatment appears to have been first devised by Tarasov.[8])

(11) The nuclei of deuterium require symmetric wave functions. They have a spin quantum number of 1, so that three spin states are available, with components 1, 0, and −1. Calling these α, β, and γ, write the possible symmetric and antisymmetric combinations for a deuterium molecule. Remembering that spin functions must be combined with rotation functions of the same symmetry property, determine

(a) Which form is ortho (i.e., the more abundant one at high temperatures) and what the ortho:para ratio is at high temperatures;

(b) Which is the stable form at very low temperatures;

(c) What the residual entropy of deuterium is if the high-temperature ratio persists as the gas is cooled.

(12) Chlorine consists of two isotopes, Cl^{35} (mole fraction α) and Cl^{37} (mole fraction $\beta = 1 - \alpha$). Determine the effect this has on the entropy of 2 moles of chlorine atoms. Now assume that the atoms combine to form molecules in a random manner; that is, the probability that any given atom will combine with Cl^{35} or Cl^{37} is directly proportional to the molar concentration of these species. Determine the mole fraction of each of the three possible types of molecules in the 1 mole of

molecular chlorine formed. Finally, show that the heteroisotopic character of chlorine contributes the same amount to the entropy of 1 mole of molecular chlorine as to 2 moles of atomic chlorine.

(13) Calculate the electronic contribution to the entropy and heat capacity of nitric oxide at $100°K$, using the partition function given in Section 6–10.

REFERENCES

1. Slater, J. C., "Introduction to Chemical Physics," Chapter XIV, New York, N.Y., McGraw-Hill Book Company, Inc., 1939.
2. Giauque, W. F., and Jones, W. M., *J. Am. Chem. Soc.*, **70**, 120 (1948).
3. Koehler, J. K., and Giauque, W. F., *J. Am. Chem. Soc.*, **80**, 2659 (1958).
4. Pauling, L., *J. Am. Chem. Soc.*, **57**, 2680 (1935).
5. Bjerrum, N., *Science*, **115**, 385 (1952).
6. Lonsdale, K., *Proc. Roy. Soc. (London)*, A**247**, 421 (1958); Gränicher, H., *ibid.*, p. 453; Pitzer, K. S., and Polissar, J., *J. Phys. Chem.*, **60**, 1140 (1956).
7. Purcell, E. M., and Pound, R. V., *Phys. Rev.*, **81**, 279 (1951).
8. Tarasov, V. V., *Doklady Akad. Nauk. SSSR*, **46**, 22 (1945); *Compt. rend. acad. sci. URSS*, **46**, 20 (1945); *C. A.*, **39**, 5163[6] (1945). (Note misprint in *C.A.*, where (T/Θ) is given instead of $(T/\Theta)^2$.) See also DeSorbo, W., *J. Chem. Phys.*, **21**, 168, 764 (1953).

GENERAL REFERENCES

Fowler, R. H., "Statistical Mechanics," London, Cambridge University Press, 1936. This important standard work gives the fullest account of Fowler's "saddle point" or "steepest descent" method.

Fowler, R. H. and Guggenheim, E. A., "Statistical Thermodynamics," London, Cambridge University Press, 1939. Includes an important survey of applicatations of statistical mechanics to chemical problems; treatment based on Fowler's method.

Gurney, R. W., "Introduction to Statistical Mechanics," New York, N.Y., McGraw-Hill Book Company, 1949. A very elementary introduction for the beginner.

ter Haar, D., "Elements of Statistical Mechanics," New York, N.Y., Rinehart & Company, Inc., 1954. A thorough treatment from a rather advanced viewpoint, stressing classical statistical mechanics and kinetic theory more than most recent books. The references to original sources are very extensive. This book contains an interesting appendix on the third law.

Hill, T. L., "Statistical Mechanics," New York, N.Y., McGraw-Hill Book Company, Inc., 1956. Covers recent developments in theory and applications of statistical mechanics. Primarily for the advanced student and specialist.

Mayer, J. E., and Mayer, M. G., "Statistical Mechanics," New York, N.Y., John Wiley & Sons, Inc., 1940. Contains a thorough presentation of Mayer's important work on the nonideal gas; though this treatment is generally valid, some of the conclusions have been modified by more recent work.

Rushbrooke, G. S., "Statistical Mechanics," London, Oxford University Press, 1949. An introductory text, though not so elementary as that of Gurney.

Contains an elementary presentation of the important method of the grand partition function.

Schrödinger, E., "Statistical Thermodynamics," London, Cambridge University Press, 1946. This very brief book covers the fundamental theory of statistical thermodynamics, including a relatively simple account of Fowler's saddle point method.

Tolman, R. C., "The Principles of Statistical Mechanics," London, Oxford University Press, 1938. A thorough critique of the logical foundations of statistical mechanics.

chapter 7

The Thermodynamics of Mixtures and Solutions

IN MOST OF THE TOPICS thus far considered little or no attention has been given to the composition of the system under consideration, except that it has been assumed, more or less tacitly, that no matter enters or leaves it; that is, that it is a closed system. In most cases absence of chemical reactions has also been assumed. In this chapter open systems, in which the amount of matter may vary, will be considered, and thermodynamic laws for processes involving the addition or removal of matter will be developed. These laws are also needed for the general treatment of chemically reacting systems.

7–1. The Chemical Potential

When a change involves addition of matter to a system (or its removal), the change in the energy of the system must include not only the effects of heat and work, represented by the two terms on the right hand side of Eq. (2–9):

$$dU = T\ dS - p\ dV$$

but also terms accounting for the energy brought into the system by the added matter. Now if dn_1 moles of substance 1 are added, the added energy will be proportional to dn_1 and may be written $\mu_1\ dn_1$. It should be noted that μ_1 is not simply the molar energy of the added substance, since some energy change may be involved in the process of mixing. Adding $\mu_1 dn_1$, and similar terms for other substances, to the above equation, we get

$$dU = T \ dS - p \ dV + \sum_i \mu_i \ dn_i \qquad (7\text{–}1)$$

The quantities μ_i were introduced, in slightly different form,* by Gibbs[1] and called by him the *potentials*; they are now practically always called the *chemical potentials*. Similar equations for dH, dA, and dG can be derived by applying the usual Legendre transformations (see Sections 3–4 and 3–9) to this equation for dU. This gives

$$dH = T \ dS + V \ dp + \sum_i \mu_i \ dn_i \qquad (7\text{–}2)$$

$$dA = -S \ dT - p \ dV + \sum_i \mu_i \ dn_i \qquad (7\text{–}3)$$

and

$$dG = -S \ dT + V \ dp + \sum_i u_i \ dn_i \qquad (7\text{–}4)$$

Eqs. (7–1) through (7–4) are known as the *Gibbs equations*. From them we can see that the chemical potential is given by any of the following expressions:

$$\mu_i = \left(\frac{\partial U}{\partial n_i}\right)_{S,V,n_j} = \left(\frac{\partial H}{\partial n_i}\right)_{S,p,n_j} = \left(\frac{\partial A}{\partial n_i}\right)_{T,V,n_j} = \left(\frac{\partial G}{\partial n_i}\right)_{T,p,n_j} \qquad (7\text{–}5)$$

in which the subscript n_j indicates that the differentiations are to be performed with all n's other than n_i constant. The last of these expressions is sometimes used alone as the definition of the chemical potential. This appears undesirable, however, since the significance of the chemical potential is far wider than any one of these relations would suggest.

To show what the significance of the chemical potential is, consider a system made up of two parts, α and β (Figure 15). Let the parts be in thermal equilibrium, but not in equilibrium with respect to flow of substance 1 from α to β. In particular, let a small positive amount dn_1 move spontaneously from α to β, so that $dn_1{}^\beta = - dn_1{}^\alpha = dn_1 > 0$, superscripts being used to indicate the parts. Although the parts are open

---

* Gibbs used $\mu_i \ dm_i$, where m_i is the mass of substance i, instead of $\mu_i \ dn_i$. His potentials were therefore specific quantities, while those defined here are molar quantities.

systems, the system as a whole is closed. The parts need not be at the same pressure, for they may be separated by a mechanically rigid membrane permeable to substance 1. (This situation is actually realized in osmotic experiments.) We assume, however, that the flow of substance 1 from α to β is the only irreversible process occurring. Now applying Eq. (7–1) to each part gives

$$dU^\alpha = T \ dS^\alpha - p^\alpha \ dV^\alpha - \mu_1^\alpha \ dn_1 \qquad \text{(a)}$$
$$dU^\beta = T \ dS^\beta - p^\beta \ dV^\beta + \mu_1^\beta \ dn_1 \qquad \text{(b)}$$

(7–6)

Of course, T is the same in both parts, since thermale quilibrium has been assumed. For the system as a whole

$$dW = -p^\alpha \ dV^\alpha - p^\beta \ dV^\beta$$

Then adding Eq. (7–6) gives

$$dU = T \ dS + dW - (\mu_1^\alpha - \mu_1^\beta) \ dn_1$$

where dU and dS refer to the energy and entropy changes of the entire system. Since by the first law $dQ = dU - dW$, this is equivalent to

$$(\mu_1^\alpha - \mu_1^\beta) \ dn_1 = T \ dS - (dU - dW) = T \ dS - dQ \qquad \text{(7–7)}$$

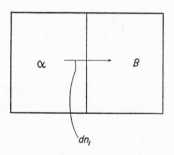

FIGURE 15. DIAGRAM ILLUSTRATING FLOW OF A SMALL AMOUNT OF MATTER FROM ONE PHASE TO ANOTHER.

Now by the second law the quantity on the right must be positive; and since dn_1 is also positive,

$$\mu_1^\alpha > \mu_1^\beta \qquad \text{(7–8)}$$

Substance 1 therefore flows from a region where its chemical potential is higher to one where it is lower.

If we modify this argument by starting with the two parts of the system at equilibrium with respect to the migration of substance 1, so that the transfer of a small quantity of it is a reversible process, then the right side of Eq. (7–7) becomes zero, and Eq. (7–8) must be replaced by

$$\mu_1{}^\alpha = \mu_1{}^\beta \tag{7-9}$$

Notice the generality of the conditions under which this criterion of equilibrium has been derived; no assumption was made as to whether the process was adiabatic, nor was constancy of temperature, pressure, or volume required. Analogous equations can, of course, be derived for other components of the system, provided they can migrate from one part of the system to the other. However, if flow of any substance from one part to the other is prevented by a membrane impermeable to that substance, then its chemical potential need not be equal in the two parts at equilibrium.

It is worth noting that there are close analogies among the three intensive properties T, p, and μ, which determine equilibria with respect to what might be called "flow" processes. Thus

(1) Temperature determines equilibrium with respect to heat flow; heat flows from regions of high temperature to regions of low temperature. The flow stops, and equilibrium is attained, when the temperature is uniform.

(2) Pressure determines equilibrium with respect to volume change; high-pressure portions of a system expand, increasing their volumes at the expense of low-pressure portions. This process ceases, and equilibrium is attained, when the pressure is uniform.**

(3) The chemical potential determines equilibrium with respect to the flow of matter; matter of any given type flows from regions where its chemical potential is high to regions where it is low. The flow ceases, and equilibrium is attained, when the chemical potential is uniform.

7-2. Partial Molar Quantities

As pointed out in Section 7–1, the chemical potential is equal to $(\partial G/\partial n_i)_{T,p,n_j}$. In this aspect it is seen to be one of a group of properties called *partial molar quantities* (or *partial molal quantities*; the two terms are used interchangeably). These will now be treated generally.

Let Y be any extensive thermodynamic property, such as volume,

---

** This statement needs modification if gravitational, electric, or magnetic fields produce nonnegligible effects.

entropy, enthalpy, or heat capacity. Then the partial molar value of Y, for each substance i in a mixture, is defined by

$$y_i \equiv \left(\frac{\partial Y}{\partial n_i}\right)_{T,p,n_j} \tag{7-10}$$

It should be noted that y_i is an intensive property, since it is a derivative of an extensive property with respect to a mole number (this follows from Section 1–5); it is for this reason that a lower-case letter is used for it. It is often represented by a bar over the letter, but this is an unnecessary complication. If the substance i is pure, we have

$$y_i^* = \left[\left(\frac{\partial Y}{\partial n_i}\right)_{T,p,n_j}\right]_{n_j = 0}$$

and this is simply the molar value of the property Y for pure i; the asterisk is used here, and will be used generally, to denote the value a thermodynamic function takes for a pure substance.

An extensive property, as defined in Section 2–6, is a first-degree homogeneous function of the mole numbers when the temperature and pressure are fixed. It therefore follows from Euler's theorem (Eq. (1–18)) that

$$Y = \sum_i n_i \left(\frac{\partial Y}{\partial n_i}\right)_{T,p,n_j} = \sum_i n_i y_i \tag{7-11}$$

From this we can find the change in Y accompanying the process of mixing at constant temperature and pressure. If we start with n_1 moles of substance 1, n_2 moles of substance 2, etc., the value of Y before mixing will be

$$Y_{unm} = \sum_i n_i y_i^*$$

After mixing, Y is given by Eq. (7–11). The change in Y on mixing is therefore

$$\Delta Y \equiv Y - Y_{unm} = \sum_i n_i(y_i - y_i^*) \tag{7-12}$$

In particular, this may be applied to enthalpy. The change in enthalpy

$$\Delta H = \sum_i n_i (h_i - h_i^*) \tag{7-13}$$

is generally called the *heat of mixing*, since it is the heat that must be added to maintain constant temperature when mixing occurs at constant pressure; like a heat of reaction, it will be negative if the process is exothermic. If we divide both sides of Eq. (7–13) by the total number of moles, we get the molar heat of mixing, given by

$$\Delta h = \sum_i x_i (h_i - h_i^*) \qquad (7\text{–}14)$$

The quantity $h_i - h_i^*$ is often called the *relative partial molar enthalpy* and is designated by l_i.

The term *heat of solution* is used for the heat of mixing when one substance (denoted by the subscript 1) is regarded as a solvent, and another (denoted by the subscript 2) as a solute. To be more specific, the *integral heat of solution* is the heat absorbed when 1 mole of solute dissolves in enough solvent to produce a solution of the required concentration, the process occurring at constant temperature and pressure. This means that $n_2 = 1$ mole and, if the required mole fraction of the solute is x_2, $n_1 = x_1/x_2$ moles. The integral heat of solution is, then, given by

$$h_2 - h_2^* + \frac{x_1}{x_2}(h_1 - h_1^*) = l_2 - \frac{x_1}{x_x} l_1$$

The *differential heat of solution* is the heat absorbed per mole of added solute when an infinitesimal amount of solute dissolves in a solution of given concentration. Since the small amount dn_2 of solute has an enthalpy $h_2^* \, dn_2$ but contributes to the solution the amount $h_2 \, dn_2$, the change in enthalpy is $(h_2 - h_2^*) \, dn_2$. Dividing this by dn_2, we find that the differential heat of solution is $h_2 - h_2^*$, or l_2. The differential heat of solution of the solvent, $h_1 - h_1^*$, is usually called the *heat of dilution*.

7–3. The Gibbs-Duhem and Analogous Equations

At any specified temperature and pressure the value of any extensive property Y depends only on the mole numbers, and so if these vary, the change in Y must be

$$dY = \sum_i \left(\frac{\partial Y}{\partial n_i} \right)_{T,p,n_j} dn_i = \sum_i y_i \, dn_i$$

But differentiation of Eq. (7–11) gives

$$dY = \sum_i (y_i \, dn_i + n_i \, dy_i)$$

Subtracting the first of these from the second gives

$$\sum_i n_i \, dy_i = 0 \qquad (7\text{–}15)$$

This equation, which results only from the mathematical properties of first-degree homogeneous functions, is a generalized from of the *Gibbs-Duhem equation*. The Gibbs-Duhem equation itself is

$$\sum_i n_i \, d\mu_i = 0 \qquad\qquad (7\text{--}16)$$

Since the chemical potential is equal to the partial molar Gibbs free energy, this is merely a particular example of Eq. (7–15). Either may be divided by the total number of moles, giving the forms

$$\sum_i x_i \, dy_i = 0 \qquad \sum_i x_i \, d\mu_i = 0 \qquad\qquad (7\text{--}17)$$

7–4. Determination of Partial Molar Quantities

If means are available for determining the property Y of a mixture, then the most obvious and straightforward way to determine y_2 (for example) is to make up several mixtures containing the same amount of component 1 but differing amounts of component 2, determine Y for each of these, and plot Y as ordinate against n_2 as abscissa. The slope of the resulting curve is $(\partial Y/\partial n_2)_{n_1} = y_2$. In practice this method is often not very satisfactory, because measuring the slope of a curve drawn from empirical data is one of the least accurate of graphical procedures.

The error can be reduced by defining a calculable quantity which gives an approximation to Y or y_2 and using the graphical procedure to determine only a small correction term. If the correction is, say, 10 per cent of the total, then a given relative error in this term produces only one tenth as large a relative error in the total quantity. Two methods of doing this will be described.

If the change of Y on mixing, given by Eq. (7–12), is plotted against n_2 for constant n_1, the slope will be

$$\left(\frac{\partial \Delta Y}{\partial n_i}\right)_{n_1} = y_2 - y_2{}^*$$

and so y_2 is obtained by adding the slope of the curve to $y_2{}^*$. This method is good when ΔY can be measured directly, and is not large compared to Y itself.

Another procedure involves defining an *apparent molar quantity*. From Eq. (7–11) we see that

$$y_2 = \frac{Y - n_1 y_1}{n_2}$$

The apparent molar value of Y for component 2, $y_2^\dagger$, is defined by replacing y_1 in this equation by y^*_1; thus

$$y_2^\dagger = \frac{Y - n_1 y_1^*}{n_2}$$

or

$$Y = n_1 y_1^* + n_2 y_2^\dagger$$

Differentiating with respect to n_2 at constant n_1 gives

$$y_2 = y_2^\dagger + n_2 \left(\frac{\partial y_2^\dagger}{\partial n_2}\right)_{n_1}$$

Thus it is necessary to determine $(\partial y_2^\dagger/\partial n_2)_{n_1}$ by plotting $y_2^\dagger$ against n_2 and measuring the slope; this is then substituted into the equation above. This method is valuable for dilute solutions, where n_2 is small, since this makes the correction term small. Note that $n_2(\partial y_2^\dagger/\partial n_2)_{n_1}$ is represented by the distance AB in Figure 16.

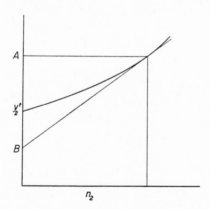

FIGURE 16. GRAPH FOR CALCULATION OF PARTIAL MOLAR QUANTITIES.

Whatever method is used, it need be applied to only one component, for once y_1 or y_2 is known, the other can be calculated from Eq. (7–11).

Finally, these methods assume that the variation of Y with composition is known only as a table of empirical data. If a mathematical relation connecting Y with n_1 and n_2 is available, y_1 and y_2 can be found by direct differentiation.

7–5. Relations Among the Partial Molar Quantities

Any relation among extensive thermodynamic properties can be converted to one among partial molar quantities by differentiating with respect to one of the mole numbers, and reversing the order of differentiation if the original equation involved derivatives. To illustrate this consider the Gibbs-Helmholtz equation

$$G = H + T\left(\frac{\partial G}{\partial T}\right)_{p,n_i}$$

the subscript n_i indicating that all mole numbers are held constant in this differentiation. Differentiating with respect to n_i at constant T, p, and n_j gives

$$\left(\frac{\partial G}{\partial n_i}\right)_{T,p,n_j} = \left(\frac{\partial H}{\partial n_i}\right)_{T,p,n_j} + T\left(\frac{\partial^2 G}{\partial n_i \partial T}\right)_{p,n_j}$$

Changing the order of differentiation in the last term gives

$$\left(\frac{\partial^2 G}{\partial n_i \partial T}\right)_{p,n_j} = \left(\frac{\partial^2 G}{\partial T \partial n_i}\right)_{p,n_j} = \left[\frac{\partial}{\partial T}\left(\frac{\partial G}{\partial n_i}\right)_{T,p,n_j}\right]_{p,n_i} = \left(\frac{\partial \mu_i}{\partial T}\right)_{p,n_i}$$

Notice that although μ_i is obtained by differentiating G with respect to n_i with all other n's constant, the differentiation of μ_i with respect to T is carried out with *all* n's constant. Using this last relation, we find

$$\mu_i = h_i + T\left(\frac{\partial \mu_i}{\partial T}\right)_{p,n_i} \tag{7–18}$$

7–6. Ideal Mixtures

Just as the theory of gases is simplified by considering an idealized type of gas as a first approximation to the behavior of a real gas, so also an idealized type of mixture is valuable in developing the theory of solutions or mixtures. As a practical working approximation, however, the range of usefulness of the ideal solution law is much more restricted than that of the ideal gas law.

There are several equivalent ways of defining ideal mixtures. The definition which will be used here is: *a mixture is said to be ideal if the chemical potential of each of its constituents is given by*

$$\mu_i = \mu_i^* + RT \ln x_i \qquad (7\text{-}19)$$

It is easily shown from this definition that there is no heat of mixing when an ideal mixture is formed. We see from Eq. (7–18) that

$$h_i = -T^2 \left[\frac{\partial(\mu_i/T)}{\partial T} \right]_{p,n_i} \qquad (7\text{-}20)$$

Alternatively, this may be derived by suitably modifying Eq. (3–20). Rewriting Eq. (7–19) to read

$$\frac{\mu_i}{T} = \frac{\mu_i^*}{T} + R \ln x_i$$

and applying Eq. (7–20) lead to

$$h_i = h_i^*$$

since the mole fractions are independent of temperature. Eq. (7–13) then shows that the heat of mixing is zero.

Similarly, we may modify Eq. (3–13) to read

$$\left(\frac{\partial \mu_i}{\partial p} \right)_{T,n_i} = v_i \qquad (7\text{-}21)$$

Since the mole fractions do not depend on the pressure, differentiation of Eq. (7–19) with respect to p gives

$$v_i = v_i^*$$

and so the change of volume on mixing is also zero.

The partial molar entropies are found by differentiating Eq. (7–19) with respect to T, which gives

$$s_i = -\left(\frac{\partial \mu_i}{\partial T} \right)_{p,n_i} = s_i^* - R \ln x_i \qquad (7\text{-}22)$$

From this and Eq. (7–12) we see that the entropy of mixing is given by

$$S = \sum_i n_i(s_i - s_i^*) = -R \sum_i n_i \ln x_i \qquad (7\text{-}23)$$

This is the same as the entropy of mixing of ideal gases or of isotopes.

The chemical potential of a pure vapor is given by

$$\mu_i = \mu'_i + RT \ln f_i/p_u$$

where μ'_i is the same as the g' of Section 4–7. For a constituent of a gas mixture we shall also apply this equation, regarding it as the definition of fugacity in this case. Now if the vapor is in equilibrium with a liquid, either pure or mixed, the chemical potential must be the same in the two phases. Therefore for the pure substance i

$$\mu_i^* = \mu'_i + RT \ln \frac{f_i^*}{p_u}$$

and for the mixture

$$\mu_i = \mu_i^* + RT \ln x_i = \mu'_i + RT \ln \frac{f_i}{p_u}$$

from which we get

$$f_i = x_i f_i^*$$

If the fugacities are practically equal to the corresponding vapor pressures or, more generally, if the f/p ratio is practically the same for the vapor of the pure liquid as for the vapor of the mixture, this becomes

$$P_i = x_i P_i^*$$

where P_i represents the partial vapor pressure of substance i in the mixture. This expression is known as *Raoult's law* and is frequently used as the definition of an ideal mixture.

Practically ideal mixtures are found among chemically similar compounds whose molecular dimensions are of at least the same order of magnitude. The following pairs are among those that have been reported to form nearly ideal mixtures[2]: 1,2-dibromoethane, 1,2-dibromopropane; benzene, toluene; benzene, diethyl ether; stannic chloride, carbon tetrachloride; methanol, ethanol; chlorobenzene, bromobenzene; carbon disulfide, carbon tetrabromide; and carbon tetrachloride, cyclohexane.

7–7. Nonideal Mixtures; Rational Activities and Activity Coefficients

Not many liquid mixtures are nearly ideal, and the relatively simple relations derived in the preceding section are not widely applicable. Just as in the case of the nonideal gas, however, we find it convenient to preserve the forms of these relations by introducing the activity. For liquid mixtures the activity is defined by

$$\mu_i = \mu_i^0 + RT \ln a_i \qquad (7\text{--}24)$$

for each substance i. The definition of the *standard chemical potential* μ_i^0 can be chosen for convenience; for each choice, there is a corresponding activity scale. Most of the discussion of activities of nonelectrolytic solutions in this book will be based on one of two widely used conventions. In convention I the pure components are chosen as standard states, so that

$$\mu_i^0 \equiv \mu_i^*$$

for each substance. This convention, which is closely analogous to that used for ideal mixtures, is most useful for mixtures with unlimited miscibility. In convention II the meaning of Eq. (7–24) is completed by stipulating that

$$a_i/x_i \rightarrow 1 \text{ as } x_1 \rightarrow 1$$

For component 1, the solvent, this is the same as convention I, and $\mu_1^0 = \mu_1^*$. However, for other substances, the solutes, the standard chemical potential is defined by reference to a state of zero concentration, or infinite dilution, as it is usually called. This state is therefore called a *reference state* for the solutes; it is not a standard state, since the chemical potential does not have its standard value for substances at infinite dilution — in fact, it does not have any finite value. When the standard chemical potential is defined by reference to a state of infinite dilution, there is, in general, no real standard state. As with gases, it is possible in some cases to find a concentration at which the activity is unity, and to regard this as a standard state for calculations based on chemical potential, but the partial molar enthalpy and the partial molar entropy will not generally have their standard values at this concentration. When it is necessary to indicate that a standard chemical potential is defined by reference to a state of infinite dilution, it will be denoted by μ''_i. With either convention, it is often convenient to have a name and symbol for the ratio a_i/x_i, which will be called the *activity coefficient* of component i and designated by γ_i.

To evaluate μ''_i we note that

$$\mu_i = \mu''_i + RT \ln \gamma_i x_i \qquad (i \neq 1)$$

or

$$\mu''_i + RT \ln \gamma_i = \mu_i - RT \ln x_i$$

and so, since $\ln \gamma_i \to 0$ as $x_i \to 0$,

$$\mu''_i = \lim_{x_i \to 0} (\mu_i - RT \ln x_i) \qquad (7\text{--}25)***$$

This is analogous to Eq. (4–17) for ideal gases. If several solutes are present, this equation is ambiguous, since the condition $x_i \to 0$ does not tell us whether the concentrations of the other solutes are to be reduced to zero also. In this case it should be modified to

$$\mu''_i = \lim_{x_1 \to 1} (\mu_i - RT \ln x_i) \qquad (7\text{--}25a)$$

since the condition $x_1 \to 1$ assures that all solute concentrations approach zero.

The advantage of convention II is that the same reference state is used for all components of the mixture, and this is a physically accessible state even in cases of limited miscibility. This is particularly valuable where solid solutes are involved. It is also important when the activity of one component of a binary mixture is to be calculated from that of the other component; with convention I this is possible only if data are available for the entire concentration range from pure solvent to pure solute.

It is clear that the activity coefficients, γ_i, are constants equal to 1 for ideal solutions, if convention I is used. For real solutions the deviations of the activity coefficients from this value serve as measures of the deviation of the solution from ideality.

Other thermodynamic properties are readily expressed in terms of activities or activity coefficients. Thus by differentiating Eq. (7–24) in the form

$$\mu_i = \mu_i^0 + RT \ln a_i = \mu_i^0 + RT \ln \gamma_i + RT \ln x_i$$

with respect to T at constant pressure and composition, we find

$$s_i = s_i^0 - R \ln a_i - RT \left(\frac{\partial \ln a_i}{\partial T}\right)_{p,x}$$

$$= s_i^0 - R \ln a_i - RT \left(\frac{\partial \ln \gamma_i}{\partial T}\right)_{p,x} \qquad (7\text{--}26)$$

*** The use of convention II requires that the limit on the right side of Eq. (7–25) must exist. Experimentally, this requirement is generally found to be met by solutions of nonelectrolytes, but it introduces complications into the treatment of electrolytic solutions.

where $s_i{}^0$ has been written for $-(\partial \mu_i{}^0/\partial T)_p$; this quantity is called the *standard molar entropy*. The subscript x outside the derivative symbols in Eq. (7–26) indicates that all mole fractions are constant. By combining Eqs. (7–24) and (7–26) we find, since $h_i = \mu_i + Ts_i$,

$$h_i = h_i{}^0 - RT^2 \left(\frac{\partial \ln a_i}{\partial T}\right)_{p,x} = h_i{}^0 - RT^2 \left(\frac{\partial \ln \gamma_i}{\partial T}\right)_{p,x} \qquad (7\text{--}27)$$

where $h_i{}^0$ has been written for $\mu_i{}^0 + Ts_i{}^0$; this is called the *standard molar enthalpy*. Finally, by differentiating Eq. (7–24) with respect to pressure, we get

$$v_i = v_i{}^0 + RT \left(\frac{\partial \ln a_i}{\partial p}\right)_{T,x} = v_i{}^0 + RT \left(\frac{\partial \ln \gamma_i}{\partial p}\right)_{T,x} \qquad (7\text{--}28)$$

If the reference state is the pure substance, then the standard values μ_i, h_i, s_i, and v_i are simply their values for the pure substance. If the reference state is infinite dilution, a procedure analogous to that for nonideal gases (Section 4–7) is used to determine the standard values of these functions. Remembering that $\gamma_i = 1$ in the reference state, we see from Eq. (7–27) that

$$h''_i = \lim_{x_i \to 0} h_i \qquad (7\text{--}29)$$

This can be combined with Eq. (7–25) to yield

$$s''_i = \lim_{x_i \to 0} (s_i + R \ln x_i) \qquad (7\text{--}30)$$

These relations are closely analogous to those for the nonideal gas. Finally, it can be seen from Eq. (7–28) that the standard molar volume v''_i is equal to the partial molar volume at infinite dilution.

7–8. The Colligative Properties; the Determination of Solvent Activities

Among the commonest methods of determining solvent activities are the four phenomena known as *colligative properties*. These are the lowering of vapor pressure, the lowering of the freezing point, the raising of the boiling point, and the osmotic pressure. All depend on the activity of the solvent and can be used to determine it.

The difference in chemical potential between solvent in solution and pure solvent is

$$\mu_1 - \mu_1{}^* = RT \ln a_1$$

But in terms of fugacity, this is also given by

$$RT \ln \frac{f_1}{f_1{}^*}$$

Comparing these two equations gives

$$a_1 = \frac{f_1}{f_1{}^*} \approx \frac{P_1}{P_1{}^*} \tag{7-31}$$

the approximation in terms of vapor pressures being sufficient in many practical cases. Notice that P_1 is the partial vapor pressure of the solvent, not the total vapor pressure of the solution. However, it is equal to the total vapor pressure when the solute is not volatile, and it is in this case that the method is most useful.

The freezing-point method can be applied to practically any solution which freezes at a convenient temperature, provided that the solid which forms when freezing occurs is pure solvent. If a solid solution containing both solvent and solute forms, the freezing point is unpredictable; it may even increase, instead of decreasing, when solute is added.

To derive an expression for freezing-point depression in terms of activity, consider pure liquid and solid solvent in equilibrium at the freezing point, T_0. The condition for equilibrium may be written

$$\frac{\mu_1{}^s}{T} = \frac{\mu_1{}^l}{T}$$

where s refers to the solid, l to the liquid. Now if solute is gradually added to the liquid, and the temperature lowered so that equilibrium is maintained, this equation must continue to hold, and so

$$d\left(\frac{\mu_1{}^s}{T}\right) = d\left(\frac{\mu_1{}^l}{T}\right)$$

So far as the solid is concerned, only the temperature variation of $\mu_1{}^s/T$

need be considered, since the composition does not vary. (Constant pressure is, of course, assumed.) Therefore

$$d\left(\frac{\mu_1{}^s}{T}\right) = \left[\frac{\partial}{\partial T}\left(\frac{\mu_1{}^{*s}}{T}\right)\right]_p dT = -\frac{h_1{}^{*s}}{T^2} dT$$

For the liquid, however, both temperature and composition variations are involved. Thus we have

$$d\left(\frac{\mu_1{}^l}{T}\right) = \left[\frac{\partial}{\partial T}\left(\frac{\mu_1{}^l}{T}\right)\right]_{p,x_1} dT + \left[\frac{\partial}{\partial x_1}\left(\frac{\mu_1{}^l}{T}\right)\right]_{p,T} dx_1$$

The coefficient of dT in this equation is equal to $-h_1{}^l/T^2$; that of dx_1 is found from

$$\frac{\mu_1}{T} = \frac{\mu_1{}^*}{T} + R \ln a_1$$

to be

$$R\left[\frac{\partial}{\partial x_1}(\ln a_1)\right]_{p,T}$$

Combining these results, we have

$$-\frac{h_1{}^{*s}}{T^2} dT = -\frac{h_1{}^l}{T^2} dT + R\left[\frac{\partial}{\partial x_1}(\ln a_1)\right]_{p,T} dx_1$$

When $x_1 = 1$ — that is, when the solvent is pure — the equilibrium temperature is the freezing point of the pure solvent, T_0. If we designate the freezing point of the solution by T_f, integration gives

$$-\int_{T_0}^{T_f} \frac{h_1{}^{*s}}{T^2} dT = \int_{T_0,1}^{T_f,x_1} \left\{-\frac{h_1{}^l}{T^2} dT + R\left[\frac{\partial}{\partial x_1}(\ln a_1)\right]_{p,T} dx_1\right\} \quad (7\text{--}32)$$

The description of the experiment suggests evaluating this line integral along the equilibrium curve (AC in Figure 17). However, since the integrand is an exact differential — the differential of $\mu_1{}^l/T$ — the same result can be obtained by integrating along other paths. In particular, a useful form of the integral is found by choosing the path ABC. Along AB $x_1 = 1$; that is, we are dealing with pure solvent, and so $h_1{}^l = h_1{}^{*l}$ and $dx_1 = 0$.

Along BC, the temperature has the constant value T_f, and a_1 must be

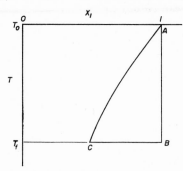

FIGURE 17. VARIATION OF FREEZING POINT OF SOLUTION WITH
MOLE FRACTION OF SOLVENT (SCHEMATIC).

evaluated at this temperature; for this reason it will be designated $a_1(T_f)$.
We thus find

$$-\int_{T_0}^{T_f} \frac{h_1^{*s}}{T^2}\, dT = -\int_{T_0}^{T_f} \frac{h_1^{*l}}{T^2}\, dT + R \int_1^{x_1} \frac{\partial}{\partial x_1} [\ln a_1(T_f)]\, dx_1$$

Remembering that when $x_1 = 1$, $\ln a_1 = 0$, we get from this

$$\int_{T_0}^{T_f} \frac{h_1^{*l} - h_1^{*s}}{T^2}\, dT = R \ln a_1(T_f)$$

The numerator in the integrand is the heat of fusion, Δh_{fus}. Therefore

$$\ln a_1(T_f) = -\int_{T_f}^{T_0} \frac{\Delta h_{fus}}{RT^2}\, dT \qquad (7\text{--}33)$$

the purpose of exchanging the limits of integration being to put the lower
temperature in the lower limit.

To this point the treatment is exact, and all the quantities on the
right of Eq. (7–33) are experimentally measurable, provided that the pure
liquid solvent can be supercooled to the temperature T_f. The heat of fusion
can be calculated as a function of temperature from its value at T_0 and
heat capacity data for the solid and supercooled liquid solvent. If heat
capacities for the supercooled liquid are not available, this is not a serious
difficulty, since equations for c_p at temperatures above T_0 can usually
be extrapolated into the region between T_f and T_0 without much error.
In fact, in most cases the heat capacity difference between the liquid and
solid can be regarded as constant, and in many cases it is sufficient to

treat the heat of fusion as constant. This last approximation makes it possible to integrate Eq. (7–33) to

$$\ln a_1(T_f) = \frac{\Delta h_{fus}}{R} \left(\frac{1}{T_0} - \frac{1}{T_f} \right) \qquad (7\text{–}34)$$

If this is to be reduced to the familiar equation for dilute solutions

$$\Theta_f = K_f m \qquad (7\text{–}35)$$

where $\Theta_f \equiv T_0 - T_f$, K_f is a constant, and m the molality, several approximations must be made. Since the activity coefficient, γ_1, is equal to 1 in the pure solvent, it does not differ greatly from 1 in dilute solution. We therefore have $a_1 \approx x_1$, and

$$\ln a_1 \approx \ln x_1 = \ln (1 - x_2) = -x_2 - \tfrac{1}{2}x_2{}^2 - \dots \qquad (7\text{–}36)$$

Furthermore, since for dilute solutions T_0 and T_f do not differ greatly,

$$\frac{1}{T_0} - \frac{1}{T_f} = \frac{T_f - T_0}{T_0 T_f} \approx - \frac{\Theta_f}{T_0{}^2}$$

Substituting these into Eq. (7–34) gives

$$\frac{\Delta h_{fus}\Theta_f}{RT_0{}^2} = x_2 + \tfrac{1}{2}x_2{}^2 + \dots$$

or, neglecting higher powers of x_2,

$$\Theta_f = \frac{RT_0{}^2}{\Delta h_{fus}} x_2 \qquad (7\text{–}37)$$

Finally, we note that a molality of m means that there are m moles of solute per kilogram of solvent; that is, per $1000/M_1$ moles of solvent, where M_1 is the molecular weight of the solvent. Therefore,

$$x_2 = \frac{m}{m + \dfrac{1000}{M_1}} \approx \frac{m}{\dfrac{1000}{M_1}} = \frac{mM_1}{1000}$$

the last approximation resulting from the fact that m is small in dilute solutions. This leads to

$$\Theta_f = \frac{RT_0{}^2 M_1}{1000 \, \Delta h_{fus}} m \qquad (7\text{–}38)$$

By comparing Eqs. (7–35) and (7–38), we find

$$K_f = \frac{RT_0^2 M_1}{1000\,\Delta h_{fus}} \tag{7-39}$$

Both these equations are dimensionally inconsistent, but they can be made consistent by writing 1000 g/kg instead of merely 1000. Both are only approximations at nonzero concentrations. However, if K_f is determined experimentally by measuring Θ_f at various molalities, and its value is extrapolated to zero concentration, the limiting value may be used in Eq. (7–39) to calculate the heat of fusion accurately.

The treatment of boiling-point elevation is so closely analogous to that of freezing-point depression that it will not be necessary to reproduce it in detail. The fact that the treatment of freezing-point lowering is valid only if the solid phase is pure solvent has as its analogy in the treatment of boiling-point elevation the fact that the vapor must be pure solvent; that is, the solute must be nonvolatile. The equations analogous to Eqs. (7–33) through (7–39) (omitting Eq. (7–36)) are

$$\ln a_1(T_b) = -\int_{T_0}^{T_b} \frac{\Delta h_v}{RT^2}\,dT \tag{7-40}$$

$$\ln a_1(T_b) = -\frac{\Delta h_v}{R}\left(\frac{1}{T_0} - \frac{1}{T_b}\right) \tag{7-41}$$

$$\Theta_b \approx \frac{RT_0^2}{\Delta h_v}\,x_2 \approx \frac{RT_0^2 M_1}{1000\,\Delta h_v}\,m = K_b m \tag{7-42}$$

where T_0 is the boiling point of the solvent, T_b that of the solution, and $\Theta_b \equiv T_b - T_0$. Some of these differ in sign from the corresponding equations in the treatment of freezing-point depression because the boiling-point elevation and heat of vaporization differ in sign from strict analogs of the freezing-point depression and heat of fusion.

The fourth of the colligative properties, osmotic pressure, is illustrated in Figure 18. The partition AB separating the two arms, α and β, is a *semipermeable membrane*; that is, it permits solvent to pass through it but blocks the passage of solute. If solution is placed in α and solvent in β, both at pressure p_0 and the same temperature, solvent will flow from β to α, flow in this direction reducing the concentration difference. This flow can be stopped by applying an extra pressure, π, (making the total

$p_0 + \pi$) to the solution; pressures on the solution greater than $p_0 + \pi$ will cause the flow to reverse. The equilibrium pressure difference, π, between the solution and solvent is called the *osmotic pressure*.

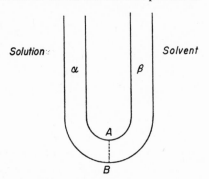

FIGURE 18. SCHEMATIC DIAGRAM OF OSMOTIC EXPERIMENT.

To find the relation between osmotic pressure and activity, consider the apparatus filled on both sides with solvent at pressure p_0, the two sides being at the same temperature; the system will, of course, be in equilibrium. If solute is now added slowly to α, and the pressure is simultaneously increased so that equilibrium is maintained, then at all times

$$\mu_1{}^\alpha = \mu_1{}^\beta$$

Since, however, the material in β is pure solvent at constant temperature and pressure, its chemical potential is constant. Therefore we must have

$$d\mu_1{}^\alpha = 0$$

From this point on we refer only to portion α of the system, and so we can simplify the notation by dropping the superscript α. Since both pressure and composition vary in α,

$$d\mu_1 = \left(\frac{\partial \mu_1}{\partial x_1}\right)_{p,T} dx_1 + \left(\frac{\partial \mu_1}{\partial p}\right)_{x_1,T} dp = 0 \qquad (7\text{-}43)$$

At the start of the process, $p = p_0$ and $x_1 = 1$; at the end, when x_1 has reached its final value, $p = p_0 + \pi$. Therefore

$$\int_{1,p_0}^{x_1,p_0+\pi} \left[\left(\frac{\partial \mu_1}{\partial x_1}\right)_{p,T} dx + \left(\frac{\partial \mu_1}{\partial p}\right)_{x_1,T} dp\right] = 0 \qquad (7\text{-}44)$$

As in the treatment of the freezing point, the description of the experiment suggests integrating along the equilibrium curve, AC in Figure 19, but

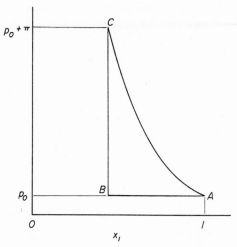

FIGURE 19. VARIATION OF OSMOTIC PRESSURE OF SOLUTION WITH MOLE FRACTION OF SOLVENT (SCHEMATIC).

since the integrand is the exact differential $d\mu_1$, the same result is found by integrating along other paths. The path ABC leads to a convenient form of the expression. Along AB only the composition varies, the pressure remaining fixed at the value p_0, and

$$\left[\left(\frac{\partial \mu_1}{\partial x_1}\right)_{p,T}\right]_{p=p_0} = \frac{\partial}{\partial x_1}(\mu_1{}^* + RT \ln a_1) = RT \frac{\partial \ln a_1(p_0)}{\partial x_1}$$

where the notation $a_1(p_0)$ indicates that the activity is determined at the pressure p_0. This gives

$$\int_{AB} d\mu_1 = RT \int_1^{x_1} \frac{\partial \ln a_1(p_0)}{\partial x_1} dx_1 = RT \ln a_1(p_0)$$

Along BC only the pressure varies; the integral becomes

$$\int_{BC} d\mu_1 = \int_{p_0}^{p_0+\pi} \left(\frac{\partial \mu_1}{\partial p}\right)_{x_1,T} dp = \int_{p_0}^{p_0+\pi} v_1 \, dp$$

With the insertion of these values, Eq. (7–44) becomes

$$- RT \ln a_1 = \int_{p_0}^{p_0+\pi} v_1 \, dp \qquad (7\text{–}45)$$

where the activity is measured at the pressure p_0, and the partial molar volume of the solvent at the final concentration of the solution. This equation is thermodynamically exact, but approximations are always introduced to make it more wieldy. The first of these is to regard the liquid as incompressible; that is, to consider v_1 constant. This leads to

$$-RT \ln a_1 = \pi v_1 \qquad (7\text{--}46)$$

This approximation is almost exact unless the pressure is very high; if more accuracy is needed, v_1 can be regarded as varying linearly with p. If the solution is very dilute, $\ln a_1 \approx - x_2$ (Eq. (7–36)) and so

$$\pi v_1 = RT x_2 \qquad (7\text{--}47)$$

For dilute solutions $n_2 \ll n_1$, and therefore

$$x_2 = \frac{n_2}{n_1 + n_2} \approx \frac{n_2}{n_1}$$

Using this in Eq. (7–47) gives

$$\pi v_1 n_1 = \pi V_1 = n_2 RT \qquad (7\text{--}48)$$

where V_1 can be loosely interpreted as the total volume of the solvent or, for very dilute solutions, as the volume of the solution. This is the well-known van't Hoff equation. Since n_1/V is the molar concentration, c, this may be written

$$\pi = cRT \qquad (7\text{--}49)$$

In the early days of physical chemistry, a great deal of speculation resulted from the superficial resemblance of Eq. (7–48) to the ideal gas law, and attempts were made to find some analogy between the phenomona of gas pressure and osmotic pressure. Nowadays it should be superfluous to point out that the resemblance is fortuitous.

Although any of the colligative properties can be used to determine the activity of the solvent, practical considerations often determine which is best in any particular instance. Freezing- and boiling-point determinations are usually easiest experimentally. However, the freezing-point method cannot be used directly at any temperature other than the freezing point, and the use of the boiling-point method at any temperature other than the normal boiling point is complicated by the necessity of operating at other than atmospheric pressure. The vapor-pressure method is somewhat more troublesome in most cases, and much more so if the solute is volatile; it can, in principle, be used at any temperature between the triple point and the critical temperature of the solvent. Osmotic pressure is generally the most difficult to determine; for concentrated solutions of solutes of low molecular weight, it may be as high as several hundred bars; moreover, for many solutions semipermeable membranes are not available. However, for polymer solutions, other colligative properties are so small as to be scarcely measurable, while osmotic pressure is a few millibars or less; and simple cellulosic membranes are suitable. For these reasons osmotic pressure has become very important in the study of solutions of polymers.

7–9. Solvent Activity at Other Temperatures and Pressures

As pointed out in the preceding section, the colligative properties permit direct determination of the activity of the solvent only under rather limited conditions. For this reason it is often important, when we have the activity at one temperature and pressure, to be able to calculate it at another temperature or, more rarely, at another pressure. Equations for doing this are easily derived.

Since for the solvent the pure state is a standard state, Eq. (7–27) becomes

$$\left[\frac{\partial \ln a_1}{\partial T}\right]_{p,x} = \frac{h_1^* - h_1}{RT^2} = -\frac{l_1}{RT^2}$$

and integration gives

$$\ln a_1(T_2) - \ln a_1(T_1) = \int_{T_1}^{T_2} \frac{h_1^* - h_1}{RT^2} \, dT \tag{7–50}$$

For small changes $h_1^* - h_1$ can be treated as constant, and the integration is simple. For larger changes the variation of this quantity with temperature must be considered. From

$$\left[\frac{\partial (h_1^* - h_1)}{\partial T}\right]_{p,x} = c_{p1}^* - c_{p1}$$

we see that

$$h_1^* - h_1 = h_1^*(T'_1) - h_1(T'_1) + \int_{T'_1}^{T} (c_{p1}^* - c_{p1}) \, dT \tag{7–51}$$

Therefore, we need to have the activity at one temperature (T_1), the relative partial molar enthalpy at one temperature (T'_1), not necessarily the same as T_1, and relative partial molar heat capacities over the necessary range of temperatures. With this information we can use Eq. (7–51) to determine $h_1^* - h_1$ as a function of T, and substitute the result into Eq. (7–50) to determine $a_1(T_2)$.

This procedure is satisfactory if the c_p data are available in the form of an empirical function of T. If only tabulated c_p values are at hand, it involves the rather tedious process of double graphical integration. In this case a procedure similar to that of Section 5–4 can be used. We note that

$$RT \ln a_i = \mu_i - \mu_1^* = h_i - h_1^* - T(s_i - s_1^*) \qquad (7\text{–}52)$$

Knowing a_i and $h_i - h_1^*$ at the temperature T_1, we apply this equation to calculate $s_i - s_1^*$ at this same temperature. Then $h_i - h_1^*$ is calculated at T_2 by means of Eq. (7–51). Next $s_i - s_i^*$ is calculated at T_2 by the equation

$$s_i(T_2) - s_1^*(T_2) = s_i(T_1) - s_1^*(T_1) + \int_{T_1}^{T_2} \frac{c_{pi} - c_{p1}^*}{T} \, dT$$

These are then recombined by Eq. (7–52) to obtain a_i at T_2.

Pressure variation of activity can be treated similarly, with Eq. (7–28) as the starting point. Since this is seldom needed, the details will not be given.

7–10. Application of the Gibbs-Duhem Equation to Activities

If we substitute the fundamental equation for activity,

$$\mu_i = \mu_i^0 + RT \ln a_i$$

into the Gibbs-Duhem equation (Eq. (7–17))

$$\sum_i x_i \, d\mu_i = 0$$

we find, since μ_i^0 is a constant at constant temperature and pressure,

$$\sum_i x_i \, d(\ln a_i) = 0 \qquad (7\text{–}53)$$

Now since

$$\sum_i x_i = 1$$

we also have

$$\sum_i x_i \, d(\ln x_i) = \sum_i dx_i = 0$$

Subtracting this from Eq. (7–53) gives

$$\sum_i x_i \, d(\ln \gamma_i) = 0 \qquad (7\text{–}54)$$

since $\ln \gamma_i = \ln a_i - \ln x_i$.

This will now be applied to a solution consisting of solvent and a single solute. The pure solvent ("infinitely dilute solution") will be taken as the standard state for the solvent and as the reference state for the solute. Since $\ln \gamma_1 \to 0$ as $x_2 \to 0$, one may try to express $\ln \gamma_1$ as a series of powers of x_2, with no constant term. Thus

$$\ln \gamma_1 = Ax_2 + Bx_2{}^2 + \ldots \tag{7-55}$$

where A and B are constants, at least at fixed temperature and pressure. Substituting this into Eq. (7-54) and using the fact that $x_1 = 1 - x_2$ gives

$$(1 - x_2) (A + 2Bx_2 + \ldots) \, dx_2 + x_2 \, d \, (\ln \gamma_2) = 0$$

or

$$\left(\frac{A}{x_2} + 2B - A + \ldots \right) dx_2 + d(\ln \gamma_2) = 0$$

Integration of this gives

$$A \ln x_2 + (2B - A)x_2 + \ldots + \ln \gamma_2 = \text{const.} \tag{7-56}$$

Now as $x_2 \to 0$, $\ln \gamma_2 \to 0$ and $\ln x_2 \to -\infty$. This can be reconciled with Eq. (7-56) only by taking $A = 0$. If any lower power of x_2 (for example $x_2{}^{\frac{1}{2}}$) had been included in Eq. (7-55), similar reasoning would have shown that its coefficient must vanish also. Thus we conclude that lowest power of x_2 which can appear in an equation such as Eq. (7-55) has an exponent which exceeds 1.

Actually it is often found that for solutions of nonelectrolytes

$$\ln \gamma_1 = \frac{w}{RT} x_2{}^2 + \ldots \tag{7-57}$$

where w is a constant, independent of temperature and composition. For many solutions this one term is sufficient; Guggenheim[3] has proposed the name *strictly regular solutions* for these. (Previously Hildebrand had introduced the term *regular solution*; this will be discussed later.) If the solute is an electrolyte, $\ln \gamma_1$ can be expressed at very low concentrations by

$$\ln \gamma_1 = Bx_2{}^{\frac{3}{2}} \tag{7-58}$$

Further treatment of electrolytic solutions will, however, be deferred to Chapter 9.

Returning to Eq. (7–56), we can easily evaluate the constant of integration by setting $\ln \gamma_2 = 0$ when $x_2 = 0$. This shows that

$$\ln \gamma_2 = -2Bx_2 + \ldots \tag{7–59}$$

Thus if the deviation of γ_1 from 1 is negative, that of γ_2 is positive, and vice versa. (It should be emphasized that this is true only when the infinitely dilute state is used as the reference state for the solute.)

Eqs. (7–57) and (7–59) show that for very dilute solutions (near $x_2 = 0$) the activity coefficients can be expressed by

$$\gamma_1 \approx e^{wx_2^2/RT} \approx 1 + \frac{w}{RT} x_2^2$$

and

$$\gamma_2 \approx e^{-2wx_2/RT} \approx 1 - \frac{2w}{RT} x_2$$

and so γ_1 and γ_2 differ from 1 only by second- and first-degree terms in x_2, respectively. We can, therefore, take as approximations that both γ_1 and γ_2 are equal to 1, and so

$$a_1 = x_1 \qquad a_2 = x_2$$

the first of these being the better approximation. Then Eq. (7–31), applied to the first of these, gives Raoult's law

$$P_1 = x_1 P_1^*$$

For component 2 we have

$$\mu_2 = \mu''_2 + RT \ln x_2 = \mu'_2 + RT \ln \frac{f_2}{p_u}$$

and so

$$\frac{f_2}{p_u x_2} = \exp \frac{\mu'_2 - \mu''_2}{RT}$$

or

$$P_2 \approx f_2 = Kx_2 \tag{7–60}$$

where K is independent of concentration. This is known as *Henry's law*. Note that these two laws differ in that the constant in Henry's law cannot be identified with P_2^*, since the law applies only to dilute solutions of component 2, not to the pure substance. These results are commonly summed up in the rule, *in dilute solutions Raoult's law can be applied to the solvent, Henry's law to the solute.*

Integration of Eq. (7–54) for a two-component system makes it possible to determine solute activity from data on solvent activity, which in turn can be calculated from colligative property measurements. We note that since $x_2 = 0$ is the reference state for both solvent and solute, both activity coefficients are equal to 1 in this state. Using this as the lower limit of integration gives

$$\ln \gamma_2 = -\int_{x_2=0}^{x_2} \frac{x_1}{x_2} \, d(\ln \gamma_1) = -\int_0^{\ln \gamma_1} \frac{x_1}{x_2} \, d(\ln \gamma_1) \qquad (7\text{--}61)$$

If $\ln \gamma_1$ is expressed as a function of x_1 or x_2 (in the form of an empirical equation, for example), the integration is easy. Thus if

$$\ln \gamma_1 = Bx_2^{\frac{3}{2}}$$

then $d(\ln \gamma_1) = \frac{3}{2}Bx_2^{\frac{1}{2}} \, dx_2$, and

$$\ln \gamma_2 = -\int_0^{x_2} \frac{1-x_2}{x_2}(\tfrac{3}{2}Bx_2^{\frac{1}{2}}) \, dx_2 = -\tfrac{3}{2}B \int_0^{x_2} (x_2^{-\frac{1}{2}} - x_2^{\frac{1}{2}}) \, dx_2$$

$$= -B(3x_2^{\frac{1}{2}} - x_2^{\frac{3}{2}})$$

If graphical integration is necessary, however, a difficulty arises from the behavior of the integrand, which approaches infinity at the lower limit of integration. Two procedures for circumventing this difficulty will be described.

Consider a dilute solution, whose properties will be designated by primes, and replace zero in the lower limit of integration by x_2'. Then

$$\ln \gamma_2 - \ln \gamma'_2 = -\int_{x_2=x'_2}^{x_2} \frac{x_1}{x_2} \, d(\ln \gamma_1)$$

$$= -\int_{\ln \gamma'_1}^{\ln \gamma_1} \frac{x_1}{x_2} \, d(\ln \gamma_1)$$

There is no difficulty in carrying out this integration graphically, since the point at which the integrand becomes infinite is not included in the range of integration. If several values of x'_2 are chosen and the integration performed for each, then $\ln \gamma_2 - \ln \gamma'_2$ can be plotted against x'_2 on another graph. Now as $x'_2 \to 0$, $\ln \gamma_2 - \ln \gamma'_2 \to \ln \gamma_2$, and so $\ln \gamma_2$ can be found by extrapolating this graph to $x'_2 = 0$. Since this method requires several area measurements, it is rather tedious, particularly if no planimeter is available.

The following method, which does not have this disadvantage, is applicable whenever $\ln \gamma_1$ is proportional to $x_2{}^2$ (or a higher power of x_2) in very dilute solution. Integrating by parts, we find from Eq. (7–61)

$$\ln \gamma_2 = -\left. \frac{x_1}{x_2} \ln \gamma_1 \right]_{x_2=0}^{x_2} + \int_{x_2=0}^{x_2} \ln \gamma_1 \, d\left(\frac{x_1}{x_2}\right)$$

The integrated part vanishes at the lower limit, since $\ln \gamma_1$ is proportional to $x_2{}^2$. The integral can be simplified by noting that

$$d\left(\frac{x_1}{x_2}\right) = d\left(\frac{1 - x_2}{x_2}\right) = d\left(\frac{1}{x_2} - 1\right) = -\frac{1}{x_2{}^2} \, dx_2$$

Incorporating this into the expression for $\ln \gamma_2$ gives

$$\ln \gamma_1 = -\frac{x_1}{x_2} \ln \gamma_1 - \int_0^{x_2} \frac{\ln \gamma_1}{x_2{}^2} \, dx_2 \tag{7–62}$$

The integrand in this equation remains finite as $x_2 \to 0$ because of the condition that $\ln \gamma_1 \sim x_2{}^2$ near zero concentration. This makes possible the direct graphical evaluation of the integral.

Application of these methods requires very accurate experimental measurements; with crude measurements the graphs are erratic near zero concentration.

7–11. Statistical Thermodynamics of Solutions

The treatment of solution is one of the most difficult applications of statistical mechanics; except for a few qualitative remarks, it is beyond the scope of this book. Even a qualitative understanding of this topic, however, is helpful in understanding why solutions exhibit ideal behavior or various types of deviation from it.

Most of the work on the statistics of liquids and liquid mixtures has been based on some kind of lattice model. In these models the liquid, whether pure or mixed, is pictured very much like a crystal; it is assumed that there is a geometrically regular array of sites which the molecules can occupy. This underestimates the number of configurational states possible, since actually the molecules are not confined to any rigid pattern. However, when this model is used to compare the number of states — and therefore the entropy — of a mixture with that of its pure components, this error tends to cancel out.

Let us consider a mixture in which (a) each site can be occupied by one molecule of any of the types occurring in the mixture, and (b) the interaction energy between two molecules depends only on their distance apart, and not on what kinds of molecules they are. Now in the pure state, a molecule of type A, for example, has as its neighbors other molecules of the same type, while in a mixture, some or all of its neighbors will probably be of other types. The process of mixing involves, therefore, the breaking up of A-A neighboring pairs (and also B-B pairs, etc.) and the formation of other types, such as A-B and A-C. We have specified, however, that the interaction energy of these new pairs must be the same as that of the old ones, and so no energy change occurs on mixing. This model also leads to a zero volume of mixing, and in any case, pressure-volume effects can ordinarily be neglected in condensed systems. We therefore find that the heat of mixing is also zero.

Since any molecule can occupy any site without affecting the energy of the system, the sites are occupied at random. This means that the problem of finding the entropy of mixing is exactly the same as in the mixing of isotopes in a crystal, which is treated in Section 6–16, and the equation derived there can be applied here also:

$$\Delta S = -R \sum_i n_i \ln x_i$$

This is the same as Eq. (7–23) for ideal mixtures. Since the enthalpy change on mixing is also that of an ideal mixture, we can conclude that mixtures based on this model are ideal.

Two types of deviation from the ideal solution model will be considered. In one of these the interaction energy between like molecules is different from that between unlike molecules, and so there is an energy change on mixing. If a pair of like molecules in close proximity has greater energy than a pair of unlike molecules at the same distance, then the energy of mixing (and also the heat of mixing, since they differ only trivially) is negative. Clearly the different configurations which the molecules of the mixture can take up are not equally probable, since configurations in which a relatively high proportion of neighboring pairs consist of unlike molecules have relatively low energy. With the probabilities of the possible configurations unequal, the entropy of mixing is lower than that of the ideal mixture. However, the difference is often so small that the entropy of mixing has practically its ideal value. If unlike pairs have higher energy than like pairs, the heat of mixing will be positive. For these solutions there is a tendency for like molecules to cluster together, since this reduces the energy of the mixture. If this effect is great enough, it may lead to a separation into two phases. As with the solutions with negative heat of mixing, these solutions must have lower entropy of mixing than an ideal solution, but the difference is often negligible. To solutions of these two types — with ideal entropy of mixing but nonzero heat of mixing — Hildebrand[4] gave the name *regular solutions*.

Another type of deviation from the behavior of ideal solutions is caused by a large discrepancy in size between the types of molecules in the mixture, as when a polymer is dissolved in a solvent of low molecular weight. In this case the model in which any one site in the lattice may be occupied by one molecule of any type in the mixture is not adequate. Instead, we must picture each of the larger molecules as taking up several adjacent sites, or even several hundred when the solute is a polymer. Since this model is most often applied to solutions containing long, flexible solute molecules, the several adjacent sites occupied by a single solute molecule need not be in a straight line or any other special geometrical pattern. Clearly such a molecule has many more configurations available than a molecule which occupies only one site. Moreover, a polymer molecule can take full advantage of all the many configurations available to it only when it is reasonably free from interference from other polymer molecules; that is, in dilute solution. In the pure polymer, the number of configurations is limited by the fact that most or all of the sites adjacent to a given molecule are occupied by other molecules. Thus the process of dissolving increases the number of configurations more than it would for an ideal solution, and the entropy of mixing is greater. By treating these ideas mathematically, Flory[5] has derived the following expression for the entropy of mixing when N molecules of z-mers (polymers containing z monomer units in each molecule) are dissolved in n molecules of solvent:

$$\Delta S = -k \left(n \ln \frac{n}{n + zN} + N \ln \frac{zN}{n + zN} \right) \qquad (7\text{--}63)$$

When $z = 1$, this reduces to the formula for an ideal mixture. If each unit of the polymer occupies about as much space as a molecule of solvent, as is usually assumed, the ratios in Eq. (7–63) may be identified with the volume fractions of solvent and solute, ϕ_1 and ϕ_2. We then have

$$\Delta S = -k(n \ln \phi_1 + N \ln \phi_2) \qquad (7\text{–}64)$$

Such solutions are highly nonideal — a fact which must be remembered when osmotic pressure is used to determine the molecular weights of polymers. If any confidence is to be placed in such measurements, the ratio of osmotic pressure to concentration must be extrapolated to zero concentration, and the limiting value used in calculating molecular weight.

7–12. The Molal Activity Scale

Activities discussed up to this point have been defined in part by specifying that $a_i/x_i \to 1$ either as $x_i \to 1$ or as the solution approaches infinite dilution. Activities defined in this manner are often called *rational activities*. There are several advantages in the use of rational activities; among others they are equal to mole fractions for all components in ideal solutions, and for the solvent in dilute solutions. For the latter reason rational activities are practically always used for the solvent even when another scale is used for the solute. For solutes in highly nonideal solutions, such as electrolytic solutions, the advantages of rational activities largely disappear, and it may be more convenient to have an activity which approximates the molality, rather than the mole fraction, in dilute solution. This is referred to as the *practical activity*; in its definition we retain Eq. (7–24) for all solute species:

$$\mu_i = \mu_i^0 + RT \ln a_i \quad (i = 2, 3, \ldots)$$

but complete the definition by specifying that

$$\frac{a_i}{m_i} \to 1 \text{ as } x_1 \to 1 \quad (i = 2, 3, \ldots)$$

where m_i is the concentration of substance i expressed as a molality. This means that the *practical activity coefficients*, a_i/m_i, approach 1 as the solution approaches infinite dilution. It might be desirable to have distinct symbols for activities on different scales, but it is not customary to do this; for activity coefficients distinct symbols are sometimes used. However, since the fundamental equation (Eq. (7–24)) takes the same form for all activities, there is something to be said for the practice of using the same symbols for all. This will be done in this book, except where there is some danger of confusion.

Conversion of activities from one scale to another is not difficult, particularly if both are based on the same reference state (e. g., infinite dilution). If we distinguish the practical activity and the corresponding standard chemical potential by primes, we have from Eq. (7–24)

$$\mu_i = \mu_i{}^{0\prime} + RT \ln a'_i = \mu_i{}^0 + RT \ln a_i$$

since the chemical potential is not affected by our choice of activity scales. From this we find

$$\frac{a'_i}{a_i} = \exp\left(\frac{\mu_i{}^0 - \mu_i{}^{0\prime}}{RT}\right)$$

At fixed temperature and pressure, the quantity on the right is constant; it can be evaluated by considering the fact that both a'_i/m_i and a_i/x_i approach 1 at infinite dilution. Therefore the ratio

$$\frac{a'_i/m_i}{a_i/x_i} = \frac{a'_i/a_i}{m_i/x_i}$$

also approaches 1. This gives

$$\frac{a'_i}{a_i} = \lim_{x_1 \to 1} \frac{m_i}{x_i}$$

Now the molality is the concentration expressed in moles of solute per kilogram of solvent; that is, if w_1 is the mass of solvent,

$$m_i = \frac{n_i}{w_1/1 \text{ kg}}$$

At low concentrations x_i differs only negligibly from n_i/n_1. Therefore we have

$$\lim_{x_1 \to 1} \frac{m_i}{x_i} = \frac{n_1}{w_1/1 \text{ kg}}$$

which is simply the number of moles of solvent in a kilogram of solvent. Notice that this is the value of a'_i/a_i at all concentrations, even though it is the value of m_i/x_i only at infinite dilution. It follows that even in ideal solutions, for which $a_i = x_i$ at all concentrations, $a'_i = m_i$ only in the limit of infinite dilution. Even if an infinitely dilute reference state is used for an ideal solution, the rational activity coefficient will be unity; this is not true of the practical activity coefficient.

Another activity scale based on molarity is sometimes used. However, the dependence of molarity on temperature introduces complications into relations based on this scale, and so its use is generally undesirable.

PROBLEMS

(1) If U is regarded as a function of S, V, and the n's, show that it is a first-degree homogeneous function of these variables, and apply Euler's theorem to prove that

$$U = TS - pV + \sum_i \mu_i \, dn_i \qquad (7\text{–}65)$$

(2) Eq. (7–16) was derived under the assumption of constant temperature and pressure. Show that if this restriction is removed, the Gibbs-Duhem equation becomes

$$S \, dT - V \, dp + \sum_i n_i \, d\mu_i = 0 \qquad (7\text{–}66)$$

(3) A substance whose formula will be represented by A in phase α associates into n-mers, of formula A_n, in phase β. Show that Eqs. (7–8) and (7–9) must be replaced by

$$n\mu_A{}^\alpha \geqslant \mu_{A_n}{}^\beta$$

if the chemical potential is calculated on the basis of the molecular weight of the n-mer in phase β. However, if the association in phase β is ignored and the monomeric molecular weights used in calculating chemical potentials, then Eqs. (7–8) and (7–9) are retained. It follows that in applying relations derived from Eq. (7–9), one must use the same molecular weights in all phases, regardless of association. (See the discussion of this point by Bijvoet and Peerdeman.[6])

(4) At 20°C the density of ethanol-water mixtures at several concentrations is as follows:

x_{EtOH}	Density/(g/cm³)
0.350	0.8959
0.360	0.8935
0.370	0.8911
0.380	0.8887
0.390	0.8864

Determine the partial molar volumes of the two components in a mixture containing 37.0 mole per cent ethanol, and calculate the volume change on mixing. The densities of pure ethanol and pure water are 0.7893 and 0.9982 g/cm³.

(5) Let Y be any extensive property of a binary mixture and define $\bar{y}$ by

$$Y = (n_1 + n_2)\bar{y}$$

Show that

$$y_1 = \bar{y} + x_2 \left(\frac{\partial y}{\partial x_1} \right)_{T,p}$$

(6) Show that for a volatile solute, with infinitely dilute reference state,

$$a_2 = \frac{f_2}{K} \approx \frac{P_2}{K}$$

the Henry's law constant, K, being given by

$$K = \lim_{x_2 \to 0} \frac{P_2}{x_2}$$

(7) (a) To two immiscible solvents, α and β, in contact a solute is added; it goes partly into each solvent, and is unassociated in both. If activities are based on an infinitely dilute reference state in both solutions, show that a_2^α/a_2^β is a constant whose value is the limit of x_2^α/x_2^β as both concentrations approach zero.

(b) Show that if the solute exists as unassociated molecules A in solvent α, but as n-mers A_n in solvent β, $a_2^{\alpha n}/a_2^\beta$ is a constant whose value is the limit of $x_2^{\alpha n}/x_2$.

(8) Adams[7] defined activity of a solute by

$$a_2^c = \lim_{x_2 \to 0} x_2 \exp\left(\frac{\mu_2^c - \mu_2}{RT}\right)$$

the superscript c denoting a given fixed concentration. Show that the activity defined in this manner is identical with the rational activity based on an infinitely dilute reference state.

(9) The following data for aqueous solutions of sucrose at 50°C are taken from the work of Perman[8] and smoothed to eliminate apparent discrepancies:

x_2	γ_1
0.01	0.9994
0.02	0.9976
0.03	0.9952
0.04	0.9920
0.05	0.9877
0.06	0.9815
0.07	0.9732
0.08	0.9638
0.09	0.9533
0.10	0.9429

Calculate γ_2 when $x_2 = 0.10$, using either or both of the graphical methods given in Section 7–10. (Note that when γ_1 is given as 0.9994, its logarithm is known to only one significant figure; the reliability of the point calculated from this value is correspondingly low.)

(10) Show that for a solution obeying Flory's equation (Eq. (7–63))

$$\ln a_1 = \frac{N(z-1)}{n+zN} + \ln\left(\frac{n}{n+zN}\right)$$

provided the solution is athermal; that is, there is no heat of mixing when it is formed.

REFERENCES

1. Gibbs, J. W., Collected Works, Vol. 1, p. 65, New York, N.Y., Longmans, Green, & Co., 1928.
2. Meyer, K. H., and Van der Wyk, A. J. A., *Helv. Chim. Acta*, **23**, 488 (1940).
3. Guggenheim, E. A., "Mixtures," Chap. IV, London, Oxford University Press, 1952.
4. Hildebrand, J. H., *J. Am. Chem. Soc.*, **51**,, 66 (1929); Hildebrand, J. H., and Scott, R. L., "The Solubility of Nonelectrolytes," pp. 46–47, New York, N.Y., Reinhold Publishing Corp., 1950.
5. Flory, P. J., *J. Chem. Phys.*, **10**, 51 (1942).
6. Bijvoet, J. M., and Peerdeman, A. F., *J. Chem. Educ.*, **35**, 240 (1958).
7. Adams, L. H., *Chem. Rev.*, **19**, 1 (1936).
8. Perman, E. P., *Trans. Faraday Soc.*, **24**, 330 (1928).

chapter 8

Chemical Equilibria
and Phase Equilibria

THERE IS PROBABLY no application of thermodynamics to chemistry more important practically than the calculation of the equilibrium conditions for chemical reactions. By this means it is possible to determine certain necessary, but not sufficient, conditions for a reaction to proceed to a given yield. In industrial research the effort and funds expended on the search for suitable catalysts for desired reactions is enormous; in the absence of thermodynamic studies, much of this effort might be wasted on attempts to make the reaction take place under circumstances in which it is thermodynamically impossible. In this chapter two related problems are considered: how far it is thermodynamically possible for a reaction to proceed, and how many phases can coexist in equilibrium in a single system.

8-1. Fundamental Equilibrium Expression for Chemical Reactions

Consider a chemical reaction symbolized, as in Chapter 5, by

$$\sum_i y_i Y_i \rightarrow \sum_i z_i Z_i$$

Let this reaction proceed in a closed system. Despite the fact that the total mass of the system is constant, the number of moles of each reactant and product changes. Now if the degree of advancement, ξ, of the reaction increases by an infinitesimal amount $d\xi$, the amount of Y_i decreases by $y_i \, d\xi$, and that of Z_i increases by $z_i \, d\xi$. Thus

$$dn_{Y_i} = -y_i \, d\xi \quad \text{and} \quad dn_{Z_i} = z_i \, d\xi$$

Eq. (7-1) then takes the form

$$dU = T \, dS - p \, dV - \left(\sum_i y_i \mu_{Y_i} - \sum_i z_i \mu_{Z_i} \right) d\xi \qquad (8\text{-}1)$$

By the first law $dQ = dU + p \, dV$; rearranging Eq. (8-1) thus gives

$$\left(\sum_i y_i \mu_{Y_i} - \sum_i z_i \mu_{Z_i} \right) d\xi = T \, dS - (dU + p \, dV) = T \, dS - dQ$$

The second law states that the quantity on the right must be zero for reversible changes and positive for irreversible ones. The reaction can therefore proceed naturally — that is, irreversibly — only if

$$\sum_i y_i \mu_{Y_i} - \sum_i z_i \mu_{Z_i} > 0 \qquad \text{(a)}$$

and equilibrium occurs if $\qquad\qquad\qquad\qquad\qquad\qquad$ (8-2)

$$\sum_i y_i \mu_{Y_i} - \sum_i z_i \mu_{Z_i} = 0 \qquad \text{(b)}$$

The quantity on the left was introduced by De Donder[1] and called by him the *affinity*; this term had been used previously, but only in a qualitative sense. De Donder used A as the symbol for the affinity, but since this has been used here for the Helmholtz free energy, the two-letter symbol Af will be used instead.

If the reaction takes place at constant temperature and pressure, the affinity is the negative of the Gibbs free energy change, $-\Delta g$. The connection of the affinity with chemical equilibrium is, however, more general than that of Δg, in analogy to the fact that the chemical potential has more general properties than is indicated by its role as a partial molar Gibbs free energy.

8-2. The Equilibrium Constant

If Eq. (7-24) is substituted into the definition of affinity, there results

$$Af = Af^0 - RT \ln \left(\frac{a_{Z_1}{}^{z_1} a_{Z_2}{}^{z_2} \ldots}{a_{Y_1}{}^{y_1} a_{Y_2}{}^{y_2} \ldots} \right) \qquad (8\text{-}3)$$

where the standard affinity, Af^0, is the quantity which results from using standard chemical potentials in the expression for the affinity. The quantity in parentheses in Eq. (8–3) is called the *reaction quotient* and is designated by Q_a. At equilibrium $Af = 0$, and the reaction quotient must take a value which depends only on Af^0 and T, not on the activities. This value is referred to as the *equilibrium constant*, K_a. Thus we see that

$$RT \ln K_a = Af^0 \tag{8–4}$$

and the affinity is given by

$$Af = RT \ln \frac{K_a}{Q_a} \tag{8–5}$$

Since the reaction can proceed only if the affinity is positive, Q_a must be less than K_a. As the reaction proceeds, Q_a increases; when it reaches the value K_a, equilibrium has been attained, and no further progress of the reaction takes place. If we start with $Q_a > K_a$, the direction of the reaction, if it occurs at all, must be backwards.

In most practical work, K_a and Q_a are approximated by various simplified expressions. A few examples will be given.

If some or all of the reactants or products are gases, $a_i = f_i/p_u \approx p_i/p_u$ for these substances, and so the numerical value of the pressure or fugacity is substituted for the activity.

If some or all of the reactants or products are pure solids or liquids, the pure liquid or solid state is chosen as the standard state for these substances, so that its activity is 1; it can, therefore, be dropped from the expression for K_a or Q_a. Of course, this does not mean that its chemical potential can be omitted in calculating the affinity.

If some or all of the reactants or products are solutes in a dilute solution, the activity is often approximated by means of the mole fraction, molality, or molarity.

It is customary to designate these approximations to the equilibrium constant by the use of an appropriate subscript in place of a. Thus if pressures or mole fractions are used, we have K_p or K_x, respectively. To be more specific, when all reactants and products are either gases or pure condensed phases, and the ideal gas law is used, the equilibrium constant becomes

$$K_p = \frac{p_{Z_1}{}^{z_1} p_{Z_2}{}^{z_2} \cdots}{p_{Y_1}{}^{y_1} p_{Y_2}{}^{y_2} \cdots} \, p_u{}^{-\Delta n} \tag{8–6}$$

where Δn is the increase in the number of moles of gas accompanying a unit increase in the degree of advancement, as in Section 5–3, and no terms are included for the condensed phases. The equilibrium constant defined in this way is dimensionless; however, the term $p_u^{-\Delta n}$ is often omitted from the definition, and the dimensions are then pressure units to the Δn power.

8–3. Variation of the Equilibrium Constant with Temperature

The Gibbs-Helmholtz equation (Eq. (7–20)) can be applied to the standard chemical potentials, yielding

$$\left[\frac{\partial(\mu_i^0/T)}{\partial T}\right]_p = -\frac{h_i^0}{T^2}$$

If the standard affinity is divided by T and this equation is applied, we find

$$\left[\frac{\partial(Af^0/T)}{\partial T}\right]_p = \frac{\partial}{\partial T}\left(\sum_i y_i \frac{\mu_{Y_i}^0}{T} - \sum_i z_i \frac{\mu_{Z_i}^0}{T}\right)$$

$$= \sum_i z_i \frac{h_{Z_i}^0}{T^2} - \sum_i y_i \frac{h_{Y_i}^0}{T^2} = \frac{\Delta h^0}{T^2}$$

We then find from Eq. (8–4) that

$$\left[\frac{\partial(\ln K_a)}{\partial T}\right]_p = \frac{\Delta h^0}{RT^2} \tag{8–7}$$

This is known as *van't Hoff's equation*; it makes possible the calculation of an equilibrium constant at other temperatures if it is known at one temperature, provided the necessary enthalpy data are available. If the variation of Δh^0 with temperature can be neglected, as is often true for short temperature ranges, Eq. (8–7) integrates to

$$\ln K_a(T_2) - \ln K_a(T_1) = \frac{\Delta h^0}{R}\left(\frac{1}{T_1} - \frac{1}{T_2}\right) \tag{8–8}$$

Integration is also possible when the standard heat capacities are available as functions of temperature, and the standard heat of reaction is known at one temperature. If only tabulated heat capacities are to be used, the double graphical integration can be avoided by separating the standard affinity into a Δh^0 term and a $T\Delta s^0$ term and calculating each of these at the new temperature, as in Section 5–4.

8–4. Calculation of Equilibrium Constants from Calorimetric or Spectroscopic Data

It has been pointed out that the affinity is equal to the negative of the Gibbs free energy change when the reaction is carried out at constant temperature and pressure. This provides the usual method of calculating the affinity. The standard enthalpy change for the reaction can be determined from heats of formation or of combustion. The entropy of each species involved is determined from calorimetric data, with the help of the third law, or by statistical methods. These are then combined by means of the relation

$$Af^0 = -\Delta g^0 = T \, \Delta s^0 - \Delta h^0$$

Thermodynamic tables list the necessary information in a variety of forms. Some give standard affinities of formation with the sign changed, designating them as "Standard [Gibbs] free energies of formation." In others the standard heats of formation and standard entropies are listed. Some include the symbol $h_0{}^0$, referring to the standard enthalpy at $0°K$; the functions then listed are $h^0 - h_0{}^0$ and $(\mu^0 - h_0{}^0)/T$. No value can be assigned to $h_0{}^0$, but its presence serves as a reminder that the functions listed must be combined in such a manner that it cancels out. No difficulty should be found in using any of these, if it is clearly understood exactly what data are given. For example, if we add $(\mu^0 - h_0{}^0)/T$ for the reactants, using appropriate stoichiometric coefficients, and subtract a similar sum for the products, and finally multiply by T, we get $Af^0 + \Delta h_0{}^0$. Then by subtracting the sum of $h^0 - h_0{}^0$ for the reactants from a similar sum for the products, we find $\Delta h^0 - \Delta h_0{}^0$. Adding this to the quantity previously determined gives $Af^0 + \Delta h^0$. Finally, Δh^0 is calculated from standard heats of formation and subtracted from this, yielding the standard affinity.

Finally, it should be pointed out that this procedure is often reversed, experimental equilibrium constants being used in Eqs. (8–4) and (8–7) to yield valuable thermodynamic information.

8–5. The Statistical Mechanics of Chemical Equilibrium

Although classical thermodynamic methods have sufficed for deriving the equation of chemical equilibrium (Eq. (8–4)), it is interesting to show that this same relation can be obtained by statistical methods. Only a rather simple case will be treated here, but it is sufficiently involved to show the form which the equilibrium constant must take.

Consider a closed, ideal, gaseous system consisting initially of $N_A{}^0$ molecules of A, and $N_B{}^0$ molecules or atoms of B. These may react to form C, according to the equation

$$A + 2B \leftrightharpoons 2C$$

To list all the possible states of this system, we must first consider the divers ways in which the matter may be distributed among the substances A, B, and C; then for each of these distributions the possible combinations of translational and other energy states of the constituent molecules is needed. The possible distributions of the matter among A, B, and C are easily listed, for if at any time X molecules of A have reacted, then $2X$ molecules of B have reacted, and $2X$ molecules of C have formed. Therefore the number of molecules of each must be given by

$$N_A = N_A{}^0 - X$$
$$N_B = N_B{}^0 - 2X$$
$$N_C = 2X$$

where X may take any integral value from zero to a maximum determined by the limiting amount of A or B present.

If we sum $\exp(-\epsilon_i/kT)$ for all states of given X, we find the partition function for a mixture of N_A molecules of A, N_B molecules of B, and N_C molecules of C. This is given by the methods shown in Sections 6–9, 6–10, and 6–11 as

$$Z(X) = \frac{z_A{}^{N_A} z_B{}^{N_B} z_C{}^{N_C}}{N_A! \ N_B! \ N_C!}$$

where z_A, for example, is the partition function for a single molecule of A. Note that in this equation the energies of A, B, and C must be measured from the same zero point. Finally, the partition function for the reacting system is the sum of this over all values of X:

$$Z = \sum_{X \geqslant 0} Z(X)$$

What we want to find is the average value of X when the system is in equilibrium. However, the calculation can be enormously simplified by assuming that the average value is the same as the most probable value. This is a general principle of statistical mechanics for macroscopic systems, although we have proved it only for certain properties of the Einstein crystal. Since the probability of any given value of X is simply $Z(X)/Z$, we need only find the value of X that makes $Z(X)$ a maximum. This is simplified by dealing with $\ln Z(X)$ instead of $Z(X)$ itself. Thus

$$\ln Z(X) = (N_A{}^0 - X) \ln z_A + (N_B{}^0 - 2X) \ln z_B + 2X \ln z_C$$
$$- \ln (N_A{}^0 - X)! - \ln (N_A{}^0 - 2X)! - \ln (2X)!$$

We now differentiate this, treating X as a continuous variable. The derivatives of the factorial terms are found by Stirling's formula to be

$$\frac{d}{dX}(\ln N!) = \frac{d}{dX}(N \ln N - N) = \frac{dN}{dX}(\ln N)$$

Thus for a maximum we find

$$\frac{\partial[\ln Z(X)]}{\partial X} = 0 = -\ln z_A - 2 \ln z_B + 2 \ln z_C + \ln N_A + 2 \ln N_B - 2 \ln N_C$$

or

$$\frac{z_C{}^2}{z_A z_B{}^2} = \frac{N_C{}^2}{N_A N_B{}^2}$$

If we now multiply each term on both sides by the appropriate power of $kT/p_u V$ and use the fact that $p_i = N_i kT/V$, we find

$$\frac{(p_C/p_u)^2}{(p_A/p_u)(p_B/p_u)^2} = \frac{(z_C kT/p_u V)^2}{(z_A kT/p_u V)(z_B kT/p_u V)^2} \tag{8-9}$$

Now, considering translational properties alone, we find from Eqs. (6–34), (6–35), and (6–39) that

$$g'_{tr} = u_{tr} + pv - Ts'_{tr} = -RT \ln \frac{z_{tr} kT}{p_u V}$$

where

$$z_{tr} = \frac{(2\pi m k T)^{3/2} V}{h^3}$$

(We do not need to use u', since u is constant for ideal gases at fixed temperature.) From Eq. (6–46)

$$a_r = g_r = -RT \ln z_r$$

since rotation makes no contribution to pressure. Similar expressions hold for vibration and electronic contributions if necessary. Thus finally we can combine these to get

$$g' = -RT \ln \frac{zkT}{p_u V}$$

where $z = z_{tr} z_r \ldots$ Now applying this to Eq. (8-9), after taking logarithms, gives

$$\ln K_p = \frac{-\Delta g'}{RT} = \frac{A f^0}{RT}$$

which is Eq. (8-4).

The application of the canonical ensemble to this problem, as carried out here, is rather cumbersome; it is used because the more powerful method of the grand canonical ensemble has not been developed. With the latter tool available, the statistical mechanics of chemical equilibrium can be treated in a more elegant and general manner.*

8-6. Phase Equilibrium in Nonreacting Systems; the Phase Rule

It is well known that pure water and its vapor can coexist in equilibrium at a variety of temperatures and pressures, but that the temperature and pressure cannot be chosen independently. If the pressure is chosen, there will be at most one temperature at which both phases can coexist at this pressure. If any other temperature is chosen, the water will either all evaporate or all condense, leaving only one phase. If only one phase is desired, both temperature and pressure can, within limits, be chosen arbitrarily; if three phases are to be present, there is only one temperature and pressure at which this is possible, and neither can be chosen arbitrarily. On the other hand, adding another substance — sucrose, for example — to the water, permits us to choose one more property at will, though still within limits. Thus we can choose a temperature, then choose a pressure lower than the vapor pressure of water at this temperature, and still have both liquid and vapor present by suitably fixing the concentration.

Before making this discussion more general, we need exact definitions of some of the terms used. A *phase* is a portion of a system, set off by

* See, for example, Rushbrooke's text, listed under GENERAL REFERENCES at the end of Chapter 6.

definite geometrical boundaries, and having uniform intensive properties; or several such portions identical in their intensive properties. As an example, in a system consisting of a piece of ice in liquid water, the ice and the liquid water are two phases; they are clearly marked off by definite boundaries, and the intensive properties are uniform throughout each. Of course, some of the intensive properties (the density, for example) are different in different phases. If the system contains several pieces of ice, they constitute one phase, in accordance with the second part of the definition. Since gases do not form definite boundaries with other gases but always mix, there cannot be more than one gaseous phase in any system. There is no theoretical limit to the number of liquid phases in one system; Hildebrand[2] quotes an example of seven liquid phases in a system containing mercury, gallium, phosphorus, perfluorokerosene, aniline, water, and hexane. Any number of solid phases may be present; there may even be several solid phases of the same chemical composition, such as rhombic and monoclinic sulfur. This definition is not entirely satisfactory for colloidal systems, and in fact the concept of phase is rather vague in these systems.

The number of intensive properties of a system (temperature, pressure, mole fractions, etc.) which can be selected arbitrarily (within limits) before the state of the system is fixed is called the *number of degrees of freedom*, or the *variance*, of the system. Alternatively, the variance may be regarded as the number of intensive properties that can be altered independently without changing the number of phases. In a system of liquid water and its vapor, the variance is 1; for an aqueous sucrose solution and its vapor, it is 2.

J. W. Gibbs[3] derived a highly important rule dealing with situations involving phase equilibria. The purpose of Gibbs' rule is to make possible the calculation of the number of phases which can coexist in a given system, or, if the number of phases is given, of the number of degrees of freedom. To derive this rule, consider a system of C nonreacting components, having P phases. All the intensive properties of any one phase can be fixed by specifying the chemical potential of each of the C components, and the temperature and pressure; that is, by a total of $C + 2$ variables. However, once we have specified these variables for one phase, we have specified them for the entire system, since (1) thermal equilibrium requires that the temperature be uniform throughout the system; (2) mechanical equilibrium requires that the pressure be uniform throughout; (3) equilibrium with respect to flow of component 1 from one part of the system to another requires that the chemical potential of component 1 should be uniform throughout, and similarly for the other components. Therefore, specifying the values of $C + 2$ variables is sufficient to fix the intensive properties of the entire system. However, not all of these can be independent, for in each phase the chemical potentials are connected by the Gibbs-Duhem equation (Eq. (7–16)). There are P of these equations, since there is one in each phase; therefore out of the $C + 2$ variables the number which are independent — that is, the number of degrees of freedom — is given by

$$F = C + 2 - P$$

This is the Gibbs phase rule.

Alternatively, we may prefer to use instead of the chemical potentials the mole fractions or percentage composition. Though more convenient for many purposes, this choice makes the derivation of the phase rule more complicated, for it is not immediately obvious that fixing the temperature, pressure, and composition of one phase fixes those of all phases in equilibrium with it. It does have this effect, however, since fixing these variables in one phase fixes the chemical potentials in that phase and so, by the reasoning in the last paragraph, in all phases in equilibrium with it. Corresponding to the Gibbs-Duhem equation connecting the chemical potentials, we have among the mole fractions the relation

$$\sum_i x_i = 1$$

in each phase.

It has been tacitly assumed in this derivation that every component is present in every phase. However, the result is valid even if this is not true. If component 1, for example, is missing from some of the phases, μ_1 remains undefined in those phases. However, μ_1 is still an intensive variable having a uniform value throughout all phases in which component 1 occurs, and so the absence of this component in some phases does not alter the facts that the number of intensive variables is $C + 2$, and the number of Gibbs-Duhem equations connecting them is P.

The number 2 in the phase rule arises, as the derivation shows, from the fact that for most purposes temperature and pressure are the only variables, other than chemical potentials, that are relevant to the phase equilibrium. It is conceivable that the phase rule might be applied to an equilibrium which is affected by other variables as well, such as magnetic field strength,[**] and in this case 2 would be replaced by a larger number.

[**] An example of a phase equilibrium affected by magnetic field strength is that between the normal and superconducting states of a metal.

Of more interest in chemical work are cases in which experimental conditions prevent arbitrary varying of pressure or temperature. This situation occurs when condensed systems are studied in open containers; the pressure is then fixed by the atmosphere and is no longer considered a variable. The phase rule must then be modified to

$$F = C + 1 - P$$

Finally, it is common to study three-component condensed systems with both temperature and pressure fixed, only composition variables being investigated. For this situation the phase rule becomes

$$F = C - P$$

8–7. The Phase Rule for Reacting Systems

Two different but equivalent procedures are available for treating phase equilibria in reacting systems. In the original method of Gibbs the phase rule, in the unmodified form

$$F = C + 2 - P$$

is used, but a distinction is made between the number of different chemical species, or constituents (here denoted by C'), and the number of components (C). The latter is the smallest number of substances whose concentrations, when specified, suffice to fix the composition of the entire system. As Ricci[4] has pointed out, there is an element of reasoning in a circle involved in this approach. In the other treatment, apparently first proposed by De Donder[5] the number of constituents is used, and the number of auxiliary restrictions (R) resulting from the chemical reactions is calculated and subtracted from the formula for the variance. The rule then takes the form

$$F = C' + 2 - P - R$$

The latter approach, expanded to meet the objections of Ricci[4], is presented first. The student should be acquainted with both methods, since for various systems one or the other approach is the easier and more instructive.

In the derivation of the phase rule for nonreacting systems the assumption was made that the intensive variables were connected by only P equations, one in each phase. In reacting systems additional relations apply, and the number of degrees of freedom is correspondingly reduced.

Rules can be developed for handling these systems, but in some instances the application of them may be rather complex; good judgment and understanding of principles are needed for reliable results in these cases.

There are three main types of relations which may occur among the intensive variables in reacting systems and not in nonreacting systems, and which reduce the number of degrees of freedom. These are (1) chemical equilibria, (2) stoichiometric relations, and (3) electrical neutrality conditions in ionic solutions. These will be discussed separately.

To every *independent* chemical equilibrium corresponds an equation connecting the chemical potentials (Eq. (8–2b)). Each such equilibrium therefore reduces the variance by 1. The significance of the term *independent* in this usage is that no one of the reactions is equal to any linear combination of the others. As an illustration of this, consider the set of reactions

$$C + O_2 \leftrightharpoons CO_2$$

$$C + CO_2 \leftrightharpoons 2CO$$

$$H_2O + C \leftrightharpoons H_2 + CO$$

$$2H_2 + O_2 \leftrightharpoons 2H_2O$$

$$CO + H_2O \leftrightharpoons CO_2 + H_2$$

It is easily verified that subtracting the second equation from the third yields the fifth. The equilibria represented by these equations are therefore not independent. If the equilibrium condition (Eq. (8–2b)) for the second equation is subtracted from that for the third, that for the fifth results. Thus the fifth reaction imposes no restriction on the chemical potentials not already imposed by the second and third equations. If the fifth reaction is deleted from the set, the remaining four are still not independent, for the fourth can be obtained by multiplying the first three by 1, 1, and − 2, respectively, and adding. If the fourth one is also deleted (or if any two of the original five are removed), the remaining three are independent. For this system, therefore, $R = 3$. If there are two phases (solid carbon and gas),

$$F = 6 + 2 - 2 - 3 = 3$$

The particular variables chosen as the degrees of freedom may be, for example, temperature, pressure, and the partial pressure of hydrogen. Whether a given set of reactions is independent can usually be determined by inspection, but a systematic method is given in Appendix VII.

There may be instances in which it is difficult to decide whether the effect of a very slow reaction should be considered. If the system can come to equilibrium, except with respect to this reaction, in a time short compared to that required for the reaction to reach equilibrium, then the concept of a sort of partial equilibrium, in which the slow reaction is disregarded, is valid; whether it is useful will depend on the problem to which it is applied. Thus in a system containing ethanol, acetic acid, water, and ethyl acetate at, let us say, 30°C, it would be possible to establish vapor-liquid equilibrium and withdraw and analyze samples of the liquid and vapor while only a negligible amount of reaction occurs. Therefore it would be valid to treat this as a four-component system, unless we are interested in long-term equilibria. If the esterification (or its reverse) is hastened by a catalyst, this might no longer be true.

If some constituents are introduced into the system only by a chemical reaction which produces them *in situ*, and if two or more of these go exclusively into the same phase, their concentrations will be related by stoichiometric ratios. For example, consider the reaction

$$(NH_4)_2CO_3 \ (s) \leftrightarrows 2NH_3(g) + H_2O \ (g) + CO_2 \ (g)$$

If the three gases are introduced into the system only by this reaction, then in the gas phase the ratios $x_{NH_3}/x_{H_2O} = 2$ and $x_{NH_3}/x_{CO_2} = 2$ are both fixed by the stoichiometry of the reaction. (The ratio $x_{H_2O}/x_{CO_2} = 1$ is not independent of these.) These stoichiometric requirements reduce the number of degrees of freedom by 2. Since there is also a chemical equilibrium, there are three auxiliary restrictions altogether. If the system consists only of solid ammonium carbonate and its gaseous decomposition products, there are four constituents and two phases, and so the variance is

$$F = 4 + 2 - 2 - 3 = 1$$

If, however, extra carbon dioxide is introduced into this system, the ratio x_{NH_3}/x_{CO_2} is no longer fixed, and there is one more degree of freedom. As a second example, consider a system consisting of $CaCO_3$ (s), CaO (s), and CO_2 (g). Here there are three constituents, and one chemical equilibrium

$$CaCO_3 \ (s) \leftrightarrows CaO \ (s) + CO_2 \ (g)$$

If calcium oxide and carbon dioxide are introduced into the system only by this reaction, stoichiometry requires that

$$n_{CaO} = n_{CO_2}$$

However, these two products go into different phases, and so the requirement that they be present in equimolar amounts does not place any restriction on the concentrations in any phase. It does not matter, therefore, whether extra carbon dioxide is introduced or not; in neither case does any stoichiometric restriction on the concentrations occur. Since there are three constituents, three phases (the two solids are immiscible and so form separate phases), and one chemical equilibrium, the variance is

$$F = 3 + 2 - 3 - 1 = 1$$

An intermediate type of system, somewhat more difficult to consider, consists of a liquid A and its gaseous decomposition products, B and C, B being more soluble in liquid A than C is. As examples of such systems we might have, for A, B, and C, respectively, phosgene, chlorine, and carbon monoxide, or phosphorus pentachloride, phosphorus trichloride, and chlorine. Both these systems, at suitably chosen temperature and pressure, behave in the manner described. The stoichiometric requirement is that the numbers of moles of B and C must be equal, but their ratio in any phase would depend of the relative amounts of the phases. This can be seen by considering two extreme cases. If the amount of vapor is very small, the decomposition products must stay mostly in the liquid phase, and their mole fractions in that phase must be practically equal. The vapor phase will consist largely of C because of its higher volatility. On the other hand, if the amount of liquid is very small, the mole fractions of the decomposition products must be nearly equal in the vapor phase, while in the liquid phase B must be more concentrated that C because of its higher solubility. This shows that the ratio x_B/x_C is not stoichiometrically fixed in either phase; the only auxiliary restriction is the chemical equilibrium, and $R = 1$. Then

$$F = 3 + 2 - 2 - 1 = 2$$

In agreement with this, we can fix the temperature, and then vary the concentrations by varying the total volume for a fixed amount of material.

If the solubility of the gaseous decomposition products in the liquid phase is very slight, the variation of composition which can be brought about becomes very slight, and this situation merges in practice into the case in which all the decomposition products go into the gas phase, and no composition variation is possible.

In ionic solutions, still another requirement appears if we regard the ions as constituents — the requirement of electrical neutrality. For example, consider the system containing H_2O, HCl, H_3O^+, $AgCl$, Ag^+,

Cl^-, $AgCl_2^-$. Here we have seven constituents, the electroneutrality condition

$$n_{H_3O^+} + n_{Ag^+} = n_{Cl^-} + n_{AgCl_2^-}$$

and three independent chemical equilibria,

$$HCl + H_2O \rightleftharpoons H_3O^+ + Cl^-$$

$$AgCl\ (s) \rightleftharpoons Ag^+ + Cl^-$$

$$AgCl\ (s) + Cl^- \rightleftharpoons AgCl_2^-$$

This makes four extra restrictions, and so the number of degrees of freedom is

$$F = 7 + 2 - 3 - 4 = 2$$

The number of components, C, in the Gibbs treatment corresponds to $C' - R$ in this discussion. Alternatively, the number of components can be regarded as the minimum number of substances from which the system could be made up experimentally in any concentration permitted to it, using only reactions that occur in the system. This can be illustrated with the systems already considered. In the system consisting of carbon and its oxides, hydrogen, oxygen, and water, six constituents are present, and $C' - R = 6 - 3 = 3$. In agreement with this, we can make up this system by introducing carbon, hydrogen, and oxygen in the proper ratio, and permitting them to react according to the equations given. The ammonium carbonate system can be made up from solid ammonium carbonate alone, provided that the decomposition products are present in their stoichiometric ratios; there is, therefore, one component, and $C' - R = 4 - 3 = 1$. If, however, the concentrations are to be varied, one or more of the decomposition products will have to be added (or removed) directly, and the number of components will be two or three. The example used to illustrate ionic systems can be made up from H_2O, HCl, and AgCl; this makes three components, and $C' - R = 7 - 4 = 3$. For the calcium carbonate, phosgene, and phosphorus pentachloride systems this method is misleading, yielding one component instead of the correct number, two.

As a final example, for a system consisting of methane, ethane, propane, and butane, there are four components, unless catalysts are present to make reactions among these occur. This system could be made up from only two substances (carbon and hydrogen), but this would involve reactions which do not occur in the system. Of course, if catalysts are introduced into the system so that hydrocarbons could be formed from their elements and converted into each other, the number of components would be smaller than the number of constituents, and might be as low as two.

PROBLEMS

(1) By substituting suitable dn's for a chemical reaction into Eqs. (7–1) through (7–4), show that

$$A f = -\left(\frac{\partial U}{\partial \xi}\right)_{S,V} = -\left(\frac{\partial H}{\partial \xi}\right)_{S,p} = -\left(\frac{\partial A}{\partial \xi}\right)_{T,V} = -\left(\frac{\partial G}{\partial \xi}\right)_{T,p}$$

(2) Giauque and Archibald[6] measured the pressure of water vapor in equilibrium with magnesium hydroxide and magnesium oxide. The values found were 26.55 millibars at 463.1°K, 72.52 millibars at 485.0°K. Calculate the standard affinity at each of these temperatures for the reaction

$$Mg(OH)_2 \ (s) \ \rightarrow \ MgO \ (s) \ + \ H_2O \ (g)$$

using the bar as the standard pressure. Calculate Δh^0, assuming that it is constant over this range of temperature. Then determine Δs^0 at each of the temperatures. How would these values be changed by the choice of the atmosphere as the standard pressure?

(3) The standard affinity of formation of nitric oxide (NO) is -86.69 kjoules/mole·deg at 25°C, and its heat of formation is 90.37 kjoules/mole·deg. If it is decided that the reaction

$$\tfrac{1}{2}N_2 \ (g) + \tfrac{1}{2}O_2 \ (g) \ \rightarrow \ NO \ (g)$$

is suitable for practical production of NO only if K_p is at least 0.01, find the temperature necessary. Since the heat capacities of diatomic gases do not differ greatly, Δc_p may be considered zero.

(4) From the tables in Appendix II find $A f^0$, Δh^0, and $\Delta c_p{}^0$ at 25°C for the reaction

$$H_2O \ (l) \ \rightarrow \ H_2O \ (g)$$

Assuming that $\Delta c_p{}^0$ is constant, derive an expression for the standard affinity as a function of temperature. Finally, determine the temperature at which the standard affinity is zero, and compare this with the boiling point of water. (The final equation can be solved graphically or by trial and error; once an approximate value is found, Newton's method may be used to find a better one.)

(5) According to the ideal gas law, the molar concentration c, of a gas is equal to RT/p. Using this, derive a relation between K_p and K_c for a gas reaction. Show that

$$\frac{d(\ln K_c)}{dT} = \frac{\Delta u^0}{RT^2}$$

(6) Discuss the systems described below in terms of the phase rule, determining the variance of each.

(a) Hydrogen sulfide is introduced into a warm evacuated container, where it partially decomposes into hydrogen and solid sulfur.

(b) Sulfur dioxide is mixed with oxygen in the presence of a solid catalyst which promotes the reaction

$$SO_2 + \tfrac{1}{2}O_2 \rightarrow SO_3$$

The system is entirely gaseous, the catalyst not being considered part of it.

(c) N_2O_4 is introduced into a system in which it decomposes partially into NO_2, which in turn decomposes partially into NO and O_2. Only gases are present.

(d) A one-phase liquid system is made by mixing ethanol and formic acid. Since formic acid is a rather strong acid, it catalyzes the esterification. Hydronium and formate ions will naturally be present also.

(e) Pure water is introduced into an evacuated space. Solid $Ag(NH_3)_2Cl$ is then added. In solution the complex ion $Ag(NH_3)_2^+$ partially decomposes to simple silver ion and ammonia, and some $AgCl$ is precipitated. A vapor space is left in the container above the condensed phases.

REFERENCES

1. De Donder, Th., and Van Rysselberghe, P., "The Thermodynamic Theory of Affinity," p. 32, Stanford, Calif., Stanford University Press, 1936.
2. Hildebrand, J. H., and Scott, R. L., "The Solubility of Electrolytes," Frontispiece, New York, N.Y., Reinhold Publishing Corp., 1950.
3. Gibbs, J. W., Collected Works, pp. 63, 96, New York, N.Y., Longmans, Green, & Co., 1928.
4. Ricci, J. E., "The Phase Rule and Heterogeneous Equilibrium," pp. 10-12, New York, N.Y., D. Van Nostrand Co., Inc., 1951.
5. Van Rysselberghe, P., *J. Phys. Chem.*, **36**, 1733 (1932).
6. Giauque, W. F., and Archibald, R. C., *J. Am. Chem. Soc.*, **59**, 568 (1937).

chapter 9

Electrolytic Solutions
and Electrochemical Cells

THE THERMODYNAMIC TREATMENT of electrolytic solutions involves several complications not found in solutions of nonelectrolytes. These result from the impossibility of transferring ions of one type to or from a solution without simultaneously transferring other ions so as to maintain electrical neutrality. The difficulties are analogous to those that arise in treating heats of formation of ions.

The thermodynamics of electrolytic solutions underlies the theory of electrochemical, or galvanic, cells. The theoretical and practical importance of electrochemical cells is large and varied. They furnish the best means of determining the activities of electrolytes and sometimes of nonelectrolytes; practically all measurements of pH are made by them. Equilibrium constants for ionic reactions, including solubility products, acid and base ionization constants, and dissociation constants of complex ions, can be determined by electrochemical measurements. Several analytical and industrial procedures, such as potentiometric titrations, polarography, and electroplating, depend on special types of electrochemical cells. Finally, the familiar use of certain galvanic cells as portable sources of electrical energy should be mentioned.

The scope of this book must limit the treatment of electrochemistry to the basic principles of applying thermodynamics to electrolytic solutions and electrochemical cells.

9–1. Chemical Potentials, Activities, and Activity Coefficients of Electrolytes

If we attempt to define the chemical potential of sodium ion in an aqueous solution of sodium chloride by applying one of the relations of Eq. (7–5), so that, for example,

$$\mu_{Na^+} = \left(\frac{\partial G}{\partial n_{Na^+}}\right)_{T,p,n_{Cl^-},n_{H_2O}}$$

we see immediately that this has no operational meaning, since we cannot vary the number of moles of sodium ions while keeping the number of moles of chloride ions constant. However, if we add dn moles of sodium chloride to a constant amount of water, we can write formally

$$dG = \left(\frac{\partial G}{\partial n_{Na^+}}\right)_{T,p,n_{Cl^-},n_{H_2O}} dn_{Na^+} + \left(\frac{\partial G}{\partial n_{Cl^-}}\right)_{T,p,n_{Na^+},n_{H_2O}} dn_{Cl^-}$$

$$= (\mu_{Na^+} + \mu_{Cl^-}) \, dn$$

Now the quantity in parentheses is experimentally measurable, since the operation of adding sodium chloride to water, unlike that of adding only sodium ion to water, can actually be carried out. Similarly, if we add to a constant amount of water dn moles of chloride ion in the form of calcium chloride, we must also add $\frac{1}{2}dn$ moles of calcium ion, and we find that

$$dG = (\tfrac{1}{2}\mu_{Ca^{++}} + \mu_{Cl^-}) \, dn$$

Again the quantity in parentheses is measurable. As a third example, if we remove dn moles of silver ion from a solution by the reaction

$$\tfrac{1}{2}Cu + Ag^+ \rightarrow Cu^{++} + Ag$$

we simultaneously add $\frac{1}{2}dn$ moles of cupric ion. This leads to

$$dG = (\tfrac{1}{2}\mu_{Cu^{++}} - \mu_{Ag^+}) \, dn$$

In all these measurable combinations the corresponding combinations of charges are zero. This can be generalized as follows: Consider a process in which ions of type i, charge z_i, are added to a solution, which is kept electrically neutral by means of ions of type j, charge z_j. These ions of type j must be added if z_i and z_j are of opposite signs, removed if they are of the same sign. Then the combination

$$\frac{\mu_i}{z_i} - \frac{\mu_j}{z_j}$$

represents an electrically neutral combination of ions and is a physically measurable quantity. The charge is usually measured in terms of a unit positive charge equal in magnitude to the charge on an electron. The z's are then small positive or negative integers. If we are dealing with addition of a salt to a solution, an equivalent but slightly different formulation is commonly used. If the salt on dissolving dissociates so that one mole gives ν_+ moles of cation, of charge z_+, and ν_- moles of anion, of charge z_-, then

$$\nu_+ z_+ + \nu_- z_- = 0$$

and the measurable combination

$$\nu_+ \mu_+ + \nu_- \mu_-$$

is called the chemical potential of the salt.

The activities of ions, which are practically always referred to molality rather than mole fraction, present similar complications. We can write formally, in analogy with nonelectrolytes,

$$\mu_{Na^+} = \mu^0_{Na^+} + RT \ln a_{Na^+}$$

$$a_{Na^+} = \gamma_{Na^+} m_{Na^+}$$

and

$$\gamma_{Na^+} \rightarrow 1 \text{ as } m_{Na^+} \rightarrow 0$$

but these are not meaningful, since the quantity on which they are all based, the chemical potential of the sodium ion, has not been defined in terms of any experimentally possible operation. However, combining the equations for sodium ion and chloride ion, we find

$$\mu_{NaCl} = \mu_{NaCl} + RT \ln a_{Na^+} a_{Cl^-} \tag{9-1}$$

The product $a_{Na^+} a_{Cl^-}$ is called the activity of the salt; its square root is the *mean ionic activity*, generally designated by $a_\pm$. This gives as alternative forms of Eq. (9-1):

$$\mu_{NaCl} = \mu_{NaCl} + RT \ln a_{NaCl} = \mu^0_{NaCl} + RT \ln a^2_\pm$$

$$= \mu^0_{NaCl} + 2\,RT \ln a_\pm \tag{9-2}$$

Similarly we define the *mean ionic activity coefficient* and *mean ionic molality* by the relations

$$\gamma^2_\pm = \gamma_+\gamma_- \text{ and } m^2_\pm = m_+m_-$$

Then

$$a_\pm = \gamma_\pm m_\pm, \text{ and}$$

$$\mu_{NaCl} = \mu^0_{NaCl} + 2RT \ln m_\pm + 2RT \ln \gamma_\pm$$

Since

$$\gamma_\pm \to 1 \text{ as } m \to 0,$$

$$\mu^0_{NaCl} = \lim_{m\to0} (\mu_{NaCl} - 2RT \ln m_\pm) \tag{9-3}$$

Experimentally, it is found that this limit exists. If we had tried to treat NaCl like a nonelectrolyte, the right side of this equation would have been replaced by

$$\lim_{m\to0} (\mu_{NaCl} - RT \ln m)$$

This limit, however, does not exist. Thus the somewhat more complicated treatment given here is necessary. Notice that if NaCl is the only salt present, or at least the only source of either sodium or chloride ions, then $m_+ = m_- = m_\pm = m$. This simple relation does not hold with more complicated types of salts.

For a salt of the 1-2 type such as $CaCl_2$, we have

$$\mu_{CaCl_2} = \mu_{Ca^{++}} + 2\mu_{Cl^-} = \mu^0_{CaCl_2} + RT \ln a_{Ca^{++}} + 2RT \ln a_{Cl^-}$$

$$= \mu^0_{CaCl_2} + RT \ln a_{Ca^{++}}a_{Cl^-}{}^2 \tag{9-4}$$

If we now define the mean ionic molality as the cube root of $a_{Ca^{++}}a_{Cl^-}{}^2$, the last equation becomes

$$\mu_{CaCl_2} = \mu^0_{CaCl_2} + RT \ln a_\pm{}^3 = \mu^0_{CaCl_2} + 3RT \ln a_\pm \tag{9-5}$$

The mean ionic molality and mean ionic activity coefficient are defined analogously, so that

$$\gamma_\pm{}^3 = \gamma_{Ca^{++}} \gamma_{Cl^-}{}^{-2} \text{ and } m_\pm{}^3 = m_{Ca^{++}}m_{Cl^-}{}^2 \text{ and } a_\pm = \gamma_\pm m_\pm$$

Again, since

$$\gamma_\pm \to 1 \text{ as } m_\pm \to 0$$

$$\mu^0_{CaCl_2} = \lim_{m_\pm\to0} (\mu_{CaCl_2} - 3RT \ln m_\pm) \tag{9-6}$$

Notice, however, that in this case $m_{\pm}$ is not equal to m even when $CaCl_2$ is the only solute, for then

$$m_{Ca^{++}} = m, \quad m_{Cl^-} = 2m, \text{ and}$$

$$m_{\pm} = [m(2m)^2]^{1/3} = 4^{1/3}\, m$$

This leads to

$$\mu^0{}_{CaCl_2} = \lim_{m \to 0} (\mu_{CaCl_2} - 3RT \ln 4^{1/3}\, m)$$

$$= \lim_{m \to 0} (\mu_{CaCl_2} - 3RT \ln m) - RT \ln 4 \qquad (9\text{--}7)$$

Finally, this can be generalized for any type of salt. We have

$$\mu_{salt} = \nu_+\mu_+ + \nu_-\mu_-$$

$$= \mu_{salt} + RT \ln(a_+{}^{\nu+}a_-{}^{\nu-}) \qquad (9\text{--}8)$$

If we define

$$a_{\pm}{}^{(\nu_+ + \nu_-)} = a_+{}^{\nu+}a_-{}^{\nu-} = a_{salt} \qquad (9\text{--}9)$$

this becomes

$$\mu_{salt} = \mu^0{}_{salt} + (\nu_+ + \nu_-)RT \ln a_{\pm} = \mu^0{}_{salt} + RT \ln a_{salt} \quad (9\text{--}10)$$

We have also, as usual, $a_{\pm} = \gamma_{\pm}m_{\pm}$, where

$$\gamma_{\pm}{}^{(\nu_+ + \nu_-)} = \gamma_+{}^{\nu+}\gamma_-{}^{\nu-} \text{ and } m_{\pm}{}^{(\nu_+ + \nu_-)} = m_+{}^{\nu+}m_-{}^{\nu-} \qquad (9\text{--}11)$$

If only one salt is present, the mean ionic molality becomes

$$\left[(\nu_+m)^{\nu+} (\nu_-m)^{\nu-}\right]^{\frac{1}{\nu_+ + \nu_-}} = \left[\nu_+{}^{\nu+} \nu_-{}^{\nu-}\right]^{\frac{1}{\nu_+ + \nu_-}} m \qquad (9\text{--}12)$$

and

$$\mu^0{}_{salt} = \lim_{m \to 0} \left[\mu_{salt} - (\nu_+ + \nu_-)RT \ln m\right] - RT \ln(\nu_+{}^{\nu+} \nu_-{}^{\nu-}) \quad (9\text{--}13)$$

9-2. The Debye-Hückel Limiting Law

Two theories have been held regarding the behavior of strong electrolytes in very dilute solution. One of these, originating with Arrhenius, assumed that an equilibrium occurs between ions and unionized salt, and that the ions affect thermodynamic properties exactly as molecules do. Thus incomplete dissociation was given as the explanation for the fact that 0.1 m NaCl, for example, shows a freezing point depression greater than that of 0.1 m sucrose, but less than twice as great. For weak electrolytes this theory is substantially correct, but its application to strong electrolytes led to several difficulties. Because of these it was gradually replaced by a view that ionization of strong electrolytes is complete, but the ions, because of their mutual interactions, are not equivalent to molecules in their effects on thermodynamic properties. Most current theory is based on the mathematical treatment of this idea by Debye and Hückel[1] in 1923. The derivation of the Debye-Hückel limiting law — that is, a law giving the activity coefficients of ions in extremely dilute solution, will be outlined here.

Two main ideas are involved in the Debye-Hückel treatment. One is that, because of electrostatic interactions, the ions will so arrange themselves that among the nearest neighbors of any given positive ion negative ions will predominate, and vice versa. This statement refers to the time average of the ionic configurations, which of course are not static. The other is that the difference in chemical potential between an ion and a molecule is equal to the electrostatic work necessary to charge the molecule until it carries the same amount of electricity as the ion.

The exact nature of this charging process must be made clear. Two such processes have been used, and some confusion may arise if it is not made clear which is used here. In the Debye charging process all ions are considered discharged at the start, and all are charged simultaneously. Thus if the final charge on an ion is e_i, its charge at any stage is $e_i\xi$, where ξ is the degree of advancement of the charging process. This leads to the total electrostatic charging work, which must then be differentiated with respect to the number of ions to find the electrostatic contribution to the chemical potential. In Güntelberg's charging process, attention is fixed on a single ion, and only this one ion is charged from zero to its final charge, all other ions having their normal fixed charges during this process. This gives directly the electrostatic work per ion, which, when multiplied by Avogadro's number to convert it to a molar basis, can be identified with the electrostatic contribution to the chemical potential. These two charging processes can be shown to give the same result for any treatment in which the approximation of Eq. (9-14) is introduced[2]; without this approximation the problem is enormously complicated, and only limited progress has been made on it. In this treatment the Güntelberg charging process is used.

If the charge on an ion is $z\epsilon$, where $-\epsilon$ is the charge of an electron, then the electrostatic energy of the ion at a point where the potential is ψ is $z\epsilon\psi$. The concentration of ions of a given type at any given point will therefore be proportional to $e^{-z\epsilon\psi/kT}$; thus for positive ions

$$c_+ = c_+{}^0 e^{-z_+ \epsilon\psi/kT}$$

By considering the case where $z = 0$, we see that $c_+{}^0$ is the average, or bulk, concentration of positive ions. This must be expressed in ions per cubic centimeter. A similar equation holds for the negative ions. The charge density at any point is then

$$\rho = (z_+ c_+ + z_- c_-)\epsilon = (z_+ c_+{}^0 e^{-z_+ \epsilon\psi/kT} + z_- c_-{}^0 e^{-z_- \epsilon\psi/kT})\epsilon$$

Since this derivation is confined to very dilute solutions, in which ψ is small, we can expand the exponential, retaining only the constant and linear terms of the series. This gives

$$\rho = (z_+ c_+{}^0 + z_- c_-{}^0)\epsilon + (z_+{}^2 c_+{}^0 + z_-{}^2 c_-{}^0)\frac{\epsilon^2 \psi}{kT} \tag{9-14}$$

The first term is identically zero because of the electrical neutrality of the solution.

We now borrow from electrostatic theory an equation due to Poisson

$$\nabla^2 \psi = -\frac{4\pi\rho}{D}$$

where ∇^2, called the *Laplacian operator*, means

$$\frac{\partial^2}{\partial x^2} + \frac{\partial^2}{\partial y^2} + \frac{\partial^2}{\partial z^2}.$$

and D is the dielectric constant. Substituting gives

$$\nabla^2 \psi = (z_+{}^2 c_+{}^0 + z_-{}^2 c_-{}^0)\frac{4\pi\epsilon^2}{DkT}\,\psi = \kappa^2\,\psi$$

Notice that the coefficient on the right is necessarily positive, and so it is justifiable to designate it by κ^2.

If we now concentrate on the region around some specified positive ion, it is appropriate to change to polar coordinates centered at the specified positive ion, and assume spherical symmetry of the potential. The angular dependence of ψ then vanishes, and it can be shown that the equation becomes

$$\frac{1}{r^2}\left[\frac{\partial}{\partial r}\left(r^2\,\frac{\partial\psi}{\partial r}\right)\right] = \kappa^2\psi$$

The complete solution of this equation is

$$\psi = \frac{Ae^{-\kappa r}}{r} + \frac{Be^{\kappa r}}{r}$$

Since the second term approaches infinity with increasing r, its coefficient must be zero. The exponential in the remaining term is expanded, and again only two terms are retained. Thus

$$\psi = \frac{A}{r} - A\kappa \qquad (9\text{--}15)$$

This expression gives the potential in the immediate neighborhood of a given ion. For very small distances from the ion the potential due to the ion itself must dominate over that due to other ions; its value is $z_+\epsilon/rD$. This is clearly identifiable with the first term in Eq. (9–15), and so we find that $A = z_+\epsilon/D$. The other term, $-A\kappa = -z_+\epsilon\kappa/D$, then gives the potential due to neighboring ions.

Finally, the deviation of the activity coefficient from unity is ascribed to the work needed in the imaginary process of charging the ion from a discharged state to the actual state. If a small amount of electricity $\epsilon\,dz_+$ (during this process we must allow z_+ to take nonintegral values) is brought to the ion, the work done is

$$dW = \psi\epsilon\,dz_+ = -A\kappa\epsilon\,dz_+ = -\frac{\epsilon^2\kappa}{D}z_+\,dz_+$$

Integrating this from 0 to the final charge on the ion, we find

$$W = kT\ln\gamma_+ = -\frac{\epsilon^2\kappa}{D}\int_0^{z_+}z_+\,dz_+ = -\frac{\epsilon^2\kappa z_+^2}{2D}$$

We use kT, instead of RT, because the work on only a single ion, not a mole of ions, is involved. Thus we finally arrive at an expression for the activity coefficient. However, because the units chosen for the derivation are not convenient in applications, it is usually expressed differently. The *ionic strength* is defined as

$$I \equiv \tfrac{1}{2}(z_+^2 C_+ + z_-^2 C_-)$$

where C_+ is the concentration of the positive ion in moles per liter. Thus $C_+ = 1000c_+^0/N_a$. Using this value gives

$$\ln \gamma_+ = -\left(\frac{\pi N_a}{500\, DkT}\right)^{\frac{1}{2}} \frac{\epsilon^3}{DkT} I^{\frac{1}{2}} z_+^2$$

If we convert to common logarithms by dividing both sides by ln 10, and insert numerical values, using the dielectric constant for water, we find

$$\log \gamma_+ = -Cz_+^2 I^{\frac{1}{2}}$$

where C has the following values[3]:

20°C	0.5046
25°C	0.5091
30°C	0.5139

A similar equation applies to negative ions.

It will be noticed that this theory gives the activity coefficient of ions of a single type — a quantity which, according to Section 9–1, is physically meaningless. The reason is that we have considered a quantity which cannot be measured experimentally — the work of charging of a single ion. However, since this theory cannot be subjected to experimental test except when it is applied to neutral combinations of ions, it remains true that there is no operational definition of single ion activities.

To apply the theory to mean ionic activity coefficients, we find from Eq. (9–9),

$$\log \gamma_\pm = \frac{\nu_+ \log \nu_+ + \nu_- \log \nu_-}{\nu_+ + \nu_-} = -CI^{\frac{1}{2}}\left(\frac{\nu_+ z_+^2 + \nu_- z_-^2}{\nu_+ + \nu_-}\right)$$

$$= -CI^{\frac{1}{2}} z_+ z_- \left(\frac{\nu_+ z_+^2 + \nu_- z_-^2}{\nu_+ z_+ z_- + \nu_- z_+ z_-}\right)$$

By making use of the fact that $\nu_+ z_+ = -\nu_- z_-$, we find that the quantity in parentheses reduces to -1. Therefore

$$\log \gamma_\pm = CI^{\frac{1}{2}} z_+ z_- \tag{9–16}$$

Notice that this is always negative, since the z's are necessarily of opposite sign.

For 1–1 type electrolytes, the ionic strength becomes simply the molarity (or the molality, since they do not differ appreciably in dilute aqueous solution). For other electrolytes, it is given by

$$I = \tfrac{1}{2}(C_+z_+{}^2 + C_-z_-{}^2) = \tfrac{1}{2}m(\nu_+z_+{}^2 + \nu_-z_-{}^2) \qquad (9\text{--}17)$$

For mixed electrolytes the theory still applies; the ionic strength in this case is defined by

$$I = \tfrac{1}{2}\sum C_i z_i{}^2 \qquad (9\text{--}18)$$

the summation being over all types of positive and negative ions in the solution.

The Debye-Hückel limiting law is reasonably accurate only at extreme dilution, especially for ions of high charge. Even for 1–1 electrolytes the deviations are likely to be appreciable at any ionic strength above about 0.001.

9–3. Activities of Electrolytes by the Gibbs–Duhem Equation

The activity of the solvent in an electrolytic solution can be determined by any of the methods described for nonelectrolytes. The freezing point and vapor pressure methods are most often used. Osmotic measurements have been made with electrolytes, but they are too difficult to be practical for general use in determining activities. For dilute solutions of a nonvolatile solute a technique for measuring osmotic pressure by using the surface of the solution itself as the semipermeable membrane has been developed. Another method often used for electrolytes is the isopiestic method, although this can also be used for nonelectrolytic solutions if the solute is nonvolatile and the solvent volatile. This method actually merely compares the solvent activity of the unknown solution with that of a reference solution, which must have the same solvent and a nonvolatile solute. The two solutions, each in its own open container, are placed inside a larger closed container and kept at constant temperature. If the solvent activities are not initially equal, solvent will distill from the solution in which its activity is higher into the other one. When equilibrium is attained, the two solutions are analyzed. Since the activities are equal, the activity of the unknown solution at the equilibrium concentration is determined if that of the reference solution is known.

Once the solvent activity is known as a function of concentration, that of the solute can be found by integrating the Gibbs–Duhem equation. Application of this method to electrolytes, however, is complicated by the custom of using practical, instead of rational, activities; moreover, $\ln \gamma_1$ in extremely dilute solutions is proportional to the 3/2 power of the concentration instead of the square, and so the integrand of Eq. (7–62) does not approach a finite limit at infinite dilution.

An expression will be derived for facilitating this integration in the case of a solution having only one solvent and one solute. In what follows the subscript 1 will denote the solvent, $+$ the cation, and $-$ the anion; and $\nu \equiv \nu_+ + \nu_-$. The Gibbs–Duhem equation becomes

$$n_1 \, d\mu_1 + n_+ \, d\mu_+ + n_- \, d\mu_- = 0$$

We now introduce n_k, the number of moles of solvent in a kilogram of solvent, and the molality m, the number of moles of solute in a kilogram of solvent. The equation then becomes

$$n_k \, d\mu_1 + m_+ \, d\mu_+ + m_- \, d\mu_- = n_k \, d\mu_1 + m(\nu_+ \, d\mu + \nu_- \, d\mu_-) = 0$$

Introducing the activities leads to

$$n_k \, d(\ln a_1) + m \, [\nu_+ \, d(\ln a_+) + \nu_- \, d(\ln a_-)] = 0$$

or

$$n_k \, d(\ln a_1) + m\nu \, d(\ln a_\pm) = 0$$

This may be applied to activities on any scale, since changing the scale changes $\ln a$ by a constant additive amount and so does not affect $d(\ln a)$. On introducing the activity coefficients, however, we must choose the scale; taking the practical scale for solute activities, we find

$$n_k \, d(\ln a_1) + m\nu \, [d(\ln \gamma_\pm) + d(\ln m)] = 0$$

since $\ln m$ and $\ln m_\pm$ differ only by a constant. Thus

$$d(\ln \gamma_\pm) = -\frac{n_k}{m\nu} \, d(\ln a_1) - d(\ln m)$$

$$= -\left[\frac{n_k}{m\nu} \frac{d(\ln x_1)}{dm} + \frac{1}{m} + \frac{n_k}{m\nu} \frac{d(\ln \gamma_1)}{dm}\right] dm$$

The first two terms can be simplified as follows. Since

$$x_1 = \frac{n_k}{n_k + m\nu} \quad \text{and} \quad \frac{d(\ln x_1)}{dm} = -\frac{\nu}{n_k + m\nu}$$

the sum of the first two terms becomes

$$-\frac{n_k}{m(n_k + m\nu)} + \frac{1}{m} = \frac{\nu}{n_k + m\nu} = -\frac{d(\ln x_1)}{dm}$$

Integration of these two terms can now be carried out, using the fact that $\ln x_1 = 0$ when $m = 0$. This gives

$$\ln \gamma_\pm = \ln x_1 - \int_0^m \frac{n_k}{m\nu} \frac{d(\ln \gamma_1)}{dm} \, dm$$

Using integration by parts, we find

$$\int_0^m \frac{n_k}{m\nu} \frac{d(\ln \gamma_1)}{dm} \, dm = \frac{n_k}{m\nu} \ln \gamma_1 \Big]_{m=0}^m + \int_0^m \frac{n_k}{m^2\nu} \ln \gamma_1 \, dm \qquad (9\text{-}19)$$

In extremely dilute solutions, $\ln \gamma_\pm = -Bm^{\frac{1}{2}}$, where B is found by comparison with Eqs. (9-16) and (9-17) to be equal to

$$B = -Cz_+z_-\left(\frac{\nu_+z_+{}^2 + \nu_-z_-{}^2}{2}\right)^{\frac{1}{2}} \ln 10 \qquad (9\text{-}20)$$

By substituting this into the Gibbs-Duhem equation, we can show that

$$\ln \gamma_1 = \frac{B}{3n_k} m^{3/2} + \dots \qquad (9\text{-}21)$$

The details are left as an exercise (see Problem 3). This shows that the integrated part of Eq. (9-19) vanishes at the lower limit despite the m in the denominator. Therefore

$$\ln \gamma_\pm = \ln x_1 - \frac{n_k}{m\nu} \ln \gamma_1 - \int_0^m \frac{n_k}{\nu} \frac{\ln \gamma_1}{m^2} \, dm \qquad (9\text{-}22)$$

The extra complexity of this equation, as compared with Eq. (7-62), results from the use of the practical activity scale. Near the lower limit the integrand is proportional to $m^{-\frac{1}{2}}$, and so it does not approach a finite limit. However, we see from Eq. (9-21) that

$$\frac{n_k}{\nu m^2} \ln \gamma_1 - \frac{B}{3} m^{-\frac{1}{2}}$$

contains no term in $m^{-\frac{1}{2}}$; if higher terms are retained, it can be shown that no negative powers of m appear, and so it remains finite at $m = 0$. Integrating the second part of this expression alone gives $-\frac{2}{3}Bm^{\frac{1}{2}}$; adding this quantity outside the integral sign permits us to rewrite Eq. (9–22) in the form

$$\ln \gamma_{\pm} = \ln x_1 - \frac{n_k}{m\nu} \ln \gamma_1 - \frac{2}{3} Bm^{\frac{1}{2}} - \int_0^m \left(\frac{n_k}{\nu} \frac{\ln \gamma_1}{m^2} - \frac{B}{3} m^{-\frac{1}{2}} \right) dm \quad (9\text{–}23)$$

In this form the integrand remains finite at all concentrations, and graphical integration presents no special difficulty.

9–4. Galvanic Cells

A *galvanic**cell is an arrangement whereby a chemical reaction can be made to result directly in the performance of electrical work, not through the intermediary of heat. Such a device is shown schematically in Figure 20. Let us consider briefly the sources of electromotive force in this device.

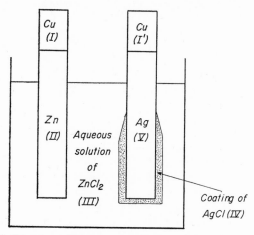

FIGURE 20. SCHEMATIC REPRESENTATION OF A TYPICAL GALVANIC CELL WITHOUT LIQUID JUNCTION.

Copper and zinc, like other metals, consist of a lattice of kernels (nuclei plus firmly attached electrons) with loose electrons ("valence electrons") free to migrate throughout the metal, and also to cross the interface into

*Named for Luigi Galvani (1737-1798), whose experiments on metallic wires inserted into the nerves and muscles of frogs were among the most important examples of early research on electricity.

other metals. If a neutral piece of copper is placed in contact with a neutral piece of zinc, there will, in general, be a tendency for a net flow of electrons across the interface. This produces a potential difference which soon brings the flow to a stop. Under this equilibrium condition a potential difference

$$\psi_{I,II} = \psi_I - \psi_{II}$$

may be considered as existing across the interface. This potential difference, however, cannot be measured, for any attempt to connect any sort of potentiometer to the two metals necessitates closing the circuit through one or more additional interfaces. The potential differences across these balance the one to be measured, so that no electromotive force exists in the circuit. (An emf exists if the interfaces are at different temperatures, as in a thermocouple.)

At the next interface, between zinc and solution, a potential difference will arise from a tendency of the zinc to go into solution in the form of ions (or the reverse). This may be formulated in either of two equivalent ways:

$$Zn^{++}(II) \rightarrow Zn^{++}(III)$$

or

$$Zn(II) \rightarrow Zn^{++}(III) + 2\epsilon^-(II)$$

where ϵ^- represents an electron. Either formulation shows that the metallic zinc phase will be left negative if the reaction occurs in the direction indicated. Thus we ascribe to this pair of phases another unmeasurable potential difference,

$$\psi_{II,III} = \psi_{II} - \psi_{III}$$

At the next two interfaces, reactions which may occur are

$$Cl^-(IV) \rightarrow Cl^-(III)$$

and

$$Ag^+(IV) \rightarrow Ag^+(V)$$

or

$$Ag^+(IV) + \epsilon^-(V) \rightarrow Ag(V)$$

These two reactions, if they proceed in the indicated directions, will tend to make the metallic silver phase positive. Thus we have another unmeasurable potential difference,

$$\psi_{III,V} = \psi_{III} - \psi_V$$

We could, of course, include potential differences $\psi_{III,IV}$ and $\psi_{IV,V}$ also. Finally, the considerations at the silver-copper interface are analogous to those at the zinc-copper interface, leading to a term

$$\psi_{V,I'} = \psi_V - \psi_{I'}$$

Adding all these potential differences, we find

$$\psi_{I,I'} = \psi_I - \psi_{I'} = \psi_{I,II} + \psi_{II,III} + \psi_{III,V} + \psi_{V,I'} \qquad (9\text{-}24)$$

At last we have reached a potential difference that can be measured; since phases I and I′ are of the same material, we can connect them without introducing additional interfaces. That the quantities on the right side of Eq. (9-24) cannot be measured was pointed out by Gibbs[4]; Guggenheim[5] carries this idea even further, asserting that these quantities not only cannot be measured, but have not even been defined in any physically meaningful manner. Guggenheim's view has been rejected by some other specialists in this field,[6] and no attempt to evaluate the controversy will be made here.

The difference $\psi_I - \psi_{I'}$ for this cell is of the order of magnitude of -1 volt, depending on temperature and concentration. This quantity, with the sign changed, will be called the *electromotive force* (emf) of the cell. Several other names have been used or suggested for one or the other of these quantities, and much confusion has arisen; the name used here appears to be generally confined to this sense.

A different viewpoint will be used in deriving the relation between emf and the thermodynamic properties of the reactions. Consider the two copper portions of the cell connected by a wire (the "outside circuit") which may include a device, such as a motor, by which an electric current can be made to do work. The reactions which occur when this cell produces a current may be summarized as follows: At the zinc-solution interface

$$Zn(II) \rightarrow Zn^{++}(III) + 2\epsilon^-(II)$$

These electrons move from the zinc to the copper (I), through the outside circuit to copper (I′) and thence to the silver. (Of course, this statement does not imply that the same two electrons make the entire journey;

since electrons have no individuality, this would be meaningless.) The two extra electrons do not remain in the silver, but react with silver chloride thus:

$$2\epsilon^-(V) + 2AgCl(IV) \rightarrow 2Ag(V) + 2Cl^-(III)$$

The net change, then, is

$$Zn(II) + 2AgCl(IV) \rightarrow Zn^{++}(III) + 2Cl^-(III) + 2Ag(V)$$

This we will call the *cell reaction*. When this reaction advances by one unit, two moles of electrons are transferred through the outside circuit.

Now it was shown in Section 8–1 that when a reaction advances by a small amount $d\xi$ in a closed system, the energy change is given by

$$dU = T\ dS - p\ dV - Af\ d\xi$$

From the viewpoint of the first law, however, the energy change can also be written

$$dU = dQ + dW = dQ - p\ dV + dW'$$

where dW' is the work, other than pressure-volume work, done on the system — in this case, the electrical work. Comparison shows that

$$T\ dS - Af\ d\xi = dQ + dW'$$

or

$$-dW' = Af\ d\xi - (T\ dS - dQ)$$

Since the quantity in parentheses must be zero or positive, we find that

$$-dW' \leqslant Af\ d\xi$$

that is, the electrical work done *by* the system per unit of advancement cannot exceed the affinity of the cell reaction, and equals it only for a reversible process.

Now suppose that as the reaction advances by one unit, z moles of electrons pass through the outside circuit from I to I'; for the cell considered here, $z = 2$. The amount of electricity carried by 1 mole of electrons is the quantity known as the *Faraday*; its value is 96,488 coulombs/mole, and it will be denoted by F. If the emf of the cell is E, the maximum amount of work it can perform when the reaction advances by $d\xi$ is $zFE\ d\xi$—that is, the product of the amount of electricity transported by the electromotive force. Therefore,

$$zFE \leqslant Af$$

the equality sign applying only at equilibrium. In most of the remainder of this chapter, only the equilibrium value will be considered.

Since, for the cell of Figure 20, the affinity of the reaction is given by

$$Af = Af^0 - RT \ln a_{Zn^{++}}a_{Cl^-}{}^2$$

the emf is given by

$$E = E^0 - \frac{RT}{2F} \ln a_{Zn^{++}}a_{Cl^-}{}^2 \tag{9-25}$$

where E^0, the *standard emf of the cell*, is defined in general by Af^0/zF, or $Af^0/2F$ in this case.

This equation is generally known as the *Nernst equation*, though Nernst's statement of it was much less rigorous than most modern formulations. If R is expressed in joules/mole·degree and F in coulombs/mole, E will be in volts. The factor F can be omitted from the equation if R is expressed as 8.617×10^{-5} volt·Faraday/degree.

The experimental determination of E is usually carried out by balancing the emf of the cell against a known potential drop supplied by a potentiometer. In this way the measurement is made with no current flowing, and the equilibrium value of the emf is obtained. (Actually, we cannot know that the current is zero, but only that it is less than the galvanometer can detect.) A similar result can be obtained by using a vacuum-tube voltmeter, since the input resistance of these instruments can be made so high that the current they draw is scarcely detectable.

The determination of the standard emf ordinarily involves extrapolation of a suitable function of E and the concentration to zero concentration. Thus from Eq. (9–25)

$$E = E^0 - \frac{3RT}{2F} \ln a_{\pm} = E^0 - \frac{3RT}{2F} \ln m_{\pm} - \frac{3RT}{2F} \ln \gamma_{\pm}$$

or

$$E + \frac{3RT}{2F} \ln m + \frac{RT}{2F} \ln 4 = E^0 - \frac{3RT}{2F} \ln \gamma_{\pm} \tag{9-26}$$

The last term on the right approaches zero with m, and so

$$E^0 = \lim_{m \to 0} \left(E + \frac{3RT}{2F} \ln m \right) + \frac{RT}{2F} \ln 4 \tag{9-27}$$

In the very low concentration region, where the Debye-Hückel limiting law applies, the right side of Eq. (9–26) becomes

$$E^0 + bm^{\frac{1}{2}}$$

where b is constant at constant temperature and pressure. Therefore, a graph of $E + \dfrac{3RT}{2F} \ln m$ plotted against $m^{\frac{1}{2}}$ is a straight line, and can be extrapolated to $m = 0$ accurately.

In practice, however, the range of validity of the Debye-Hückel limiting law is so low that the graph shows appreciable curvature even at the lowest experimentally practical concentrations. A more refined method of extrapolation, apparently first used extensively by Hitchcock,[7] can resolve this difficulty. The mean ionic activity coefficient can be expressed with improved accuracy by adding an empirical linear term to the Debye-Hückel limiting law, thus:

$$\ln \gamma_{\pm} = -Bm^{\frac{1}{2}} + B'm \qquad (9\text{--}28)$$

where B is defined as in Eq. (9–20), and B' is an empirical constant. Introducing this into Eq. (9–26) gives

$$E + \frac{3RT}{2F}(\ln m - Bm^{\frac{1}{2}}) + \frac{RT}{2F} \ln 4 = E^0 - \frac{3RT}{2F}B'm \qquad (9\text{--}29)$$

Therefore, plotting the quantity on the left side of this equation against m will give a straight line, which can be extrapolated to E^0 at $m = 0$. Because Eq. (9–28) expresses the mean ionic activity coefficients at moderate concentrations much more accurately than the Debye-Hückel limiting law, the range of linearity of this graph extends to relatively high concentrations and so a more reliable extrapolation is possible.

An additional point should be mentioned in connection with this cell. Since silver chloride is not completely insoluble, silver ions will go into solution, diffuse to the zinc electrode, and there be reduced to silver by chemical reaction with the zinc. This process is too slow to be of importance in this cell; however, it may make some analogous cells, in which a more soluble salt is involved, entirely impractical. For instance, replacement of the zinc and silver chlorides in this cell by the corresponding chlorates would give a cell in which deposition of silver on the zinc electrode would be serious.

9–5. Thermodynamic Properties from Cells Without Liquid Junctions

The cell described in the preceding section has no interface at which two solutions of different composition are in contact; for this reason it is called a cell without liquid junction. This is generally the most desirable type of cell for measuring thermodynamic properties; although cells with liquid junction have yielded important results, they are always subject to uncertainty because there is no satisfactory method of treating the effect of the liquid junction.

Before discussing the properties that can be determined from cells without liquid junction, we need a symbolism for depicting these cells. The cell described in Section 9–4 will be indicated by

$$\text{Cu, Zn} \mid \text{ZnCl}_2 \text{ (aq)} \mid \text{AgCl, Ag, Cu}$$

the vertical lines indicating solid-solution interfaces. The copper terminals could be replaced by terminals of any other metal; they are often omitted from the symbol. Additional information, such as the molality of the ZnCl_2 solution, may be included. The emf of the cell is positive if, as is true in this case, the left-hand electrode supplies electrons to the outside circuit when the cell acts as a source of energy; that is, the left-hand electrode is the negative one. Other criteria, equivalent to this one, may be used instead; thus the emf is positive if

(1) The chemical reaction at the left-hand electrode is an oxidation; or
(2) During the discharge of the cell, cations move through the cell from left to right, or anions from right to left, or both.

(a) *Determination of Activities.* The determination of activities by means of emf measurements is straightforward, provided a suitable cell can be devised. Once E^0 has been found from an equation analogous to Eq.(9–27) or (9–29), it is used, together with measured emf values, in an equation such as Eq. (9–26) to calculate $a_\pm$ and $\gamma_\pm$. Thus the cell described above may be used to measure the activity of zinc chloride in aqueous solution.

The activities of the acids HCl, HBr, and HI can be found from cells of the type

$$\text{Cu, Pt, H}_2 \text{ (g)} \mid \text{HX (aq)} \mid \text{AgX, Ag, Cu}$$

In this cell the platinum is coated with colloidal platinum, which catalyzes the oxidation reaction by which the left-hand electrode furnishes electrons to the outside circuit:

$$\tfrac{1}{2}\text{H}_2 \text{ (g)} \rightarrow \text{H}^+ + \epsilon^-$$

The reduction at the other electrode is

$$\epsilon^- + \text{AgX}^- \rightarrow \text{Ag} + \text{X}^-$$

and the over-all change is

$$\tfrac{1}{2}\text{H}_2 + \text{AgX} \rightarrow \text{Ag} + \text{H}^+ + \text{X}^-$$

(For HI the emf is negative, except at low concentrations; this means that the actual reaction is the reverse of this.) Thus $z = 1$, and

$$Af = Af^0 - RT \ln (a_{H^+}a_{X^-}/a_{H_2}^{\frac{1}{2}})$$

The emf is, therefore,

$$E = E^0 - \frac{RT}{F} \ln \frac{a_{\pm}^2}{a_{H_2}^{\frac{1}{2}}} \tag{9-30}$$

$$= E^0 + \frac{RT}{2F} \ln a_{H_2} - \frac{2RT}{F}(\ln \gamma_{\pm} + \ln m) \tag{9-31}$$

and so

$$E^0 = \lim_{m \to 0} \left(E - \frac{RT}{F} \ln a_{H_2} + \frac{2RT}{F} \ln m \right) \tag{9-32}$$

The activity of hydrogen gas can be evaluated without electrochemical measurements; in fact, at ordinary atmospheric pressure it is sufficiently accurate to identify it with the numerical measure of the partial pressure of hydrogen. Thus we can determine E^0 from Eq. (9-32), and then use this in Eq. (9-31) to calculate activity coefficients at any desired concentration.

The activity of sulfuric acid has been determined from measurements on the cell

$$\text{Pt, H}_2 \mid \text{H}_2\text{SO}_4 \text{ (aq)} \mid \text{PbSO}_4, \text{PbO}_2, \text{Pt}$$

The cell reaction is

$$\text{H}_2 + \text{PbO}_2 \text{ (s)} + 2\text{H}^+ \text{ (aq)} + \text{SO}_4^= \text{ (aq)} \to \text{PbSO}_4 \text{ (s)} + 2\text{H}_2\text{O}$$

and, if the activity of hydrogen is unity, the emf is

$$E = E^0 + \frac{RT}{2F} [\ln (m_{H^+}^2 m_{SO_4^=}) + \ln (\gamma_{H^+}^2 \gamma_{SO_4^=}) - \ln a_{H_2O}^2]$$

$$= E^0 + \frac{RT}{2F} (3 \ln m_{\pm} + 3 \ln \gamma_{\pm} - 2 \ln a_{H_2O}) \tag{9-33}$$

Since $m_{\pm} = 4^{\frac{1}{3}}m$, and $\gamma_{\pm}$ and a_{H_2O} both approach 1 at infinite dilution,

$$E^0 = \lim_{m \to 0} \left(E - \frac{3RT}{2F} \ln m \right) - \frac{RT}{2F} \ln 4$$

The data needed for evaluating E^0 can be obtained from this cell, but if activities of sulfuric acid are to be calculated, information on the activity of water is needed. This can be determined by the vapor-pressure method, for example. Alternatively, the cell

$$\text{Pt, H}_2 \mid \text{H}_2\text{SO}_4 \text{ (aq)} \mid \text{Hg}_2\text{SO}_4, \text{Hg, Pt}$$

may be used; its emf is given by

$$E = E^0 + \frac{3RT}{2F} \ln a_{\pm} \qquad (9\text{--}34)$$

which does not involve the activity of water. Comparison of Eqs. (9-33) and (9-34) can then be used as an electrochemical method of determining the activity of water in aqueous sulfuric acid. Finally, note that if the reactions for these cells are written in terms of H_3O^+ instead of H^+, the activity of water will appear to the fourth power in Eq. (9-33), and to the second in Eq. (9-34). This does not affect the determination of E^0, but it does show that the mean ionic activity depends on the formulas assigned to the ions. This effect becomes negligible at high dilutions.

As a final example of ionic activity determination, the double cell

$$\text{Ag, AgCl} \mid \text{KCl (aq, } m=m_1) \mid \text{K (in Hg)} \mid \text{KCl (aq, } m=m_2) \mid \text{AgCl, Ag}$$

has been used to determine the activity of KCl in aqueous solution. In this cell the two aqueous phases are in contact with the amalgam but not with each other. The reaction in the left half of the cell is

$$\text{Ag (s)} + \text{Cl}^- \text{ (aq, } m=m_1) + \text{K}^+ \text{ (aq, } m=m_1) \rightarrow \text{AgCl (s)} + \text{K (in Hg)}$$

with

$$E_{\text{left}} = E^0 - \frac{RT}{F} \ln \frac{a_\text{K}}{a_{\text{Cl}^-}(1)a_{\text{K}^+}(1)}$$

where $a_{\text{K}^+}(1)$ means the activity of potassium ion in the solution of molality m_1, and a_K is the activity of potassium in the amalgam. For the right half we find an analogous equation, but reversed in sign. Summing the two gives for the entire cell

$$E = \frac{2RT}{F} \ln \frac{a_{\pm}(1)}{a_{\pm}(2)} = \frac{2RT}{F} \left[\ln a_{\pm}(1) - \ln m_2 - \ln \gamma_{\pm}(2) \right]$$

If m_1 is kept fixed while m_2 is varied, then

$$\ln a_{\pm}(1) = \lim_{m_2 \to 0} \left(\frac{FE}{2RT} + \ln m_2 \right) \qquad (9\text{--}35)$$

Note that the activity of potassium in the amalgam cancels out,** as does E^0. A cell, such as this one, in which the emf depends only on a difference of concentration is called a *concentration cell*.

Activities of amalgamated metals can be found by using a concentration cell in which two amalgams of different concentrations are the electrodes. Thus we consider the cell

$$\text{Pt, Zn (in Hg; } a_{Zn} = a_1) \mid \text{ZnSO}_4 \text{ (aq)} \mid \text{Zn (in Hg; } a_{Zn} = a_2\text{), Pt}$$

The reactions at the electrodes (for positive emf) are

$$\text{left:} \quad \text{Zn } (a_1) \rightarrow \text{Zn}^{++} \text{ (aq)} + 2\epsilon^-$$

$$\text{right:} \quad \text{Zn}^{++} \text{ (aq)} + 2\epsilon^- \rightarrow \text{Zn } (a_2)$$

Adding these, we find that the net effect is merely the transfer of zinc from the left amalgam to the right one, two electrons going through the outside circuit for each atom of zinc transferred. The affinity for this process is

$$Af = RT \ln \frac{a_1}{a_2}$$

and so the emf is

$$E = \frac{RT}{2F} \ln \frac{a_1}{a_2} = \frac{RT}{2F} (\ln a_1 - \ln m_2 - \ln \gamma_2)$$

Therefore

$$\ln a_1 = \lim_{m_2 \to 0} \left(\frac{2FE}{RT} + \ln m_2 \right) \tag{9-36}$$

Since the solute is a nonelectrolyte, extrapolation is carried out by plotting $2FE/RT - \ln m_2$ against m_2 rather than $m_2^{\frac{1}{2}}$.

(b) *Ionic Equilibrium Constants.* Two examples will be given of the use of cells without liquid junctions to measure equilibrium constants for ionic reactions. The first of these is the ionization of water,

$$\text{H}_2\text{O} \rightarrow \text{H}^+ + \text{OH}^-$$

for which the equilibrium constant is

$$K_w = \frac{a_{\text{H}^+} a_{\text{OH}^-}}{a_{\text{H}_2\text{O}}} \tag{9-37}$$

** The amalgam could be replaced by a membrane permeable only to potassium ions (or only to cations), if one could be found. Some of the recently developed *permselective* membranes almost meet this requirement.

Consider the two cells

I.   Pt, H_2 | HCl (aq) | AgCl, Ag, Pt

and

II.   Pt, H_2 | aq soln of NaOH (m_1) and NaCl (m_2) | AgCl, Ag, Pt

If the hydrogen gas is kept at unit activity, or the results corrected for any deviation of the hydrogen activity from unity, the emf of the first cell is

$$E_I = E_I{}^0 - \frac{RT}{F} \ln \left(a_{H^+} a_{Cl^-}\right) \tag{9-38}$$

The value of $E_I{}^0$ is determined by the extrapolation of

$$\left(E_I + \frac{2RT}{F} \ln m_{HCl}\right)$$

to infinite dilution. Now the solution in cell II contains both the essential ions present in the solution in cell I; namely H^+ and Cl^-. Since the electrodes are also the same, we can use the same equation for the emf. Thus

$$E_{II} = E_I{}^0 - \frac{RT}{F} \ln \left(a_{H^+} a_{Cl^-}\right) = E_I{}^0 - \frac{RT}{F} \ln \frac{K_w a_{H_2O} a_{Cl^-}}{a_{OH^-}}$$

$$= E_I{}^0 - \frac{RT}{F} \left(\ln K_w + \ln \frac{m_{Cl^-}}{m_{OH^-}} + \ln \frac{a_{H_2O} \gamma_{Cl^-}}{\gamma_{OH^-}}\right) \tag{9-39}$$

Identifying m_{OH^-} and m_{Cl^-} with m_1 and m_2, respectively, we find

$$\ln K_w = \lim_{\substack{m_1 \to 0 \\ m_2 \to 0}} \left[\frac{F(E_I{}^0 - E_{II})}{RT} - \ln \frac{m_2}{m_1}\right] \tag{9-40}$$

It is generally convenient to make m_1 and m_2 equal so that the term $\ln (m_2/m_1)$ disappears.

If the ionization reaction is written

$$2H_2O \to H_3O^+ + OH^-$$

the activity of water will be squared in Eq. (9-39). This will not affect the value of K_w, but it will change the calculated value of the ratio if

$$\gamma_{Cl^-}/\gamma_{OH^-}$$

this is determined from Eq. (9-39) at appreciable concentrations.

As a second example, a method of determining the ionization constant of a weak acid (HA) will be described. Consider cell I, described above, and the following cell:

III. Pt, H$_2$ | aq soln containing $\begin{Bmatrix} \text{HA} & (m_1) \\ \text{NaA} & (m_2) \\ \text{NaCl} & (m_3) \end{Bmatrix}$ | AgCl, Ag, Pt

The emf can be expressed by

$$E_{\text{III}} = E_{\text{I}}^0 - \frac{RT}{F} \ln (a_{\text{H}^+}a_{\text{Cl}^-}) \tag{9–41}$$

The hydrogen ion activity is eliminated by means of the equation for the ionization equilibrium

$$K_A = \frac{a_{\text{H}^+}a_{\text{A}^-}}{a_{\text{HA}}} \tag{9–42}$$

This gives

$$E_{\text{III}} = E_{\text{I}}^0 - \frac{RT}{F} \ln \frac{K_A a_{\text{HA}} a_{\text{Cl}^-}}{a_{\text{A}^-}}$$

$$= E_{\text{I}}^0 - \frac{RT}{F} \left(\ln K_A + \ln \frac{m_{\text{HA}} m_{\text{Cl}^-}}{m_{\text{A}^-}} + \ln \frac{\gamma_{\text{HA}}\gamma_{\text{Cl}^-}}{\gamma_{\text{A}^-}} \right)$$

The molalities in this equation are related to m_1, m_2, and m_3 by

$$m_{\text{Cl}^-} = m_3$$

$$m_{\text{A}^-} = m_2 + m_{\text{H}^+}$$

$$m_{\text{HA}} = m_1 - m_{\text{H}^+}$$

Substituting gives

$$E_{\text{III}} = E_{\text{I}}^0 - \frac{RT}{F} \left[\ln K_A + \ln \frac{(m_1 - m_{\text{H}^+})m_3}{(m_2 + m_{\text{H}^+})} + \ln \frac{\gamma_{\text{HA}}\gamma_{\text{Cl}^-}}{\gamma_{\text{A}^-}} \right]$$

or

$$\ln K_A = \lim_{x_{\text{H}_2\text{O}} \to 1} \left[\frac{F(E_{\text{I}}^0 - E_{\text{III}})}{RT} - \ln \frac{(m_1 - m_{\text{H}^+})m_3}{(m_2 + m_{\text{H}^+})} \right] \tag{9–43}$$

The extrapolation is complicated by the fact that the answer must be known before the values of m_{H^+} can be calculated. This difficulty necessitates determining a provisional value of K_A by some other method, or by neglecting m_{H^+} in extrapolating Eq. (9–43). This provisional value is then used to calculate provisional values of m_{H^+}, and a second extrapolation is made, based on these values. This gives a second approximation to K_A. This procedure can be repeated until self-consistent results are obtained. Unless the value of K_A is relatively large (greater than about 10^{-4}) the number of extrapolations required is not excessive.

(c) *Entropy and Enthalpy Changes from Emf Measurements.* Since

$$\left(\frac{\partial \mu_i}{\partial T}\right)_{p,x} = -s_i$$

the subscript x meaning that the mole fractions of all constituents are constant, we can find, by applying this to the affinity, that

$$\left(\frac{\partial Af}{\partial T}\right)_{p,\, x_{in},x_{fin}} = \Delta s$$

In this equation *in* and *fin* refer to the initial and final states of a system undergoing reaction. Since the affinity is zFE, this gives

$$zF\left(\frac{\partial E}{\partial T}\right)_{p,x_{in},x_{fin}} = \Delta s \qquad (9\text{–}44)$$

By treating the Gibbs-Helmholtz equation in the same way, we find

$$zF\left[\frac{\partial(E/T)}{\partial T}\right]_{p,x_{in},x_{fin}} = \frac{\Delta h}{T^2} \qquad (9\text{–}45)$$

For many ionic reactions Δh can be determined more accurately by this method than by calorimetry.

These equations can, of course, be applied also to the standard emf's, giving

$$zF\left(\frac{\partial E^0}{\partial T}\right)_p = \Delta s^0 \qquad (9\text{–}46)$$

$$zF\left[\frac{\partial(E^0/T)}{\partial T}\right]_p = \frac{\Delta h^0}{T^2} \qquad (9\text{–}47)$$

9–6. Cells With Liquid Junctions

A *cell with liquid junction* contains one or more interfaces at which two solutions of different composition are in contact. Of course, such an interface cannot be sharp, since diffusion will tend to equalize concentrations on opposite sides of the interface. For this reason it is best to picture the junction as a narrow region in which the concentrations vary rapidly but continuously from their values in one phase to those in the other. In cells with liquid junctions irreversible diffusion is occurring at all times; nevertheless, rigorous equations for their emf can be derived. The information for applying these, however, is seldom available. For this reason a simpler approximate equation will be derived here.

Consider the cell

$$Cu \mid Cu(NO_3)_2 \text{ (aq, } m_1) \vdots Cu(NO_3)_2 \text{ (aq, } m_2) \mid Cu$$

the vertical dotted line indicating a liquid junction. The simplifying assumption which will be made is that the transference numbers of cupric and nitrate ions are constant over the molality range from m_1 to m_2. If this cell discharges so that 1 mole of electrons leave the left-hand electrode to the outside circuit, the following changes take place:

$$\tfrac{1}{2}Cu \rightarrow \tfrac{1}{2}Cu^{++} (1) + \epsilon^-$$

$$\tfrac{1}{2}t_+Cu^{++} (1) \rightarrow \tfrac{1}{2}t_+Cu^{++} (2)$$

$$t_-NO_3^- (2) \rightarrow t^-NO_3^- (1)$$

$$\tfrac{1}{2}Cu^{++} (2) + \epsilon^- \rightarrow \tfrac{1}{2}Cu$$

In these equations t_+ and t_- represent the transference numbers, that is, the fractions of the total current that are carried by migration of each type of ion. Alternatively, they may be regarded as the number of equivalents of each ion that migrate past a given point when one Faraday of electricity passes that point. The factor $\tfrac{1}{2}$ in the second equation is accounted for by the fact that cupric ion carries a double charge, or that a mole of cupric ion is two equivalents. The sum of these changes is

$$\tfrac{1}{2}Cu^{++} (2) + t_-NO_3^- (2) + \tfrac{1}{2}t_+Cu^{++} (1) \rightarrow$$

$$\tfrac{1}{2}Cu^{++} (1) + t_-NO_3^- (1) + \tfrac{1}{2}t_+Cu^{++} (2)$$

Using the fact that $t_+ = 1 - t_-$, we find that

$$t_-[\tfrac{1}{2}Cu^{++} (2) + NO_3^- (2)] \rightarrow t_- [\tfrac{1}{2}Cu^{++} (1) + NO_3^- (1)]$$

From this we easily find that the affinity of the composite change represented by this equation, and the corresponding emf, are given by

$$Af = \tfrac{1}{2}t_- \left[\mu_{Cu(NO_3)_2}(2) - \mu_{Cu(NO_3)_2}(1)\right] = \tfrac{1}{2}t_- RT \ln \frac{[a_\pm(2)]^3}{[a_\pm(1)]^3} \qquad (9\text{--}48)$$

and

$$E = \tfrac{3}{2}t_- \frac{RT}{F} \ln \frac{a_\pm(2)}{a_\pm(1)} \qquad (9\text{--}49)$$

This equation has been used for determining transference numbers; its accuracy, however, is seriously limited by the assumed constancy of transference numbers. This is reasonably valid only for very small concentration differences, which in turn necessitates measurement of very small emf's.

Cells having three solutions, and two liquid junctions, are commonly used; the middle solution, commonly containing KCl or NH_4NO_3, is called a salt bridge. Unlike cells with junctions which differ only in concentration, these cells have emf's which cannot be rigorously related to measurable thermodynamic properties of the solutions. They cannot, for this reason, be used in accurate evaluation of thermodynamic data, except in some cases where an extrapolation can remove the uncertainty. Cells with a salt bridge are important in providing the means of expressing the emf of a cell as the sum of the emf of two half-cells, in practical pH determination, and in several analytical procedures.

9–7. Half-Cell Emf's and Electrode Potentials

The reactions at the two solid-solution interfaces of the cell

$$Cu, Zn \mid ZnCl_2 \text{ (aq)} \mid AgCl, Ag, Cu$$

are

$$Zn \rightarrow Zn^{++} + 2\epsilon^-$$

and

$$2AgCl + 2\epsilon^- \rightarrow 2Ag + 2Cl^-$$

and the sum of these is the cell reaction. This suggests dividing the cell into two *half-cells*

$$Cu, Zn \mid ZnCl_2 \text{ (aq)}$$

and

$$ZnCl_2 \text{ (aq)} \mid AgCl, Ag, Cu$$

and expressing the emf of the cell as the sum of the emf's of the two half-cells. However, if the emf of the left-hand half-cell is defined as $\psi_{soln} - \psi_{Cu}$, it is clearly unmeasurable. Any method of breaking up the cell emf into two half-cell emf's is necessarily arbitrary; nevertheless, if the half-cell emf's are consistent, they may be added to give correct values of whole-cell emf's. This makes possible an enormous reduction in the size of electrochemical tables.

The generally accepted convention for defining half-cell emf's is as follows: For the half-cell

$$Cu, \; Zn \mid ZnCl_2 \; (aq)$$

the half-cell emf, $\mathcal{E}_I$, is equal to the whole-cell emf of the cell

I. $Cu, \; Zn \mid ZnCl_2 \; (aq) \parallel HCl \; (aq; \, a = 1) \mid H_2 \; (g; f = 1 \; atm) \; Pt, \; Cu$

or of the cell

$$Zn, \; ZnCl_2 \; (aq) \parallel HCl \; (aq; \, a = 1) \mid H_2 \; (g; f = 1 \; atm) \; Pt, \; Zn$$

the two being equal. In this diagram the pair of vertical lines indicates a salt bridge, generally consisting of a concentrated solution of KCl, though NH_4NO_3 is substituted when chloride ions must be avoided. Similarly the half-cell emf $\mathcal{E}_{II}$ of

$$ZnCl_2 \; (aq) \mid AgCl, \; Ag, \; Cu$$

is equal to the whole-cell emf of

II. $Cu, \; Pt, \; H_2 \; (g) \mid HCl \; (aq; \, a = 1) \parallel ZnCl_2 \; (aq) \mid AgCl, \; Ag, \; Cu$

In these cells the half-cell involving H_2 is called the *standard hydrogen electrode;* its half-cell emf is clearly zero. If we combine cells I and II into a composite cell

$$Cu, \; Zn \mid ZnCl_2 \; (aq) \parallel HCl \; (aq; \, a = 1) \mid H_2 \; (g) \; Pt, \; Cu-$$
$$Cu, \; Pt, \; (H_2) \mid HCl \parallel ZnCl_2 \; (aq) \mid Zn, \; Cu$$

we see that every pair of phases from one of the $ZnCl_2$ solutions to the other is matched by an identical but oppositely directed pair. These portions of the cell, therefore, contribute nothing to the emf and may be omitted. But in doing so we recover the original cell

III. $Cu, \; Zn \mid ZnCl_2 \; (aq) \mid AgCl, \; Ag, \; Cu$

and so

$$E_{III} = \mathcal{E}_I + \mathcal{E}_{II}$$

Some discussion is needed of the confused state of terminology in this field. Various writers have used the terms "emf" and "potential" more or less interchangeably, and similarly the terms "half-cell" and "electrode."

Furthermore, there has been much confusion about signs. Two principal conventions have had widespread use. In one of these a sign-invariant quantity is assigned to each electrode or half-cell, regardless of whether it is written with the metal on the right or left; this quantity is negative if the oxidation-reduction system at the electrode is a stronger reducing agent than that of the standard hydrogen electrode. In this system, when two electrodes are combined into a cell, the more negative of the two electrodes becomes the negative terminal of the cell. This system is commonly called "European," though it has not been confined to either side of the Atlantic. In the other system the sign of the quantity assigned to each electrode or half-cell depends on whether it is written with the metal on the right or left. Thus the standard value assigned to the half-cell

$$Cu, Zn \mid Zn^{++} (aq)$$

is 0.76 v, while that assigned to

$$Zn^{++} (aq) \mid Zn, Cu \text{ is } - 0.76 \text{ v.}$$

These two quantities have been called the *oxidation potential* and *reduction potential* respectively. This system is often called the "American" system, although it originated with Nernst in Germany; the use of this convention in the widely influential books of Lewis and Randall[8] and Latimer[9] presumably accounts for this designation. At its meeting in Stockholm in 1953 the International Union of Pure and Applied Chemistry made a set of recommendations which may eventually become the basis for agreement. These recommendations are described in a simple manner by Licht and deBéthune.[10] Later the International Committee on Electrochemical Thermodynamics and Kinetics (CITCE) made a slightly different, and much more detailed, set of recommendations, which have been described by Lange and Van Rysselberghe.[11] The term "electrode potential" is reserved in the IUPAC-CITCE recommendations for the so-called "European" potential. The sign-variable quantity used in the "American" system may be called the "emf of the half-cell," a term used in the IUPAC report, but not in that of the CITCE. Various other names are also recommended; for example, "chemical tension" (by CITCE) for the quantity here called "emf." As Blum[12] and Anson[13] have pointed out, the controversy over the use of sign-variable or sign-invariant quantities stems partly from the different use to which electrochemists and thermodynamicists put electrochemical measurements. The electrochemist, interested primarily in the cell itself, is likely to prefer the invariant potentials, since they are more directly related to the physical characteristics of the cell. The thermodynamicist, on the other hand, is usually interested in the cell only as a means of obtaining thermodynamic information; for this purpose it seems natural to make the sign dependent on the direction of writing, just as the sign of a heat of reaction, for example, is dependent on the direction of the reaction. For this reason it appears best to retain both quantities but give them unmistakably distinct names. The adoption of the IUPAC recommendations would accomplish this.

The quantities defined up to this point are adequate for the treatment given here, which is confined to the equilibrium condition of cells. However, several additional quantities are needed in more general treatments. In particular, it is necessary to distinguish between the emf and the potential difference between the electrodes. The quantity $\psi_I' - \psi_I$ is, in the CITCE recommendations, called the electric tension; this is equal to the emf, or "chemical tension," for a reversible cell whenever the outside circuit is open, or when the outside circuit provides a counter emf which exactly balances that of the cell, so that no current flows through the cell. If the cell reaction has a step requiring an activation energy which may cause a false equilibrium (common in cell reactions involving gases), the electric tension and chemical tension may differ even though no current is flowing. When a current is flowing, they differ because of ohmic potential drops, electrode polarization, and the development of concentration gradients in the cell; in this case the electric tension is less in absolute magnitude than the chemical tension if the direction of current flow is the same as that produced by a spontaneous discharge of the cell, and vice versa.

9–8. Formulation in Terms of Electrochemical Potentials

Guggenheim[5] has shown that the thermodynamics of electrolytes and electrochemical cells can be expressed elegantly in terms of a quantity called the *electrochemical potential*.

The driving force tending to make a molecule move from one phase to another is a difference in chemical potentials of the substance in the two phases. For ions, however, we might conceive of two driving forces, one due to chemical potential difference, the other to electrostatic potential difference. Thus this total driving force would be

$$(\mu_i{}^\alpha - \mu_i{}^\beta) + z_iF(\psi^\alpha - \psi^\beta) = (\mu_i{}^\alpha + z_iF\psi^\alpha) - (\mu_i{}^\beta + z_iF\psi^\beta)$$

α and β referring to the phases. The quantities in parentheses on the left are called *electrochemical potentials*; they are in principle measurable, but the splitting of them into chemical and electrostatic terms is arbitrary. Nevertheless, using $\bar{\mu}$ for electrochemical potentials, we write

$$\bar{\mu}_i = \mu_i + z_i F \psi \tag{9-50}$$

Then

$$\frac{\bar{\mu}_i}{z_i} - \frac{\bar{\mu}_j}{z_j} = \frac{\mu_i}{z_i} - \frac{\mu_j}{z_j} \tag{9-51}$$

By Section 9–1, these quantities are measurable.

Let us now apply this to the cell

$$\text{I} \quad \text{II} \quad \text{III} \qquad \text{IV} \quad \text{V} \quad \text{I}'$$

$$\text{Cu, Zn} \mid \text{ZnCl}_2 \text{ (aq)} \mid \text{AgCl, Ag, Cu}$$

The equilibrium relations at the phase boundaries are

$$\bar{\mu}_{e-}^{\text{I}} = \bar{\mu}_{e-}^{\text{II}}$$

$$\bar{\mu}_{\text{Zn}++}^{\text{II}} = \bar{\mu}_{\text{Zn}++}^{\text{III}}$$

$$\bar{\mu}_{\text{Cl}-}^{\text{III}} = \bar{\mu}_{\text{Cl}-}^{\text{IV}} \tag{9-52}$$

$$\bar{\mu}_{\text{Ag}+}^{\text{IV}} = \bar{\mu}_{\text{Ag}+}^{\text{V}}$$

$$\bar{\mu}_{e-}^{\text{V}} = \bar{\mu}_{e-}^{\text{I}'}$$

Even with the highest electrostatic charges on metals, the concentration of electrons in the metal is so low that the properties of the metal, other than electrostatic potential, are practically unaltered. For this reason the chemical potential of electrons in copper may be considered constant. This gives for the electric tension, Φ,

$$\Phi = \psi_{\text{I}}' - \psi_{\text{I}} = \frac{\bar{\mu}_{e-}^{\text{I}'} - \mu_{e-}^{\text{I}'}}{-F} - \frac{\bar{\mu}_{e-}^{\text{I}} - \mu_{e-}^{\text{I}}}{-F} = \frac{\bar{\mu}_{e-}^{\text{I}'} - \bar{\mu}_{e-}^{\text{I}}}{-F} \tag{9-53}$$

z being -1 for electrons. Then, making use of the equilibrium equations (Eqs. (9–52)), we find

$$\Phi_{eq} = E = \frac{\bar\mu_{\epsilon^-}^{I'} - \bar\mu_{\epsilon^-}^{I}}{-F} = \left(\frac{\bar\mu_{\epsilon^-}^{V}}{-F} - \frac{\bar\mu_{Ag^+}^{V}}{F} \right) + \left(\frac{\bar\mu_{Ag^+}^{IV}}{F} - \frac{\bar\mu_{Cl^-}^{IV}}{-F} \right)$$

$$+ \left(\frac{\bar\mu_{Cl^-}^{III}}{-F} - \frac{\bar\mu_{Zn^{++}}^{III}}{2F} \right) + \left(\frac{\bar\mu_{Zn^{++}}^{II}}{2F} - \frac{\bar\mu_{\epsilon^-}^{II}}{-F} \right)$$

Only the third of the quantities in parentheses depends on the properties of the solution; the remaining ones may be grouped into a constant, E'. Applying Eq. (9–51) to the third term leads to

$$E = E' + \left(\frac{\mu_{Cl^-}^{III}}{-F} - \frac{\mu_{Zn^{++}}^{III}}{2F} \right) = E' - \frac{1}{2F} \left(2\mu_{Cl^-}^{III} + \mu_{Zn^{++}}^{III} \right)$$

$$= E' - \frac{\mu_{ZnCl_2}^{III}}{2F} = E' - \frac{\mu^0_{ZnCl_2}}{2F} - \frac{RT}{2F} \ln \left(a_{Zn^{++}} a_{Cl^-}{}^{-2} \right)$$

Identifying the first two terms with E^0, we arrive at the Nernst equation for this cell.

Van Rysselberghe[14] has used electrochemical potentials to define an *electrochemical affinity*, analogous to the affinity defined by the use of chemical potentials. To apply electrochemical affinities to the above cell, we note that the reaction, with the circuit open, consists of the usual chemical reaction plus a net transfer of electrons from I' to I. This may be written

$$2\epsilon^- \text{ (I')} + \text{Zn (II)} + 2\text{AgCl (IV)} \rightarrow$$
$$2\text{Ag (V)} + 2\text{Cl}^- \text{ (III)} + \text{Zn}^{++} \text{ (III)} + 2\epsilon^- \text{ (I)}$$

Thus the electrochemical affinity is

$$\overline{Af} = 2\bar\mu_{\epsilon^-}^{I'} + \bar\mu_{Zn}^{II} + 2\bar\mu_{AgCl}^{IV} - 2\bar\mu_{Ag}^{V} - 2\bar\mu_{Cl^-}^{III} - \bar\mu_{Zn^{++}}^{III} - 2\bar\mu_{\epsilon^-}^{I}$$

$$= 2\mu_{\epsilon^-}^{I'} + \mu_{Zn}^{II} + 2\mu_{AgCl}^{IV} - 2\mu_{Ag}^{V} - 2\mu_{Cl^-}^{III} - \mu_{Zn^{++}}^{III} - 2\mu_{\epsilon^-}^{I}$$
$$+ F(-2\psi_{I'} + 2\psi_{III} - 2\psi_{III} + 2\psi_{I})$$
$$= Af - 2F(\psi_{I'} - \psi_I) = Af - 2F\Phi \qquad (9\text{–}54)$$

At equilibrium this becomes

$$\overline{Af} = Af - 2FE = 0$$

Now if we reduce the electric tension by allowing current to flow (assuming E positive), we find that the electrochemical affinity becomes positive, and the reaction tends to proceed forward. If Φ is made to exceed E by an outside source of emf, $\overline{Af}$ becomes negative, and the reaction tends to proceed backward. Thus the electrochemical affinity plays the same role in electrochemical reactions as the affinity does in chemical reactions.

Moreover, consider a cell with positive emf used as a source of electrical energy. It has been shown that the work which the cell can perform per unit of reaction follows the inequality

$$-W \leqslant nFE$$

The actual work it performs, neglecting losses in the outside circuit, is $nF\Phi$. Therefore irreversible processes within the cell cause a loss equal to

$$nFE - nF\Phi = Af - nF\Phi = \overline{Af}$$

Thus the electrochemical affinity measures the extent to which the actual work performed by the cell falls short of that which could be performed in a reversible discharge. Similarly, when the electrochemical affinity is negative, its magnitude may be interpreted as the extra amount of work which must be done on a cell to charge it above that necessary to charge it reversibly.

PROBLEMS

(1) Calculate by the Debye-Hückel limiting law the mean ionic molality, activity, and activity coefficient of calcium chloride in a solution which is 0.001 M in NaCl and 0.003 M in CaCl$_2$.

(2) The equilibrium of a very slightly soluble salt with its ions in solution is given by

$$K_{sp} = a_+{}^{\nu+}a_-{}^{\nu-} = a_\pm{}^\nu = m_\pm{}^\nu \gamma_\pm{}^\nu$$

where K_{sp} is the solubility product. By substituting the Debye-Hückel limiting law for $\gamma_\pm$, show how the solubility in a solution of ionic strength I is related to that in a solution of ionic strength zero. Neglect the contribution of the slightly soluble salt itself to the ionic strength, and assume that no other electrolyte present has any ion in common with the slightly soluble salt.

(3) Show that if

$$\ln \gamma_{\pm} = -Bm^{\frac{1}{2}}$$

is substituted into the appropriate form of the Gibbs-Duhem equation, integration leads to Eq. (9–21).

NOTE: It is necessary to use the series expansion of

$$\ln x_1 = \ln \frac{n_k}{n_k + m\nu} = -\ln \left(1 + \frac{m\nu}{n_k}\right)$$

which is convergent unless $m\nu > n_k$.

(4) The activity of water in NaCl solutions of various molalities at 25°C is given by:

m	a_1	m	a_1
0.1	0.99664	1.0	0.96677
0.2	0.99336	1.5	0.94945
0.3	0.99007	2.0	0.93139
0.5	0.98353	2.5	0.92144
0.7	0.97690	3.0	0.89271

Determine $\gamma_{\pm}$ at 3.0 m, using Eq. (9–23). (The calculations are best done on a machine; if a slide rule must be used, write

$$x_1 = \frac{n_k}{n_k + \nu m} = 1 - \frac{\nu m}{n_k + \nu m}$$

and calculate the last quantity by slide rule. This makes it possible to get an extra significant figure over most of the range covered. The calculation of $\gamma_1 = a_1/x_1$ may be handled similarly.)

(5) Show by substituting appropriate numerical values that at 25°C RT/F is 0.02569 v, and $(RT/F) \ln 10$ is 0.05916 v. These figures are useful in calculations concerning cells; the second figure permits us to substitute 0.05916 $\log_{10} x$ for $(RT/F) \ln x$ at 25°C.

(6) If, in the definition of half-cell emf, hydrogen gas at a fugacity of 1 bar were substituted for the more customary hydrogen gas at 1 atm, how would the standard emf's of the half-cells

$$\text{Cu} \mid \text{CuSO}_4 \text{ (aq)}$$

and

$$\text{HCl (aq)} \mid \text{Cl}_2 \text{ (}g\text{), Pt}$$

be changed?

(7) Devise cells suitable for measuring the activity of (a) $CuSO_4$ and (b) $CaCl_2$ in aqueous solution. State what molalities would have to be varied and what extrapolations made in calculating the activity. (c) Similarly show how the cell

$$\text{Pt, } H_2 \mid \text{NaOH (aq)} \mid \text{Na (in Hg)} \mid \text{NaOH (aq)} \mid H_2 \text{ Pt}$$

can be used to determine the activity of NaOH.

(8) At 25°C the emf of the cell

$$\text{Pt, } H_2 \mid \text{HCl (aq)} \mid \text{AgCl, Ag, Pt}$$

is given for various molalities of HCl by

m	E/volt	m	E/volt
0.005	0.49844	0.009	0.46937
0.006	0.48940	0.010	0.46419
0.007	0.48178	0.020	0.43022
0.008	0.47518	0.030	0.41056

Calculate E^0 by the two methods of extrapolation described. (Data from Harned and Ehlers.[15])

(9) The emf of the cell

$$\text{Ag, AgBr} \mid \text{NaBr } (m_1) \mid \text{Na (in Hg)} \mid \text{NaBr (0.1 } m) \mid \text{AgBr, Ag}$$

at 25°C is given for various molalities m_1 by

m_1	E/volt
0.2	0.03276
0.3	0.05202
0.5	0.07657
0.7	0.09327
1.0	0.11163

Calculate $a_\pm$ and $\gamma_\pm$ at 0.1 m by direct extrapolation, using the Hitchcock method; then calculate these properties at 1.0 m. (Data from Harned and Crawford.[16])

(10) The data of Harned and Ehlers[15] on the cell of Problem 8 can be fitted in the vicinity of 20°C to the empirical equation

$$E^0 = 0.22550 - 6.15 \times 10^{-4}(t - 20) - 1.2 \times 10^{-6}(t - 20)^2 \text{ v}$$

where t is the centigrade temperature. Calculate Δf^0, Δh^0, Δs^0, and $\Delta c_p{}^0$ for the cell reaction.

(11) Analyze the flow of material across the interfaces of the cell

$$\text{Pt, } H_2 \ (g) \mid \text{HA } (m_1) \mid \text{HA } (m_2) \mid \text{HA } (m_3) \mid H_2 \ (g), \text{Pt}$$

where HA is a strong monobasic acid. Designate the transference numbers across the left-hand liquid junction by t_+ and t_-, those across the right-hand liquid junction by t'_+ and t'_-. Show that the emf is given by

$$E = \frac{1}{F} \left[t'_-(\mu_3 - \mu_2) + t_-(\mu_2 - \mu_1) \right]$$

where the μ's represent $\mu_{H^+} + \mu_{A^-}$.

Extend this treatment to a cell with two end solutions of molalities m_1 and m_2, separated by many intermediate solutions, each of which differs from adjacent ones only infinitesimally. Show that for this cell, which is a good model of an actual cell with liquid junction, the emf is given by

$$E = \frac{1}{F} \int_{\mu_1}^{\mu_2} t_- \, d\mu = \frac{2RT}{F} \int_{a=a_1}^{a_2} t_- \, d(\ln a_\pm)$$

REFERENCES

1. Debye, P., and Hückel, E., *Phys. Z.*, **24**, 305 (1923).
2. Harned, H. S., and Owen, B. B., "The Physical Chemistry of Electrolytic Solutions," pp. 60-61, New York, N.Y., Reinhold Publishing Corp., 1958; Onsager, L., *Chem. Rev.*, **13**, 73 (1933).
3. Harned, H. S., and Owen, B. B., *ibid.*, p. 165; Van Rysselberghe, P., *J. Am. Chem. Soc.*, **65**, 1249 (1943).
4. Gibbs, J. W., Collected Works, p. 429, New York, N.Y., Longmans, Green, & Co., Inc., 1928.
5. Guggenheim, E. A., *J. Phys. Chem.*, **33**, 842 (1929); "Thermodynamics," Chapter X, Amsterdam, North-Holland Publishing Co., 1949.
6. CITCE, Proceedings of the Seventh Meeting, pp. 163-180, London, Butterworths Scientific Publications, 1957; *see also* Proceedings of 8th and 9th meetings.
7. Hitchcock, D. I., *J. Am. Chem. Soc.*, **50**, 2076 (1928).
8. Lewis, G. N., and Randall, M., "Thermodynamics and the Free Energy of Chemical Substances," New York, N.Y., McGraw-Hill Book Co., 1923.
9. Latimer, W. M., "Oxidation Potentials," New York, N.Y., Prentice-Hall, Inc., 1938, 1952.
10. Licht, T. S., and de Béthune, A. J., *J. Chem. Ed.*, **34**, 433 (1957).
11. Lange, E., and Van Rysselberghe, P., *J. Electrochem. Soc.*, **105**, 420 (1958).
12. Blum, W., *J. Electrochem. Soc.*, **106**, 27C (1959).
13. Anson, F. C., *J. Chem. Ed.*, **36**, 394 (1959).
14. Van Rysselberghe, P., "Electrochemical Affinity," Parts I and II, Paris, Hermann & Cie, 1955.
15. Harned, H. S., and Ehlers, R. W., *J. Am. Chem. Soc.*, **54**, 1354 (1932).
16. Harned, H. S., and Crawford, C. C., *J. Chem. Soc.*, **59**, 1903 (1937).

chapter 10

The Thermodynamics of Surfaces

IN ALL PREVIOUS DISCUSSION in this book, it has been assumed that a system can be completely described in terms of one or more homogeneous phases. However, no phase can be homogeneous throughout, for clearly molecules in its surface are subject to different forces from those acting on molecules in the interior. Thus there must be a surface region of different properties from the interior. Ordinarily the amount of matter in this surface region is so small that it can be neglected, but there are cases in which it is important. The modifications of thermodynamic theory necessary to account for surface effects form the subject of this chapter.

10–1. General Consideration of Surfaces

Let us consider a system consisting of two fluid phases. These phases may be pure or mixed; they may both be liquid, or one may be liquid and one gaseous. In the latter case the gas may be the vapor of the liquid; for very nonvolatile liquids the gas phase may be practically a vacuum, the system then consisting effectively of only one phase. Following the plan, but not the notation, of Gibbs,[1] we will regard the system of two phases, A and B, as divided into four parts. Parallel to the actual phase boundary we imagine two surfaces, one on each side of the boundary, and situated far enough from it so that the nonhomogeneous surface region will be included entirely between them. The two homogeneous portions of the phases will be designated A' and B', the nonhomogeneous surface region, S. Furthermore, we will divide the region S into two parts, the part between the phase boundary and A' being called A'' and that between the phase boundary and B' being called B'' (Figure 21). This division is rather arbitrary. In the first place, the thickness of S is not specified. In order to include the entire homogeneous region, this thickness need be no more than about two or three molecular diameters on each side of the boundary, but it may be greater. It will, however, be assumed small compared with the radii of curvature of the surface. Secondly, the position of the phase boundary is both indefinite and variable to the extent of a few molecular diameters. For this reason properties, such as energy, relating to

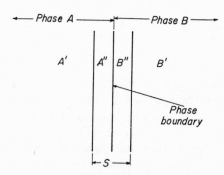

FIGURE 21. DIVISION OF TWO-PHASE SYSTEM INTO SURFACE AND HOMOGENEOUS REGIONS.

these four regions are not well defined; it is only certain combinations of them that will be found to have an operational significance. This is somewhat analogous to the treatment of electrolytic solutions, where chemical potentials of ions are formally defined, but only certain combinations of them are actually measurable.

For the regions A' and B' we can use Eq. (7–1) unchanged:

$$dU^{A'} = T^{A'} dS^{A'} - p^{A'} dV^{A'} + \sum_i \mu_i{}^{A'} dn_i{}^{A'}$$

with a similar equation for B. For S we keep the thickness constant during any variation of state that may occur; any work done on S must then be proportional to the increase in the area, σ, of the phase boundary; therefore a term $\Gamma\, d\sigma$ replaces $-p\, dV$ in the equation for S, thus:

$$dU^S = T^S dS^S + \Gamma\, d\sigma + \sum_i \mu_i{}^S dn_i{}^S \tag{10–1}$$

The arguments previously used (Sections 3–5 and 7–1) to show that temperature and each chemical potential are constant throughout a system in equilibrium are easily modified to apply to the system containing the nonhomogeneous region S, and so we may drop the superscripts from T and μ_i in these equations. Now the quantities U^S, S^S, $n_i{}^S$, and $\Gamma d\sigma$ are separated into three quantities in the following manner. Let $U^{A''}$ represent the energy that the region A'' would have if its energy per unit volume were the same as that of A'; similarly let $U^{B''}$ be the energy B'' would have if its energy per unit volume were the same as that of B'. Then define U^X by

$$U^X = U^S - U^{A''} - U^{B''}$$

Clearly U^X may be interpreted as the excess energy which the surface has over what it would have if the properties of both phases were uniform up to the boundary; it is to suggest the word "excess" that the superscript X has been chosen. In an analogous manner we define

$$S^X \equiv S^S - S^{A''} - S^{B''}$$

and

$$n_i{}^X \equiv n_i{}^S - n_i{}^{A''} - n_i{}^{B''}$$

Finally, the work term, $\Gamma\, d\sigma$, will be divided as follows:

$$\gamma\, d\sigma = \Gamma\, d\sigma + p^{A'}\, dV^{A''} + p^{B'}\, dV^{B''}$$

Thus $\gamma\, d\sigma$ is the excess of work done on the surface region over what it would be if the regions A'' and B'' could be regarded as having the same properties — in particular, the same pressure — as A' and B'; it is commonly called the *surface tension* (or *interfacial tension*, if both phases are liquid). Thus Eq. (10–1) becomes

$$dU^X + dU^{A''} + dU^{B''} = T\, dS^X + T\, dS^{A''} + T\, dS^{B''}$$
$$+ \gamma d\sigma - p^{A'}\, dV^{A''} - p^{B'}\, dV^{B''}$$
$$+ \sum_i \mu_i\, (dn_i{}^X + dn_i{}^{A''} + dn_i{}^{B''}) \quad (10\text{–}2)$$

The definition of $U^{A''}$ and similar quantities is equivalent to saying that these are the properties A'' would have if it were simply an extension of A'. Therefore Eq. (7–1) must apply to it:

$$dU^{A''} = T\, dS^{A''} - p^{A'}\, dV^{A''} + \sum_i \mu_i\, dn_i{}^{A''} \quad (10\text{–}3)$$

with a similar equation for B''. Subtracting these reduces Eq. (10–2) to

$$dU^X = T \, dS^X + \gamma d\sigma + \sum_i \mu_i dn_i{}^X \qquad (10\text{–}4)$$

If we now define $p^A = p^{A'}$ and $U^A = U^{A'} + U^{A''}$, with equations analogous to the latter for the other extensive properties, S, V, and n_i, we can combine the expressions for $dU^{A'}$ and $dU^{A''}$ into the equation

$$dU^A = T \, dS^A - p^A \, dV^A + \sum_i \mu_i \, dn_i{}^A \qquad (10\text{–}5)$$

with a similar equation for B.

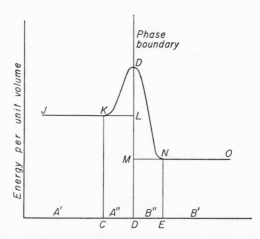

FIGURE 22. GRAPH OF ENERGY PER UNIT VOLUME PLOTTED AGAINST DISTANCE FROM INTERFACE IN A TWO-PHASE SYSTEM (SCHEMATIC).

The meaning of Eqs. (10–4) and (10–5) may be made clearer by interpreting them from a slightly different viewpoint. In Figure 22 the abscissa represents distance perpendicular to the phase boundary, extending from one region of homogeneous properties to the other. The ordinate represents the value per unit volume of some extensive property, such as the energy. The horizontal portions JK and NO represent the property in the homogeneous regions. The area under JK and to the left of KC represents $U^{A'}$; $CKLD$ represents $U^{A''}$; $DMNE$ represents $U^{B''}$; $U^{B'}$ is represented by the area below NO and to the right of NE. Finally the area $LKDNM$ represents U^X.

10–2. Equilibrium Conditions for the Surface

Let us consider an isolated liquid system, whose volatility is low enough to be neglected. For this system phase B may be considered empty, and its effect neglected. Combining Eqs. (10–4) and (10–5), we find

$$dU = T \, dS - p \, dV + \gamma \, d\sigma + \sum_i \mu_i \, dn_i \qquad (10\text{–}6)$$

where $U = U^A + U^X$, and similarly for S and n_i. Since the system is isolated, it is restricted to changes for which dU, dV, and dn_i are all zero. Also dQ is zero, and this means that $T \, dS \geqslant 0$. We then find, if γ is positive, $d\sigma \leqslant 0$. Thus the area tends to a minimum. This accounts for the spherical shape of isolated drops. In this tendency to reach a minimum area, the surface acts like a film under tension; hence the name "surface tension" for γ. This analogy should not be pushed too far, however; the molecular interpretation of surface tension and tension in a stretched film are very different.

A negative value of γ would mean that the surface tends to increase in area. Such a surface could not be stable, since its area can increase indefinitely by folding. Thus a stable interface can form only if the surface tension or interfacial tension is positive.

The same conclusion can be reached from a molecular viewpoint. With positive interfacial tension between two liquid phases, work must be done to extend the surface, and so work must be done in bringing molecules to the surface from the interior. This means that the molecule reaching the surface is subjected to a net force toward the phase from which it came. Actually, it is acted on by attractive forces from molecules in both phases, but those from its own phase are stronger. Conversely, a negative surface tension would mean that the molecule in the surface is more strongly attracted to the other phase than to its own. But if this situation held, the surface molecules from one phase would move into the other phase, and the phases would mix. Thus the formation of an interface requires a positive surface tension. This argument can be modified for the case in which one phase is a gas.

To find the pressure difference between two phases consider a two-phase system, in which phase A is of spherical shape and is immersed in phase B. By combining Eqs. (10–3) and (10–4) with a similar one for phase B we find, using U, S, and n_i without superscripts for total quantities for the entire system,

$$dU = T \, dS - p^A \, dV^A - p^B \, dV^B + \gamma \, d\sigma + \sum_i \mu_i \, dn_i$$

If the only change is the transfer of matter from one phase to the other in a closed system, $dn_i = 0$, and the last term may be omitted. If the system is in equilibrium, the transfer of a small amount of matter is reversible, and so

$$dW = dU - dQ = dU - T\,dS = -p^A\,dV^A - p^B\,dV^B + \gamma\,d\sigma$$

However, the work term can be derived from another viewpoint. The total volume change of the system is $dV^A + dV^B$, and the pressure which the system exerts on its surroundings is p^B, since phase A does not touch the surroundings. Therefore,

$$dW = -p^B(dV^A + dV^B)$$

Comparing these two expressions for dW gives

$$-p^A\,dV^A - p^B\,dV^B + \gamma\,d\sigma = -p^B(dV^A + dV^B)$$

which leads to

$$\gamma\,d\sigma = (p^A - p^B)\,dV^A \qquad (10\text{–}7)$$

Since phase A is spherical,

$$\sigma = 4\pi r^2 \text{ and } d\sigma = 8\pi r\,dr$$

$$V^A = \frac{4}{3}\pi r^3 \text{ and } dV^A = 4\pi r^2\,dr$$

and so

$$d\sigma = \frac{2}{r}\,dV^A$$

Substituting this into Eq. (10–7) gives

$$p^A - p^B = \frac{2\gamma}{r} \qquad (10\text{–}8)$$

Thus the pressure is greater on the concave side of the surface than on the convex side. If the surface is not spherical, it can be characterized by two principal radii of curvature, r_1 and r_2, and the relation of area change to volume change can be shown to be

$$d\sigma = \left(\frac{1}{r_1} + \frac{1}{r_2}\right)dV$$

The pressure difference then becomes

$$p^A - p^B = \left(\frac{1}{r_2} + \frac{1}{r_1}\right)\gamma \qquad (10\text{-}9)$$

where p^A is interpreted as the pressure on the concave side, p^B that on the convex side.

If a system of two fluid phases is affected by a gravitational field, the shape of the interfacial boundary is determined by a balance of gravitational forces and surface tension. Suppose that at some altitude the two phases are under the same pressure, p^0, and measure all altitudes from this one. Then

$$p^A = p^0 - zg\rho^A$$

and

$$p^B = p^0 - zg\rho^B$$

where z denotes altitude, g the gravitational acceleration, and ρ^A and ρ^B the densities of the fluids on the concave and convex sides of the surface. Therefore,

$$p^A - p^B = -zg(\rho^A - \rho^B)$$

and

$$-zg(\rho^A - \rho^B) = \left(\frac{1}{r_1} + \frac{1}{r_2}\right)\gamma \qquad (10\text{-}10)$$

If no point can be found at which the phases are known to be at the same pressure, z must be measured from an arbitrary zero point, and a constant added to the right side of Eq. (10-10). The constant can be evaluated if the radii of curvature are known at some point.

In principle this equation permits the determination of the surface forms of such structures as menisci, hanging drops, and films pulled up by a ring from a liquid surface. Actually it is an extremely intractable equation except in very simple cases.

A consequence of the pressure difference across a curved surface is that small droplets have higher vapor pressure than large ones. For a pure substance we have $(\partial\mu/\partial p)_T = v$; since the curved surface of a spherical drop increases the pressure on the drop by $2\gamma/r$, it increases the chemical potential by $2\gamma v/r$, since, for the small pressures involved, v may be treated as constant. Now if the vapor pressure over an uncurved surface is P^0, while that over the drop is P, the corresponding difference in chemical potential is $RT \ln (P/P^0)$, if the vapor can be regarded as ideal. Therefore

$$\ln \frac{P}{P^0} = \frac{v}{RT} \frac{2\gamma}{r} \qquad (10\text{--}11)$$

Thus the vapor pressure increases as r decreases. This effect is very small; by substituting numerical values for water at 20°C, we find that $P/P^0 = 1.11$ for $r = 10^{-6}$ cm. Nevertheless, this makes a system of droplets of various sizes unstable; the small droplets evaporate, the vapor condensing on the larger ones. Thus the small droplets disappear, and the large ones grow larger. An analogous phenomenon in connection with the solubility of small particles of solid accounts for the value of "digesting" precipitates before filtering them.

10–3. Measurement of Surface Tension; the Capillary Rise

The commonest method of measuring surface tension is by the observation of the height to which the liquid rises in a capillary tube. Figure 23, which is not drawn to scale, shows a capillary tube, C, immersed in a liquid in a container large enough so that the liquid surface away from the capillary is practically flat. Since the pressures of the two phases at a flat surface are equal, this surface is the zero point from which altitudes

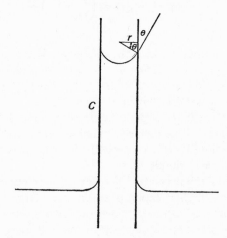

FIGURE 23. DIAGRAM SHOWING RISE OF LIQUID IN A CAPILLARY TUBE.

should be measured. The liquid level in the capillary is different from that outside; in this case (and in all cases suitable for measurement of surface tension) it is higher, and the liquid surface in the capillary forms a meniscus whose upper side is concave. It will be assumed that the radius, r, of the tube and the dimensions of the meniscus are small compared to the height, z, of the meniscus above the outside liquid level. Then z is practically constant over the entire meniscus. This means that the meniscus has constant curvature; in other words, that it is a portion of a sphere. It can be seen from Figure 23 that the radius of the capillary is related to that of the sphere by

$$r_{\text{sphere}} = \frac{r}{\cos \theta}$$

Using this value for r_1 and r_2 in Eq. (10–10), we find

$$zg(\rho^B - \rho^A) = \frac{\cos \theta}{r} (2\gamma) \qquad (10\text{–}12)$$

the superscript B referring to the liquid under the meniscus, A to the liquid or gas above the meniscus. When one phase is a gas, ρ^A is usually negligible.

Of the quantities appearing in Eq. (10-12), only θ offers any serious difficulty of measurement. Fortunately, this angle is almost always zero for water, aqueous solutions, and organic liquids in glass capillaries; optical methods are available[2] for testing whether there is appreciable deviation from zero. If θ is zero, and ρ^A is negligible, Eq. (10–12) reduces to the familiar simplified formula

$$\gamma = \tfrac{1}{2} z g \rho^B r \qquad (10\text{–}13)$$

For most liquids other than molten metals, a glass capillary of 0.1- to 0.2-mm radius is satisfactory for measuring surface tension. Corrections have been developed[2] for the case where the height of the meniscus itself is not small compared to its height above the outside liquid level. For most simple liquids the values of γ range from about 17 to 40 ergs/cm^2 (or dynes/cm). Water has the rather high value of 72.75 ergs/cm^2 at at 20°C. For molten metals the surface tension is usually several hundred, and may exceed a thousand, ergs/cm^2.

10–4. Thermal Effects of Increasing the Surface

If we apply Eq. (10–6) to a closed system, the dn's are all zero; if volume changes are negligible, we find

$$dU = T \, dS + \gamma \, d\sigma$$

This can be changed by a Legendre transformation into

$$dA = -S \, dT + \gamma \, d\sigma$$

The criterion for an exact differential now leads to

$$\left(\frac{\partial \gamma}{\partial T}\right)_{\sigma, n_i} = -\left(\frac{\partial S}{\partial \sigma}\right)_{T, n_i}$$

Since γ does not depend on σ, we can drop this subscript from the derivative of γ. Moreover, at constant T and n_i, and with pressure-volume effects neglected, any change in S must be a change in the excess surface entropy S^X, the other terms in the entropy remaining unchanged. Therefore

$$\left(\frac{\partial S}{\partial \sigma}\right)_{T, n_i} = \left(\frac{\partial S^X}{\partial \sigma}\right)_{T, n_i}$$

Since the added surface has the same excess entropy per unit area as the surface already present, the latter quantity is simply the excess surface entropy per unit area; it will be designated by s^X. Thus,

$$\left(\frac{\partial \gamma}{\partial T}\right)_{n_i} = -s^X$$

This means that if the temperature is to be kept constant as the surface area is increased, the heat required per unit increase in surface area is

$$q = Ts^X = -T\left(\frac{\partial \gamma}{\partial T}\right)_{n_i}$$

During the same process, the work done on the surface per unit increase in area is γ, and so the increase in excess surface energy per unit increase in area, u^X, is

$$u^X = \gamma - T\left(\frac{\partial \gamma}{\partial T}\right)_{n_i} \tag{10–14}$$

This may be identified with the excess surface energy per unit area. It is instructive to compare this equation with the Gibbs-Helmholtz relation

$$\Delta U = \Delta A - T \left(\frac{\partial \Delta A}{\partial T} \right)_V$$

10–5. Gibbs' Equation for Adsorption at a Surface

In Eq. (10–4), if the surface excess of each component, $n_i{}^x$, is increased in the same ratio at constant temperature and pressure, the area of the surface must be increased in this ratio also, as must the excess surface entropy and energy. Therefore U^x is a first-degree homogeneous function of S^x, σ, and $n_i{}^x$. Applying Euler's theorem to Eq. (10–4) thus leads to

$$U^x = TS^x + \gamma\sigma + \sum_i \mu_i n_i{}^x$$

If we differentiate this equation and subtract Eq. (10–4), we find

$$S^x \, dT + \sigma \, d\gamma + \sum_i n_i{}^x \, d\mu_i = 0 \qquad (10\text{–}15)$$

This equation is analogous to the Gibbs-Duhem equation, both in its method of derivation and in its final form. If we now divide by σ and introduce (in Gibbs' notation) the quantities $\Gamma_i \equiv n_i{}^x/\sigma$, the surface excess of component i per unit area, we find

$$s^x \, dT + d\gamma + \sum_i \Gamma_i \, d\mu_i = 0 \qquad (10\text{–}16)$$

Let us now apply this equation to a two-component system at constant temperature; with these restrictions it reduces to

$$d\gamma + \Gamma_1 \, d\mu_1 + \Gamma_2 \, d\mu_2 = 0 \qquad (10\text{–}17)$$

If pressure is also constant, or its effect can be neglected, the Gibbs-Duhem equation itself becomes

$$x_1 \, d\mu_1 + x_2 \, d\mu_2 = 0$$

where the x's represent mole fractions in one of the homogeneous phases. Actually, this treatment will be restricted to the one-phase case, in which phase B is a vapor of negligible content; the x's then apply to the liquid phase. Eliminating $d\mu_1$ from Eq. (10–17) by means of the Gibbs-Duhem equation gives

$$-d\gamma = \left(\Gamma_2 - \frac{x_2}{x_1} \Gamma_1 \right) d\mu_2 \qquad (10\text{–}18)$$

It can be shown that the quantity in parentheses is not affected by the arbitrary features in the definition of Γ_1 and Γ_2, such as the location of the phase boundary; thus it is a definite and measurable quantity. Gibbs[3] suggested placing the boundary in such a way that Γ_1 would vanish; the value in parentheses would then become a special value of Γ_2, which he designated $\Gamma_{2(1)}$. However, it is equivalent, and simpler in concept, merely to define $\Gamma_{2(1)}$ as the quantity in parentheses without attempting to assign values to the arbitrary quantities Γ_1 and Γ_2. Thus Eq. (10–18) becomes

$$d\gamma = -\Gamma_{2(1)} \, d\mu_2 \qquad (10\text{–}19)$$

This equation, in more general form, was first derived by Gibbs[3] and is called the *Gibbs adsorption equation*. This name is often applied also to various approximate forms of this equation, most of which Gibbs himself did not derive. For example, by using the definition of activity (Eq. (7–24),) we find

$$d\gamma = -\Gamma_{2(1)}RT \, d(\ln a_2)$$

or

$$\Gamma_{2(1)} = -\frac{a_2}{RT}\left(\frac{\partial \gamma}{\partial a_2}\right)_T \qquad (10\text{–}20)$$

This equation is exactly equivalent to the Gibbs equation, but it is often approximated by

$$\Gamma_{2(1)} = -\frac{P_2}{RT}\left(\frac{\partial \gamma}{\partial P_2}\right)_T \qquad \text{(a)}$$

$$\Gamma_{2(1)} = -\frac{x_2}{RT}\left(\frac{\partial \gamma}{\partial x_2}\right)_T \qquad \text{(b)} \qquad (10\text{–}21)$$

or

$$\Gamma_{2(1)} = -\frac{C_2}{RT}\left(\frac{\partial \gamma}{\partial C_2}\right)_T \qquad \text{(c)}$$

where P, x, and C represent partial vapor pressure, mole fraction, and molarity, respectively.

If the ratio of the amounts of the two components is the same in the surface as in the rest of the system, then $\Gamma_1/\Gamma_2 = x_1/x_2$, and $\Gamma_{2(1)}$ is zero. A positive value of $\Gamma_{2(1)}$ indicates that component 2 has concentrated in the surface. Eq. (10–21b) or (10–21c) shows that this occurs when the surface tension decreases with increasing concentration of component 2. That is, if component 2 reduces the surface tension, it concentrates in the surface, where its effect in reducing the surface energy will be greatest; but any component which increases the surface tension avoids the surface, since its presence there would increase the surface energy. A solute for which $\Gamma_{2(1)}$ is positive is said to exhibit *positive adsorption*, and vice versa.

The experimental verification of the Gibbs adsorption equation is extraordinarily difficult. When a sample is removed from the surface, new surfaces are formed, and migration to or from these new surfaces, to establish equilibrium concentrations there, starts immediately. Thus the surface sample must be completely removed in a very short time. Even more serious is the fact that the thickness of the nonhomogeneous surface layer is generally less than 10^{-7}cm; therefore even if the sample taken is only 10^{-2}cm thick, the part which actually comes from the surface is diluted with more than 100,000 times its bulk of material from the homogeneous region. Mathematically, this does not affect the value of $\Gamma_{2(1)}$; experimentally, it means that the desired quantity is a very small difference between large quantities and so is subject to greatly magnified experimental errors.

Despite these difficulties, McBain[4] and his coworkers have attacked the problem, using an apparatus requiring a high degree of ingenuity in its design and of mechanical skill in its construction. The essential feature is that a microtome blade, moving along machined rails at a speed of about 35 ft/sec, slices from the surface a layer not more than 0.1 mm thick. The concentration difference betweeen this layer and the bulk of the solution is determined directly by the very sensitive method of comparing their refractive indices in an interferometer. Both negatively and positively adsorbed solutes have been tested, and satisfactory agreement with the Gibbs equation has been found in all cases.[*]

PROBLEMS

(1) Assuming that the thickness of the liquid film in a soap bubble is negligible, show that the pressure inside the bubble exceeds that outside by $4\gamma/r$.

(2) A capillary tube of inside radius r is extended down into a liquid until its end is at a depth much greater than r. Gas is slowly forced through the capillary; each bubble, as it forms, covers only the inner cross section of the tube. Show that the minimum radius of curvature of the gas-liquid interface of the bubble is r, and so the pressure required to maintain steady flow is $p^0 + 2\gamma/r$, where p_0 is the pressure of the liquid at the depth of the end of the tube. (This is a widely used method of measuring surface tension.)

---

[*] The validity of the entire Gibbs adsorption theory has recently been challenged by de Witte.[5]

(3) Generalize the treatment of Section 10–5 to systems of C components, deriving the equation

$$-d\gamma = \sum_{i=2}^{C} \Gamma_{i(1)} \, d\mu_i$$

where

$$\Gamma_{i(1)} \equiv \Gamma_i - \frac{x_i}{x_1} \Gamma_1$$

(4) Sketch figures analogous to Figure 22, with the ordinates representing concentrations of components 1 and 2, and with phase B having negligible content. Show that arbitrarily moving the phase boundary a distance, τ, to the left would increase Γ_1 by τc_1, where c_1 refers to the concentration of component 1, in moles/cm³, in the homogeneous region. Similarly show that Γ_2 would be increased by τc_2, and so, since $c_1/c_2 = x_1/x_2$, that $\Gamma_{2(1)}$ would be unchanged. Prove also that this quantity is unaffected by moving the boundary between A'' and A'.

(5) Verify the statement on p. 242 that for water at 20°C a droplet of radius 10^{-6} cm has a vapor pressure 1.11 times that of water with a flat surface. The surface tension of water at this temperature is 72.75 dynes/cm.

REFERENCES

1. Gibbs, J. W., Collected Works, pp. 219-226, New York, N.Y., Longmans, Green, & Co., Inc., 1931 (reprinted from various issues of *Trans. Conn. Acad. Arts Sci.*, 1875-1878).
2. Adam, N. K., "The Physics and Chemistry of Surfaces," Chapter IX, Oxford University Press, 1938.
3. Gibbs, J. W., *ibid.*, p. 234-235; see also Guggenheim, E. A., "Thermodynamics," p. 215-216, 255, Amsterdam, North-Holland Publishing Co., 1949.
4. McBain, J. W., and Humphreys, C. W., *J. Phys. Chem.*, **36**, 300 (1932); McBain, J. W., and Swain, R. C., *Proc. Roy. Soc. (London)* **A 154**, 608 (1936).
5. de Witte, L., *Helv. Chim. Acta*, **42**, 583 (1959).

chapter 11

Systematic Methods of Deriving Thermodynamic Relations

IN SECTION 3–9 it was shown that by Tobolsky's method derivatives of the fundamental thermodynamic quantities can be expressed in terms of derivatives whose independent variables may be selected from T, S, p, and V; in particular, in terms of C_p, C_v, α, and κ. In this chapter more general and elegant methods of deriving interrelations among thermodynamic derivatives will be developed. In addition, a brief description will be given of a scheme which, though of little practical utility, is of interest as an illustration of the extent to which the equations of thermodynamics can be systematized and classified.

11–1. Properties of Jacobians

The few properties of Jacobians which are needed for the purpose of this book will be developed for Jacobians of two functions. All these results are applicable also to Jacobians of more functions.

Let u and v be functions of the variables x and y. The *Jacobian* of u and v with respect to x and y is defined by

$$\frac{\partial(u,v)}{\partial(x,y)} \equiv \begin{vmatrix} \left(\dfrac{\partial u}{\partial x}\right)_y & \left(\dfrac{\partial u}{\partial y}\right)_x \\[2mm] \left(\dfrac{\partial v}{\partial x}\right)_y & \left(\dfrac{\partial v}{\partial y}\right)_x \end{vmatrix} \tag{11–1}$$

Several properties follow immediately from this definition:

(1) If u and v are identical (or, for more than two functions, if any two are identical), the Jacobian is zero. This results from the theorem that a determinant vanishes if two of its rows are identical.

(2) If the independent variables (x and y) are the same (or if any two of them are the same), the Jacobian is undefined, since the definition would involve, for example, derivatives with respect to x at constant x.

(3) If the two functions (or any two of them, if there are more) are interchanged, the Jacobian changes sign but is otherwise unchanged; a similar rule applies to the independent variables. Thus

$$\frac{\partial(u,v)}{\partial(x,y)} = - \frac{\partial(v,u)}{\partial(x,y)} = - \frac{\partial(u,v)}{\partial(y,x)} = \frac{\partial(v,u)}{\partial(y,x)} \tag{11-2}$$

This follows from the fact that a determinant changes sign when any two rows, or any two columns, are interchanged.

(4) If one of the functions and one of the variables are identical, the Jacobian reduces to a simple derivative. Thus

$$\frac{\partial(u,y)}{\partial(x,y)} = \frac{\partial(y,u)}{\partial(y,x)} = \left(\frac{\partial u}{\partial x}\right)_y \tag{11-3}$$

since, for the first of the Jacobians above, the determinant becomes

$$\begin{vmatrix} \left(\dfrac{\partial u}{\partial x}\right)_y & \left(\dfrac{\partial u}{\partial y}\right)_x \\ 0 & 1 \end{vmatrix}$$

Let u and v be functions of x and y as before, and let x and y in turn be functions of r and s. To mutiply together the two Jacobians $\partial(u,v)/\partial(x,y)$ and $\partial(x,y)/\partial(r,s)$ we use the rule for multiplying determinants. This states that the product of two determinants of the same order

$$\begin{vmatrix} a_{11} & a_{12} & . & . & . \\ a_{21} & a_{22} & . & . & . \\ . & . & . & . & . \end{vmatrix} \quad \text{and} \quad \begin{vmatrix} b_{11} & b_{12} & . & . & . \\ b_{21} & b_{22} & . & . & . \\ . & . & . & . & . \end{vmatrix}$$

is another determinant of this order, and its element in the ith row and j column is

$$a_{i1}b_{1j} + a_{i2}b_{2j} + \ldots$$

Applying this to the product of the two Jacobians, we find that the element in the first row and second column (for example) is

$$\left(\frac{\partial u}{\partial x}\right)_y \left(\frac{\partial x}{\partial s}\right)_r + \left(\frac{\partial u}{\partial y}\right)_x \left(\frac{\partial y}{\partial s}\right)_r$$

which is simply $(\partial u/\partial s)_r$. Working out the other elements in the same way, we can show that

$$\frac{\partial(u,v)}{\partial(x,y)} \frac{\partial(x,y)}{\partial(r,s)} = \begin{vmatrix} \left(\dfrac{\partial u}{\partial r}\right)_s & \left(\dfrac{\partial u}{\partial s}\right)_r \\ \\ \left(\dfrac{\partial v}{\partial r}\right)_s & \left(\dfrac{\partial v}{\partial s}\right)_r \end{vmatrix} = \frac{\partial(u,v)}{\partial(r,s)} \qquad (11\text{--}4)$$

In the case of one function u of one variable x, which in turn depends on r, this reduces to the familiar formula

$$\frac{du}{dr} = \frac{du}{dx}\frac{dx}{dr}$$

11–2. Application to Thermodynamic Systems of Constant Mole Numbers

If the mole numbers are fixed in a system, the thermodynamic state is fixed in general by only two variables. In this case Jacobians of only two functions are needed. When it is unnecessary to specify the independent variables, the notation $J(u,v)$ will be used for $\partial(u,v)/\partial(x,y)$. Then, using Eq. (11–4), we find

$$\frac{J(u,v)}{J(r,s)} = \frac{\dfrac{\partial(u,v)}{\partial(x,y)}}{\dfrac{\partial(r,s)}{\partial(x,y)}} = \frac{\partial(u,v)}{\partial(r,s)} \qquad (11\text{--}5)$$

Thus $J(u,v)/J(r,s)$ may be regarded as an alternative notation for

$$\partial(u,v)/\partial(r,s)$$

but with the difference that $J(u,v)$ and $J(r,s)$ are meaningful by themselves, while $\partial(u,v)$ and $\partial(r,s)$ are not.

The first of the Maxwell equations,

$$\left(\frac{\partial T}{\partial V}\right)_S = -\left(\frac{\partial p}{\partial S}\right)_V$$

can be written in the Jacobian form

$$\frac{J(T,S)}{J(V,S)} = -\frac{J(p,V)}{J(S,V)} = \frac{J(p,V)}{J(V,S)}$$

by Eqs. (11–2) and (11–3). Multiplying by $J(V,S)$ gives

$$J(T,S) = J(p,V) \tag{11–6}$$

The other Maxwell equations may be treated similarly and lead to the same result. Thus in Jacobian notation all four of these equations reduce to this one relation. The original equations are readily recovered from Eq. (11–6) by dividing by $J(x,y)$, where x is either T or S, and y either p or V, interpreting the Jacobians according to Eqs. (11–2) and (11–3).

Equations such as

$$dU = T\,dS - p\,dV$$

can be put into Jacobian form as follows. First the equation is divided by dx at constant y, where x and y are any suitable variables. This gives

$$\left(\frac{\partial U}{\partial x}\right)_y = T\left(\frac{\partial S}{\partial x}\right)_y - p\left(\frac{\partial V}{\partial x}\right)_y$$

or

$$\frac{J(U,y)}{J(x,y)} = T\frac{J(S,y)}{J(x,y)} - p\frac{J(V,y)}{J(x,y)}$$

Multiplying by $J(x,y)$ then gives

$$J(U,y) = TJ(S,y) - pJ(V,y) \tag{11–7}$$

This equation, and the analogous ones

$$J(H,y) = TJ(S,y) + VJ(p,y) \tag{11–8}$$

$$J(A,y) = -SJ(T,y) - pJ(V,y) \tag{11–9}$$

and

$$J(G,y) = -SJ(T,y) + VJ(p,y) \tag{11–10}$$

will be needed frequently.

Several relations between Jacobians and common experimental quantities are useful. Thus if p and T are the independent variables, we find

$$J(T,S) = J(p,V) = \frac{\partial(p,V)}{\partial(p,T)} = \left(\frac{\partial V}{\partial T}\right)_p = V\alpha \qquad (11\text{--}11)$$

$$J(T,V) = -\left(\frac{\partial V}{\partial p}\right)_T = V\kappa \qquad (11\text{--}12)$$

$$J(H,p) = TJ(S,p) = -\left(\frac{\partial H}{\partial T}\right)_p = -C_p \qquad (11\text{--}13)$$

With this background we turn to the problem of evaluating $(\partial S/\partial H)_G$ in terms of derivatives with independent variables p and T; in Section 3–9 this was solved by Tobolsky's method. We find

$$\left(\frac{\partial S}{\partial H}\right)_G = \frac{J(G,S)}{J(G,H)} = \frac{-SJ(T,S) + VJ(p,S)}{-SJ(T,H) + VJ(p,H)} \quad \text{(by Eqs. (11–3) and (11–10))}$$

$$= \frac{-SJ(p,V) + VJ(p,S)}{SJ(H,T) - VJ(H,p)} \quad \text{(by Eqs. (11–2) and (11–6))}$$

$$= \frac{-SJ(p,V) + VJ(p,S)}{STJ(S,T) + SVJ(p,T) - VJ(H,p)} \quad \text{(by Eq. (11–8))}$$

$$= \frac{-SV\alpha + VC_p/T}{-STV\alpha + SV + VC_p} \quad \text{(by Eqs. (11–11) and (11–13))}$$

In the last step use has been made of the fact that if p and T are the independent variables, $J(p,T)$ reduces to one. Dividing by V converts this to the form given in Section 3–9:

$$\left(\frac{\partial S}{\partial H}\right)_G = \frac{(C_p/T) - \alpha S}{-S(T\alpha - 1) + C_p}$$

Before taking up a second example, we need to consider the Jacobian form of equations such as Eq. (1–11):

$$\left(\frac{\partial f}{\partial x}\right)_z = \left(\frac{\partial f}{\partial x}\right)_y + \left(\frac{\partial f}{\partial y}\right)_x \left(\frac{\partial y}{\partial x}\right)_z$$

Applying Eq. (11–3) leads to

$$\frac{J(f,z)}{J(x,z)} = \frac{J(f,y)}{J(x,y)} + \frac{J(f,x)}{J(y,x)}\frac{J(y,z)}{J(x,z)}$$

Clearing of fractions, we find

$$J(f,z)J(x,y) = J(f,y)J(x,z) - J(f,x)J(y,z)$$

or

$$J(f,x)J(y,z) + J(f,y)J(z,x) + J(f,z)J(x,y) = 0 \qquad (11\text{–}14)$$

Equations of this type are readily written down by the following method. First write a blank equation containing the Jacobians as in Eq. (11–14), but without the variables. Then put any one of the variables in the same position in all three terms, thus:

$$J(f, \ )J(\ , \ ) + J(f, \ )J(\ , \ ) + J(f, \ )J(\ , \ ) = 0$$

Next put the other three variables in the remaining positions in the first term in any order, and cyclically permute this order to find the order in which these variables go into the other two terms. For any given four variables, this procedure always gives the same equation regardless of the various choices permitted, though different forms of the equation appear with different choices.

This will be used in deriving the difference between C_p and C_v. We have

$$C_p - C_v = \frac{J(H,p)}{J(T,p)} - \frac{J(U,V)}{J(T,V)} = \frac{TJ(S,p)}{J(T,p)} - \frac{TJ(S,V)}{J(T,V)}$$

$$= T\frac{J(S,p)J(T,V) - J(S,V)J(T,p)}{J(T,p)J(T,V)} \qquad (11\text{–}15)$$

The numerator is now transformed by means of Eq. (11–14) with S, p, T, and V for f, x, y, and z; that is,

$$J(S,p)J(T,V) + J(S,T)J(V,p) + J(S,V)J(p,T) = 0$$

or

$$J(S,p)J(T,V) - J(S,V)J(T,p) = -J(T,S)J(p,V)$$

$$= - [J(p,V)]^2 \qquad (11\text{–}16)$$

We substitute this into Eq. (11–15). Then, with the choice of p and T as the independent variables, $J(T,p)$ becomes -1, and the other Jacobians can be interpreted by Eqs. (11–11) and (11–12). The result is

$$C_p - C_v = -T \frac{[J(p,V)]^2}{J(T,p)J(T,V)} = T \frac{(V\alpha)^2}{V\kappa} = \frac{TV\alpha^2}{\kappa}$$

A good description of the Jacobian method has been given by Crawford.[1]

11–3. Shaw's Formulation of the Jacobian Method

Shaw[2] has tabulated the Jacobians for thermodynamic functions in terms of five standard Jacobians chosen for convenience. If Shaw's table is at hand, the use of Jacobians can be considerably simplified. However, the student who wishes to make full use of the Jacobian method should understand how to use it without tables also.

Shaw denotes the five standard Jacobians as follows:

$$a \equiv J(V,T)$$

$$b \equiv J(p,V) = J(T,S)$$

$$c \equiv J(p,S)$$

$$l \equiv J(p,T)$$

$$n \equiv J(V,S)$$

(Shaw's original notation is retained, despite the fact that some of these letters are overworked already.)

With these definitions Eq. 11–16 becomes

$$b^2 + ac - nl = 0 \tag{11–17}$$

Other Jacobians can be listed in terms of these five by means of Eqs. (11–7) through (11–10). For example,

$$J(U,p) = TJ(S,p) - pJ(V,p) = -Tc + pb$$

This suffices for the calculation of the first four rows and columns of Table 1. The remaining rows and columns can then be filled in one at a time by using terms already determined. Thus, for example,

$$J(G,H) = -SJ(T,H) + VJ(p,H) = SJ(H,T) - VJ(H,p)$$

TABLE 1. VALUES OF $J(x,y)$

y \ x	p	V	T	S	U	H	A	G
p	0	b	l	c	$Tc-pb$	Tc	$-Sl-pb$	$-Sl$
V	$-b$	0	a	n	Tn	$Tn-Vb$	$-Sa$	$-Sa-Vb$
T	$-l$	$-a$	0	b	$Tb+pa$	$Tb-Vl$	pa	$-Vl$
S	$-c$	$-n$	$-b$	0	pn	$-Vc$	$Sb+pn$	$Sb-Vc$
U	$-Tc+pb$	$-Tn$	$-Tb-pa$	$-pn$	0	$-TVc-p(Tn-Vb)$	$T(Sb+pn)+pSa$	$T(Sb-Vc)+p(Sa+Vb)$
H	$-Tc$	$-Tn+Vb$	$-Tb+Vl$	Vc	$TVc+p(Tn-Vb)$	0	$T(Sb+pn)-V(Sl+pb)$	$T(Sb-Vc)-VSl$
A	$Sl+pb$	Sa	$-pa$	$-Sb-pn$	$-T(Sb+pn)-pSa$	$-T(Sb+pn)+V(Sl+pb)$	0	$SVl+p(Sa+Vb)$
G	Sl	$Sa+Vb$	Vl	$-Sb+Vc$	$-T(Sb-Vc)-p(Sa+Vb)$	$-T(Sb-Vc)+VSl$	$-SVl-p(Sa+Vb)$	0

If the row giving $J(H,x)$ has been worked out, we can use values from this row in the last expression. The result is

$$J(G,H) = S(-Tb + Vl) - V(-Tc) = -T(Sb - Vc) + VSl$$

The work of filling in the table is reduced by using the facts that $J(x,y) = -J(y,x)$ and $J(x,x) = 0$. This decreases the number of Jacobians to be listed to $8 \cdot 7/2$, or 28. Of these, six are given by the definitions, leaving only 22 to be calculated.

The value of Shaw's table is seen when it is necessary to derive a relation expressing one derivative in terms of three given ones. For example, consider the problem of expressing $(\partial A/\partial U)_S$ in terms of $(\partial U/\partial G)_p$, $(\partial S/\partial V)_H$, and $(\partial G/\partial S)_T$. To reduce the amount of writing required, these will be denoted by W, X, Y, and Z, respectively. Then from Table 1 we find

$$W = \frac{J(A,S)}{J(U,S)} = \frac{Sb + pn}{pn} \quad \text{(a)} \qquad X = \frac{J(U,p)}{J(G,p)} = \frac{-Tc + pb}{Sl} \quad \text{(b)}$$

$$Y = \frac{J(S,H)}{J(V,H)} = \frac{-Vc}{Tn - Vb} \quad \text{(c)} \qquad Z = \frac{J(G,T)}{J(S,T)} = \frac{Vl}{-b} \quad \text{(d)}$$

From (d) we find $b = -Vl/Z$; then (b) gives

$$c = \frac{pb - SlX}{T} = -\frac{\dfrac{pV}{Z} + SX}{T} l = -\frac{pV + SZX}{TZ} l$$

Using these values in (c) yields

$$n = \frac{V}{T}\left(b - \frac{c}{Y}\right) = \frac{V}{T}\left(-\frac{V}{Z} + \frac{pV + SZX}{TYZ}\right) l = \frac{V}{T}\left(\frac{-TVY + pV + SZX}{TYZ}\right) l$$

Since these expressions for b and n each contain l as a factor, it will cancel out when these values are substituted into (a). The substitution, which is facilitated by rearranging (a) first, gives

$$(W - 1)p = \frac{Sb}{n} = \frac{-SV/Z}{\dfrac{V}{T}\left(\dfrac{-TVY + pV + SZX}{TYZ}\right)} = \frac{ST^2Y}{TVY - pV - SZX} \quad \text{(11-18)}$$

This is the required relation. An alternative method is to write Eqs. (a) through (d) as a set of simultaneous linear equations in b, c, l, and n.

Since the constant terms are all zero, the set can have a solution other than $b = c = l = n = 0$ only if the determinant of the coefficients vanishes. Evaluating this determinant and setting it equal to zero leads to Eq. (11–18).

This example is rather simple, since only four of the five standard Jacobians occur in the set of equations (a) through (d). If all five occur, one of them must be treated as a known quantity and the four equations solved for the other four in terms of this one. The result is then substituted into Eq. (11–17); the "known" will appear as the square in every term and may be divided out. In some cases the procedure becomes very complex, but in these cases the complexity usually lies in the relation sought, and other methods are not likely to prove any simpler. It will be illustrated by a simple example, the derivation of a relation connecting $(\partial G/\partial H)_p$, $(\partial A/\partial S)_V$, $(\partial U/\partial H)_S$, and $(\partial G/\partial S)_T$. These will be designated by B, C, D, and E respectively. From Table 1 we find

$$B = -\frac{Sl}{Tc} \quad \text{(a)} \qquad\qquad C = -\frac{Sa}{n} \quad \text{(b)}$$

$$D = -\frac{pn}{Vc} \quad \text{(c)} \qquad\qquad E = -\frac{Vl}{b} \quad \text{(d)}$$

We can solve these for any four of the standard Jacobians in terms of the fifth; choosing a as the "known", we find from (b)

$$n = -\frac{Sa}{C}$$

Then from (c)

$$c = -\frac{pn}{VD} = \frac{pSa}{VCD}$$

Then (a) and (d) give

$$l = -\frac{TBc}{S} = -\frac{pTBa}{VCD}$$

and

$$b = -\frac{Vl}{E} = \frac{pTBa}{CDE}$$

Substituting these into Eq. (11–17) leads to

$$\left(\frac{pTBa}{CDE}\right)^2 + a\left(\frac{pSa}{VCD}\right) - \left(-\frac{pTBa}{VCD}\right)\left(-\frac{Sa}{C}\right) = 0$$

Clearing of fractions readily converts this to

$$pT^2VB^2 + SCDE^2 - STBDE^2 = 0$$

and this is the required relation.

The Jacobian method can be extended to systems of variable composition, but with more than two independent variables any general treatment must become very complex. For example, with two components there are 96 equations of the Maxwell type, and these can be represented by six typical fourth-order Jacobians, in contrast to four equations represented by one second-order Jacobian in the system of constant mole numbers.

Li[3] has constructed Jacobian tables for deriving equations for two-phase systems.

11–4. The Bridgman Tables

Bridgman[4] published the first systematic method of relating thermodynamic derivatives in 1914. This procedure is based on the fact that a derivative such as $(\partial x/\partial y)_z$ can always be expressed as the ratio of two quantities one of which does not involve y, while the other does not involve x; for example,

$$\left(\frac{\partial x}{\partial y}\right)_z = \frac{\left(\dfrac{\partial x}{\partial w}\right)_z}{\left(\dfrac{\partial y}{\partial w}\right)_z}$$

Bridgman wrote formally

$$\left(\frac{\partial x}{\partial y}\right)_z = \frac{(\partial x)_z}{(\partial y)_z} \tag{11–19}$$

To give a definite meaning to the symbols such as $(\partial x)_z$ the derivative is expressed in terms of three reference derivatives, for which Bridgman chose $(\partial V/\partial T)_p$, or $V\alpha$; $(\partial V/\partial p)_T$, or $- V\kappa$; and $(\partial H/\partial T)_p$, or C_p. The expression is then separated, necessarily somewhat arbitrarily, into a numerator and a denominator, which are identified with $(\partial x)_z$ and $(\partial y)_z$, respectively. Thus from

$$\left(\frac{\partial V}{\partial T}\right)_p = \frac{(\partial V)_p}{(\partial T)_p}$$

the choice made was $(\partial T)_p = 1$ and $(\partial V)_p = (\partial V/\partial T)_p$. Then from

$$\left(\frac{\partial U}{\partial V}\right)_p = \left(\frac{\partial H}{\partial V}\right)_p - p$$

$$= \frac{\left(\frac{\partial H}{\partial T}\right)_p - p\left(\frac{\partial V}{\partial T}\right)_p}{\left(\frac{\partial V}{\partial T}\right)_p}$$

we find

$$(\partial U)_p = C_p - pV\alpha$$

Similarly all other terms of the type $(\partial x)_p$ can be found. However, when derivatives at constant T (for example) are evaluated, another choice must be made. Thus

$$\left(\frac{\partial V}{\partial p}\right)_T = \frac{(\partial V)_T}{(\partial p)_T}$$

and neither of the symbols on the right has been assigned a meaning as yet. The choice is made by specifying that

$$(\partial x)_y = -(\partial y)_x$$

This gives $(\partial p)_T = -1$ and $(\partial V)_T = -(\partial V/\partial p)_T = V\kappa$. Note that this choice is not entirely arbitrary, since it must be consistent with the equation

$$\left(\frac{\partial x}{\partial y}\right)_z \left(\frac{\partial y}{\partial z}\right)_x \left(\frac{\partial z}{\partial x}\right)_y = -1$$

In this manner Bridgman built up complete tables of the quantities $(\partial x)_y$ To express any derivative in terms of the three reference derivatives one merely looks up the necessary quantities and substitutes into Eq. (11–19). If a relation connecting four given derivatives is required, each is expressed in terms of the three reference derivatives, and then these are eliminated from the resulting four equations.

Despite the differences in the reasoning by which the two methods were set up, Bridgman's method is simply a special case of the Jacobian method. Bridgman's symbols are the same as Jacobians with T and p as the independent variables; that is,

$$(\partial x)_y = \frac{\partial(x,y)}{\partial(T,p)}$$

Thus Bridgman's tables can be constructed from Shaw's table by choosing T and p as the independent variables (or dividing by $-l$), eliminating n, if it occurs, by means of Eq. (11–17), and interpreting the results in terms of the three reference derivatives.

11–5. The Transformations of Koenig and Prins

Koenig[5] pointed out that certain types of thermodynamic equations can be grouped into families by a set of transformations which convert any one equation in each family into the others. This method is not likely to prove of much use in deriving desired relationships; it is of interest mainly in showing the symmetry of structure of the equations of thermodynamics, and also the limitations of that symmetry.

Koenig's transformations are limited to equations which do not depend for their derivation on the extensive character of such properties as energy; this excludes, for example, the Gibbs-Duhem equation. Furthermore, they apply mainly to closed systems; although terms in μ_i and n_i can be included (and were in Koenig's original article), they are left unchanged by the transformations.

Before Koenig's transformations are applied, the equation must be written in a special form by the following rule. If both T and S occur in the equation, enclose either one of them in an absolute value symbol $(|\ |)$; similarly enclose either p or V if both occur. This has no effect on the equation, since all of these quantities are positive. The transformations are generated by moving the diagram

$$
\begin{array}{ccc}
 & -S & \\
U & & H \\
V & & -p \\
A & & G \\
 & T &
\end{array}
$$

(a)

into all the eight positions that can be reached by rotating it a multiple of 90° in the plane of the paper, or turning it over and rotating it. This gives

$$
\begin{array}{cccc}
\quad -p & \quad T & \quad V & \quad -S \\
H \quad G & G \quad A & A \quad U & H \quad U \\
-S \qquad T & -p \qquad V & T \qquad -S & -p \qquad V \\
U \quad A & H \quad U & G \quad H & G \quad A \\
\quad V & \quad -S & \quad -p & \quad T
\end{array}
$$

$$
\text{(b)} \qquad\qquad \text{(c)} \qquad\qquad \text{(d)} \qquad\qquad \text{(e)}
$$

$$
\begin{array}{ccc}
\quad -p & \quad T & \quad V \\
G \quad H & A \quad G & U \quad A \\
T \qquad -S & V \qquad -p & -S \qquad T \\
A \quad U & U \quad H & H \quad G \\
\quad V & \quad -S & \quad -p
\end{array}
$$

$$
\text{(f)} \qquad\qquad \text{(g)} \qquad\qquad \text{(h)}
$$

The transformations consist of replacing the letters in any one of these diagrams by the letters in corresponding positions in another one. The student familiar with group theory will recognize that this set of transformations constitutes a group isomorphic with the octic group.

As an illustration of the application of these transformations, consider the first Maxwell equation

$$
\left(\frac{\partial T}{\partial V}\right)_S = -\left(\frac{\partial p}{\partial S}\right)_V
$$

Putting S and V into absolute value symbols gives

$$
\left(\frac{\partial T}{\partial\, |V|}\right)_S = -\left(\frac{\partial p}{\partial_{\ast}|S|}\right)_V
\tag{11–20}
$$

(Since the subscripts merely indicate what variables are held constant, their signs are irrelevant, and we can omit the absolute value signs from them.) Using the diagrams (a) and (b) for the transformation, we must replace T by V, V by $-S$, S by p, and p by $-T$. This leads to

$$\left(\frac{\partial V}{\partial \,|-S|}\right)_p = -\left[\frac{\partial(-T)}{\partial \,|p|}\right]_S$$

Since S is positive, the absolute value of $-S$ is S; that of p is simply p. Therefore this equation becomes

$$\left(\frac{\partial V}{\partial S}\right)_p = \left(\frac{\partial T}{\partial p}\right)_S$$

which is the second Maxwell equation. Similarly the transformations (a) to (d) and (a) to (c) change Eq. (11–20) into the third and fourth Maxwell equation, respectively. The remaining four transformations merely give the same four equations again. Thus the Maxwell equations constitute a closed family of four members.

Prins[6] has proposed a modified version of Koenig's transformations which, unlike the original, does not constitute a group, but is relatively simple to apply. Prins' transformations are limited to the same type of equations as Koenig's.

The Prins transformations start with a diagram similar to Koenig's:

$$
\begin{array}{ccc}
& T & \cdot \\
& A \quad \cdot G & \\
V & \cdot & p \\
& U \cdot \quad H & \\
\cdot & S &
\end{array}
$$

(a′)

Note that T and p are on the top and right corners, respectively, with their conjugate variables, S and V, opposite them. The function appearing along any side is the one appropriate for the variables appearing at the ends of that side. For example A is the appropriate function for the variables T and V because the simplest expression for dA involves dT and dV, but not dS or dp; or, equivalently, because A is the function by which the condition for equilibrium at constant T and V is expressed. This diagram is rotated to all the positions of Koenig's diagrams, and S and V are given negative signs whenever they appear on opposite sides of the dotted line from their positions in Diagram (a'). Thus the other diagrams are

$$
\begin{array}{cccc}
\begin{array}{c}
V \\
U \quad A \\
-S \qquad T \\
H \quad G \\
p
\end{array}
&
\begin{array}{c}
-S \\
H \quad U \\
p \qquad -V \\
G \quad A \\
T
\end{array}
&
\begin{array}{c}
p \\
G \quad H \\
T \qquad S \\
A \quad U \\
-V
\end{array}
&
\begin{array}{c}
p \\
H \quad G \\
-S \qquad T \\
U \quad A \\
-V
\end{array}
\\
\text{(b')} & \text{(c')} & \text{(d')} & \text{(e')}
\end{array}
$$

$$
\begin{array}{ccc}
\begin{array}{c}
T \\
G \quad A \\
p \qquad -V \\
H \quad U \\
S
\end{array}
&
\begin{array}{c}
V \\
A \quad U \\
T \qquad S \\
G \quad H \\
p
\end{array}
&
\begin{array}{c}
-S \\
U \quad H \\
V \qquad p \\
A \quad G \\
T
\end{array}
\\
\text{(f')} & \text{(g')} & \text{(h')}
\end{array}
$$

These diagrams are used in the same way as Koenig's, except that the equation to be transformed does not have to be written in a special form; the greater convenience of the Prins transformations arises from their avoiding the need of inserting and later removing absolute value signs.

A more general set of transformations, applicable to equations with more than two independent variables, has been worked out by McKay.[7] This method is rather intricate and will not be described here.

PROBLEMS

(1) Work Problem 4, Chapter 3, by the Jacobian method.

(2) Show by using Shaw's table that $(\partial U/\partial V)_p$ and $(\partial G/\partial T)_S$ can be connected by a relation which does not involve any other derivatives.

(3) Using Shaw's table, derive the equation connecting $(\partial T/\partial V)_S$, C_v, α, and κ.

(4) Use Shaw's table and Eq. (11–17) to derive equations connecting the following:

    (a) C_p, C_v, α, and κ.

    (b) $(\partial p/\partial T)_V$, C_p, C_v, and the Joule-Thomson coefficient, $(\partial T/\partial p)_H$.

(5) From each of the following equations derive the corresponding family of equations by means of the Koenig or Prins transformations. Eliminate any duplicate equations that may appear.

    (a) $\left(\dfrac{\partial H}{\partial T}\right)_p - \left(\dfrac{\partial U}{\partial T}\right)_V = T \left(\dfrac{\partial p}{\partial T}\right)_V \left(\dfrac{\partial V}{\partial T}\right)_p$

    (b) $U - G = TS - pV$

(c) $\left(\dfrac{\partial U}{\partial V}\right)_T = T\left(\dfrac{\partial p}{\partial T}\right)_V - p$

(d) $U - A = H - G$

REFERENCES

1. Crawford, F. H., *Am. J. Phys.*, **17**, 1 (1947).
2. Shaw, A. N., *Phil. Trans. Roy. Soc. (London)*, **A234**, 299 (1935).
3. Li, J. C. M., *J. Chem. Phys.*, **26**, 909 (1957).
4. Bridgman, P. W., *Phys. Rev.*, 2nd series, **3**, 273 (1914).
5. Koenig, F. O., *J. Chem. Phys.*, **3**, 29 (1935).
6. Prins, J. A., *J. Chem. Phys.*, **16**, 65 (1948); see also *Physica*, **13**, 417 (1947).
7. McKay, H. A. C., *J. Chem. Phys.*, **3**, 715 (1935).

Derivation of Eq. (2-8) From Planck's Statement of the Second Law

The treatment of the first two laws given in Chapter 2 is one that could not be developed until thermodynamic theory had been worked out rather fully and reduced to exact mathematical form. Although such a treatment has many advantages in clarity, simplicity, and the rigor of its logic, there are many who prefer an approach more closely related to the historical development of thermodynamics. For this reason the derivation of Eq. (2-8) from Planck's statement of the second law is given here.

Planck's form of the second law is: *It is impossible to devise a machine whose only effects are the removal of heat from a reservoir and the performance of work.* (Planck actually said "the raising of a weight" instead of "the performance of work." However, the two are equivalent, and the more general form given here is easier to use.)

From Planck's statement we first prove the following theorem: *If two thermodynamically reversible machines have no effects except removing heat from a common reservoir, performing work, and rejecting heat to another common reservoir, their efficiencies must be equal.* This is proved indirectly by showing that a pair of machines which contradict this theorem would make it possible to violate Planck's principle.

The machines will be designated by A and B, and it will be assumed that at least one of them can be built to any desired scale. Thus if the amounts of heat taken by the machines from the first reservoir are $Q_1{}^A$ and $Q_1{}^B$, both being positive, we can construct the machines of such size that $Q_1{}^A = Q_1{}^B$. The hypothesis that the machines have no other effects than those listed means that they operate without change of state, or by a cyclic process which brings them back to the original state after each cycle. In either case $\Delta U^A = \Delta U^B = 0$ for a complete cycle if the operation is cyclic, or for any amount of operation if no change of state occurs. If the work done by the machines is $-W^A$ and $-W^B$, and the heat rejected to the second reservoir $-Q_2{}^A$ and $-Q_2{}^B$ (all these quantities being positive), the first law gives

$$Q_1{}^A + W^A + Q_2{}^A = 0 \quad \text{and} \quad Q_1{}^B + W^B + Q_2{}^B = 0$$

Since $Q_1{}^A = Q_1{}^B$, this leads to

$$Q_2{}^A + W^A = Q_2{}^B + W^B$$

or

$$Q_2{}^A - Q_2{}^B = W^B - W^A$$

Now let us assume that the efficiency of B is greater than that of A; that is, that

$$-\frac{W^B}{Q_1{}^B} > -\frac{W^A}{Q_1{}^A}$$

and therefore $-W^B > -W^A$. Thus

$$Q_2{}^A - Q_2{}^B = W^B - W^A < 0 \tag{A1-1}$$

Now we reverse the operation of A, so that work is done *on* it, and it takes heat from the second reservoir and rejects heat to the first. The quantities of heat and work are equal in magnitude to those involved when the machine operates in the original direction, differing only in sign. Thus

$$Q_{1r}{}^A = -Q_1{}^A \qquad W_r{}^A = -W^A \qquad Q_{2r}{}^A = -Q_2{}^A$$

where r indicates reverse operation. Equation (A1-1) thus becomes

$$-Q_{2r}{}^A - Q_2{}^B = W^B + W_r{}^A < 0$$

while

$$Q_{1r}{}^A + Q_1{}^B = Q_1{}^B - Q_1{}^A = 0$$

Thus we find that

(1) There is no net loss or gain of heat by the first reservoir.

(2) The work done by B exceeds that done on A; that is $-W^B > W_r{}^A$. Thus B can supply the work needed for A and do additional work also.

(3) There is a net removal of heat from the second reservoir, since the heat taken by A, $Q_{2r}{}^A$, is more than that supplied by B, $-Q_2{}^B$.

Therefore the composite machine, consisting of A operating in reverse and supplied with work by B, produces no effects except the removal of

heat from the second reservoir and the performance of work. This viola-
tion of Planck's principle shows that the assumption of unequal efficiencies is untenable. (Of course, an analogous argument can be used
to show that the efficiency of A cannot be higher than that of B.)

This means that if a reversible machine operates by exchanging heat
with two reservoirs, its efficiency is a property not of the machine but of
the reservoirs. The efficiency is

$$-\frac{W}{Q_1} = \frac{Q_1 + Q_2}{Q_1} = 1 + \frac{Q_2}{Q_1}$$

We now use this fact to define the temperature of the reservoirs. To do
this, we must choose a function $f(T_1, T_2)$ and specify that the equation

$$-\frac{Q_2}{Q_1} = f(T_1, T_2) \tag{A1-2}$$

will be taken as the definition of temperature.

This function cannot be completely arbitrary. For let us consider a
reversible machine taking heat Q_1 from reservoir 1 and rejecting a positive amount of heat, $-Q_2$, to reservoir 2; Eq. (A1-2) applies to these
as written. Now let another reversible machine (designated by primes)
remove heat in the amount $-Q_2$ from the second reservoir (so that $Q'_2 = -Q_2$) and reject heat $-Q'_3$ to a third reservoir, 3. Then

$$-\frac{Q'_3}{Q'_2} = f(T_2, T_3) = \frac{Q'_3}{Q_2}$$

which is found by applying Eq. (A1-2) to the second machine. Since the
second reservoir is receiving heat from the first machine and losing it to
the second at the same rate, there is no net change in this reservoir, and
it can be eliminated without effect. We are then left with a composite
machine which takes heat in the amount Q_1 from reservoir 1 and rejects
the amount $-Q'_3$ to reservoir 3. Applying Eq. (A1-2) to the composite
machine, which is also reversible, gives

$$-\frac{Q'_3}{Q_1} = f(T_1, T_3)$$

Comparison of these equations shows that

$$f(T_1, T_2) f(T_2, T_3) = f(T_1, T_3)$$

We now pick for f the simplest function that satisfies this condition, namely,

$$f(T_1, T_2) \equiv \frac{T_2}{T_1}$$

Then Eq. (A1–2) becomes

$$-\frac{Q_2}{Q_1} = \frac{T_2}{T_1} \qquad (A1\text{–}3)$$

Then if an arbitrary choice is made for the temperature of one system (such as the choice of 273.16°K for the triple point of water), this equation in principle permits other temperatures to be measured.

Now consider a machine working by means of a Carnot cycle (Section 2-8). This meets the conditions of the theorem above, and so Eq. (A1–3) can be applied. This equation is easily rearranged to

$$\frac{Q_1}{T_1} + \frac{Q_2}{T_2} = 0$$

The quantity on the left is equal to

$$\oint \frac{dQ}{T}$$

taken around a complete cycle, for in the isothermal steps T is constant, and a contribution of the form Q/T results, while the contribution of the adiabatic steps is zero.

We can now extend this result, showing that

$$\oint \frac{dQ}{T}$$

is zero for other cyclic reversible processes also. Consider a process represented by the smooth closed curve of Figure 24. If the work involved in the process is pressure-volume work, the coordinates should be p and V, as indicated; thus the area under any curve represents the work done in the corresponding process, and the area of a closed curve is the net work done in one complete cycle. For other types of work, appropriate coordinates should replace p and V; for example, if the system undergoing the change is a galvanic cell, the coordinates should be emf and amount of electricity. Now replace the original process by the process represented

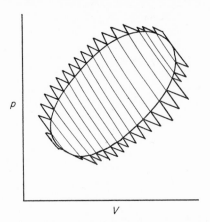

FIGURE 24. APPROXIMATION OF ANY REVERSIBLE CLOSED PROCESS (SMOOTH CURVE) BY PORTIONS OF CARNOT CYCLES (HEAVY ZIGZAG LINE).

by the heavy zigzag line; this is made up of parts of Carnot cycles, the remaining parts of which are shown as light lines. Since the unused portions of the Carnot cycles are all adiabatic, it is clear that the integral of dQ/T over the zigzag path is the sum of the integral over all the Carnot cycles; that is, it is zero. Now we can make the zigzag path approach the smooth one as nearly as desired by making the Carnot cycles sufficiently numerous and narrow. If we can show that the integral of dQ/T for the zigzag path approaches that for the smooth path, then it will be established that the integral around the smooth path is also zero.

That it is necessary to prove this is shown by the fact that there are properties of the zigzag path which do not approach the corresponding properties of the smooth path — the length, for example. Consider now the infinitesimal cyclic process represented by ABC in Figure 25. Since it is cyclic, $dU = 0$ for a complete cycle. Therefore, since the step CA is adiabatic, the first law gives

$$dQ_{AB} + dQ_{BC} = -dW$$

or, since $-dW$ is the area of ABC

$$dQ_{AB} + dQ_{BC} = \text{area } (ABC)$$

When ABC is small enough to be regarded practically as a triangle, its area is proportional to the square of AB, while dQ_{AB} and dQ_{BC} are proportional to AB itself. Therefore dQ_{AB}/T and dQ_{BC}/T differ only by an infinitesimal of higher order than either, and so their integrals are equal.

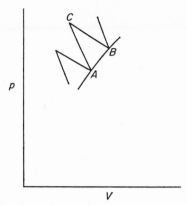

FIGURE 25. MAGNIFIED VIEW OF A SMALL PORTION OF FIGURE 24.

Thus the integral of dQ/T around any closed path is zero, and so dQ/T is an exact differential. This justifies our defining a property S by specifying that its differential is dQ/T, and so we arrive at the first part of Eq. (2–8),

$$T \, dS = dQ$$

for reversible processes.

To prove the other part, we return to the two machines A and B operating by exchanging heat with two reservoirs, but we now assume that B is irreversible. We then find that we can prove that B cannot have higher efficiency than A, but we cannot prove that A cannot have higher efficiency than B, since proving this would necessitate reversing B. Therefore if, as before $Q_1{}^A = Q_1{}^B$, then $-W^B \leqslant -W^A$. From this we find that $Q_2{}^B \leqslant Q_2{}^A$, and so

$$\frac{Q_1{}^B}{T_1} + \frac{Q_2{}^B}{T_2} \leqslant \frac{Q_1{}^A}{T_1} + \frac{Q_2{}^A}{T_2} = 0$$

The argument extending this to other irreversible closed processes is analogous to that for reversible processes, leading to the inequality

$$\frac{dQ}{T} \leqslant 0$$

Now consider an irreversible process AC, and a reversible process ABC connecting the same initial and final states (Figure 26). The irre-

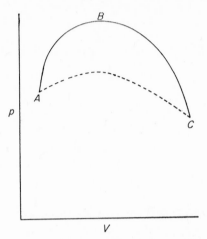

FIGURE 26. DIAGRAM OF A CYCLIC PROCESS INCLUDING AN IRREVERSIBLE PORTION.

versible process cannot properly be represented on the graph, since such properties as pressure are ill-defined for systems not in equilibrium; however, it is crudely indicated by a dotted line. For the reversible process ABC

$$\int_{ABC} \frac{dQ}{T} = S_C - S_A$$

Therefore for the entire cyclic process $ABCA$

$$\oint \frac{dQ}{T} = \int_{ABC} \frac{dQ}{T} + \int_{CA} \frac{dQ}{T} = S_C - S_A + \int_{CA} \frac{dQ}{T} \leqslant 0$$

or

$$\int_{CA} \frac{dQ}{T} \leqslant S_A - S_C$$

If the process is of infinitesimal magnitude, this becomes

$$\frac{dQ}{T} \leqslant dS$$

for irreversible processes. This is the same as the second part of Eq. (2–8), except for the inclusion of the alternative equal sign. To eliminate this alternative appears to require a special assumption, or the redefining of reversible processes to include all those processes for which $T\,dS = dQ$.

Thermodynamic Properties of Various Substances

The following table gives the standard values of heat of formation, Gibbs free energy of formation, entropy, and heat capacity at 25°C for a selected group of elements and compounds. To encourage the student to become accustomed to working with joules as well as calories, values in both units are given. For ions in solution all values are defined by the convention described in Chapter 5, so that the values for the hydrogen ion are zero.

These values are taken mostly from Circular 500 of the National Bureau of Standards, "Selected Values of Chemical Thermodynamic Properties," published in 1952.

Substance	Δh_f^0	Δg_f^0	s^0	c_p^0	Δh_f^0	Δg_f^0	s^0	c_p^0
	kjoules/mole		$\dfrac{\text{joules}}{\text{mole} \cdot \text{deg}}$		kcal/mole		$\dfrac{\text{cal}}{\text{mole} \cdot \text{deg}}$	
ALUMINUM								
Al (s)	0	0	28.32	24.33	0	0	6.769	5.817
Al^{+++} (aq)	−525	−481	−313		−125.4	−115.0	−74.9	
AlCl$_3$ (s)	−695	−637	17	89	−166.2	−152.2	40	21.3
Al(H$_2$O)$_6$Cl$_3$ (s)	−2692	−2665	38		−641.1	−542.4	90	
Al$_2$O$_3$ (s)	−1669.8	−1576.4	50.99	79.0	−399.09	−376.77	12.186	18.88
AMMONIA AND AMMONIUM								
NH$_3$ (g)	−46.2	−16.63	192.5	35.66	−11.04	−3.976	46.01	8.523
NH$_3$ (aq)	−80.8				−19.32			
NH$_4^+$ (aq)	−132.8	−79.5	112.8		−31.74	−19.00	26.97	
NH$_4$Cl (s)	−315.4	−203.9	94.6	84.	−75.38	−48.73	22.6	20.1
NH$_4$NO$_3$ (s)	−365.1				−87.27			
(NH$_4$)$_2$SO$_4$ (s)	−1179.3	−900.4	220.3	187.4	−281.86	−215.19	52.65	44.81
BARIUM								
Ba (s)	0	0	67	26.4	0	0	16	6.30
Ba^{++} (aq)	−538.4	−561	13		−128.67	−134.0	3	
BaCl$_2$ (s)	−860.1	−811	125	75	−205.56	−193.8	30	18.0
BaCO$_3$ (s)	−1218	−1139	112	85.4	−201.3	−272.2	26.8	20.40
BaSO$_4$ (s)	−1465	−1353	132	101.8	−350.2	−323.4	31.6	24.32

Substance	Δh_f^0	Δg_f^0	s^0	c_p^0	Δh_f^0	Δg_f^0	s^0	c_p^0
	kjoules/mole		$\dfrac{\text{joules}}{\text{mole} \cdot \text{deg}}$		kcal/mole		$\dfrac{\text{cal}}{\text{mole} \cdot \text{deg}}$	
BROMINE								
Br^- (aq)	−120.9	−102.82	80.71	−128.	−28.90	−24.574	19.29	−30.7
Br_2 (g)	30.7	3.14	245.35	36.0	7.34	0.751	58.639	8.60
Br_2 (l)	0	0	152		0	0	36.4	
HBr (g)	−36.2	−53.2	198.48	29.1	−8.66	−12.72	47.437	6.96
CADMIUM								
Cd (s)	0	0	51	25.9	0	0	18.5	6.65
Cd^{++} (aq)	−72.4	−77.7	−61		−17.30	−18.58	−14.6	
$CdCl_2$ (s)	−389.1	−342.6	118		−93.00	−81.88	28.3	
$CdSO_4$ (s)	−926.2	−820.0	137		−221.36	−195.99	32.8	
CALCIUM								
Ca (s)	0	0	41.6	26.3	0	0	9.95	6.28
Ca^{++} (aq)	−543.0	−553.0	−55		−129.77	−132.18	−13.2	
CaO (s)	−636	−604	40	42.8	−141.9	−144.4	9.5	10.23
$Ca(OH)_2$ (s)	−986.6	−896.8	76	85	−235.80	−214.33	18.2	20.2
$CaCl_2$ (s)	−795	−750	114	72.6	−190.0	−179.3	27.2	17.36
$CaSO_4$ (s)	−1433	−1320	107	100	−342.42	−315.56	25.5	23.8
CARBON								
C (diamond)	1.821	2.866	2.439	6.06	0.4532	0.6850	0.5829	1.44
C (graphite)	0	0	5.694	8.64	0	0	1.3609	2.06
CO (g)	−110.523	−137.27	197.91	29.14	−26.4157	−32.8079	47.301	6.96
CO_2 (g)	−393.513	−394.38	213.64	37.13	−94.0518	−94.2598	51.061	8.87
CO_2 (aq)	−412.9	−386.2	121		−98.69	−92.31	29.0	
$CO_3^=$ (aq)	−676.3	−528.1	53		−161.63	−126.22	−12.7	
CH_4 (g)	−74.85	−50.79	186.2	35.71	−17.889	−12.140	44.50	8.53
HCO_3^- (aq)	−691.11	−587.1	95		−165.18	−140.31	22.7	
CH_3OH (l)	−238.4	−166.2	127	82	−57.02	−39.73	30.3	19.5
CCl_4 (l)	−139	−68	214.4	131.75	−33.3	−16.4	51.25	31.49
$COCl_2$ (g)	−223.0	−210.5	289.2	60.7	−53.30	−50.31	69.13	14.51
$CHCl_3$ (l)	−132	−72	203	116	−31.5	−17.1	48.5	27.8
CS_2 (l)	88	64	151.0	76	21.0	15.2	36.10	18.1
CN^- (aq)	151	166	118		36.1	39.6	28.2	
HCN (g)	131	120	201.8		31.2	28.7	48.23	
C_2H_2 (g)	226.75	209	200.82	43.93	54.194	50.0	47.997	10.49
C_2H_4 (g)	52.28	68.12	219.5	43.6	12.496	16.282	52.45	10.41
C_2H_6 (g)	−84.67	−32.89	229.5	52.66	−20.236	−7.860	54.85	12.58
CH_3COOH (l)	−487	−392	160	123	−116.4	−93.8	38.2	29.5
C_2H_5OH (l)	−277.63	−174.8	160	111.5	−66.356	−41.77	38.4	26.64
C_6H_6 (l)	49.03	124.50	172.8	134	11.718	29.756	41.30	32.1
CHLORINE								
Cl^- (aq)	−176.46	−131.17	55.1	−126	−40.023	−31.350	13.17	−30.0
Cl_2 (g)	0	0	222.95	33.9	0	0	53.286	8.11
HCl (g)	−92.311	−95.265	186.67	29.1	−22.063	−22.769	44.617	6.96

Substance	$\Delta h_f{}^0$	$\Delta g_f{}^0$	s^0	$c_p{}^0$	$\Delta h_f{}^0$	$\Delta g_f{}^0$	s^0	$c_p{}^0$
	kjoules/mole		joules mole·deg		kcal/mole		cal mole·deg	
HLORINE (cont.)								
ClO_2 (g)	103	123	249		24.7	29.5	59.6	
$ClO_3{}^-$ (aq)	−98.3	−2.6	163	75	−23.50	−0.62	39.0	−18
$ClO_4{}^-$ (aq)	−131.4	−10.8	182		−31.41	−2.57	43.5	
HROMIUM								
Cr (s)	0	0	23.8	23.3	0	0	5.68	5.58
$CrO_4{}^-$ (aq)	−863	−706	38		−206.3	−168.8	9.2	
Cr_2O_3 (s)	−1128	−1047	81	118.7	−269.7	−250.2	19.4	28.38
$Cr_2O_7{}^=$ (aq)	−1461	−1257	214		−349.1	−300.5	51.1	
OBALT								
Co (s)	0	0	28	25.6	0	0	6.8	6.11
Co^{++} (aq)	−67	−51	−155		−16.1	−12.3	−37.1	
CoO (s)	−239	−213	44		−57.2	−51.0	10.5	
OPPER								
Cu (s)	0	0	33.3	24.47	0	0	7.96	5.848
Cu^{++} (aq)	64.4	65.0	−99		15.39	15.53	−23.6	
CuO (s)	−155	−127	44	44	−37.1	−30.4	10.4	10.6
Cu_2O (s)	−166.7	−146.4	101	70	−39.84	−34.98	24.1	16.7
$CuSO_4$ (s)	−769.9	−662	113	101	−184.00	−158.2	27.1	24.1
$CuSO_4 \cdot H_2O$ (s)	−1083.7	−917.1	150	131	−259.00	−219.2	35.8	31.3
$CuSO_4 \cdot 3H_2O$ (s)	−1683.1	−1400	225	205	−402.27	−334.6	53.8	49.0
$CuSO_4 \cdot 5H_2O$ (s)	−2278.0	−1880	305	281	−544.45	−499.3	73.0	67.2
uorine								
F^- (aq)	−329.1	−276.5	−9.6	−123	−78.66	−66.08	−2.3	−29.5
F_2 (g)	0	0	203.3	31.4	0	0	48.6	7.52
HF (g)	−268.6	−270.7	173.5	29.1	−64.2	−64.7	41.47	6.95
ydrogen								
H^+ (aq)	0	0	0	0	0	0	0	0
H_2 (g)	0	0	130.586	28.836	0	0	31.211	6.892
OH^- (aq)	−229.94	−157.30	−10.54	−133.9	−54.957	−37.595	−2.519	−32.0
H_2O (g)	−241.826	−228.596	188.72	33.58	−57.7979	−54.6357	45.106	8.025
H_2O (l)	−285.840	−237.192	69.94	75.30	−68.3174	−56.6902	16.716	17.996
OINE								
I^- (aq)	−55.9	−51.7	109.4	129	−13.37	−12.35	26.14	−31.0
I_2 (s)	0	0	117	55.0	0	0	27.9	13.14
HI (g)	25.9	1.3	206.33	29.2	6.20	0.31	49.314	6.97
ON								
Fe (s)	0	0	27.2	25.2	0	0	6.49	6.03
Fe^{++} (aq)	−88	−84.9	−113		−21.0	−20.30	−27.1	

Substance	Δh_f^0	Δg_f^0	s^0	c_p^0	Δh_f^0	Δg_f^0	s^0	c_p^0
	kjoules/mole		joules mole·deg		kcal/mole		cal mole·deg	
IRON (cont.)								
Fe^{+++} (aq)	−48	−105	−293		−11.4	−2.52	−70.1	
Fe$_2$O$_3$ (s)	−822	−741	90	105	−196.5	−177.1	21.5	25.0
Fe$_3$O$_4$ (s)	−1117	−1014	146		−267.0	−242.4	35.0	
LEAD								
Pb (s)	0	0	64.9	26.8	0	0	15.51	6.41
Pb^{++} (aq)	1.6	−24.3	21		0.39	−5.81	5.1	
PbO (s, yellow)	−217.9	−188.5	69	48.5	−52.07	−45.05	16.6	11.60
PbO$_2$ (s)	−276.6	−219.0	77	64	−66.12	−52.34	18.3	15.4
PbCl$_2$ (s)	−359.2	−314.0	136	77	−85.85	−75.04	32.6	18.4
PbSO$_4$ (s)	−918.4	−811.2	147	104	−219.50	−193.89	35.2	24.9
MAGNESIUM								
Mg (s)	0	0	32.5	23.9	0	0	7.77	5.71
Mg^{++} (aq)	−462.0	−456.0	118		−110.41	−108.99	−28.2	
MgO (s)	−601.8	−569.6	27	37.4	−143.84	−136.13	6.4	8.94
Mg(OH)$_2$ (s)	−924.7	−833.7	63.1	77.0	−221.00	−199.27	15.09	18.41
MgCl$_2$ (s)	−641.8	−592.3	90	71.3	−153.40	−141.57	21.4	17.04
MgSO$_4$ (s)	−1278	−1174	92	96.3	−305.5	−280.5	21.9	23.01
MgCO$_3$ (s)	−1113	−1029	66	75.5	−266	−246	15.7	18.05
MANGANESE								
Mn (s)	0	0	31.8	26.3	0	0	7.59	6.29
Mn^{++} (aq)	−219	−223	−84		−52.3	−53.4	−20	
MnO (s)	−385	−363	60	43.0	−92.0	−86.8	14.4	10.27
MnO$_2$ (s)	−521	−466	53	54.0	−124.5	−111.4	12.7	12.91
MnO$_4^-$ (aq)	−518	−425	190		−123.9	−101.6	45.4	
MERCURY								
Hg (l)	0	0	77	27.8	0	0	18.5	6.65
Hg^{++} (aq)		164.8				39.38		
Hg$_2^{++}$ (aq)		153.9				36.79		
HgO (s, red)	−90.7	−58.53	72	45.7	−21.68	−13.990	17.2	10.93
HgCl$_2$ (s)	−264.9	−210.66	196	102	−63.32	−50.350	46.8	24.3
Hg$_2$SO$_4$ (s)	−742.0	−623.9	200.7	132.0	−177.34	−149.12	47.98	31.55
NICKEL								
Ni (s)	0	0	30.1	26.0	0	0	7.20	6.21
Ni^{++} (aq)	−64	−46	−159		−15.3	−11.1	−38.1	
NiO (s)	−244	−216	38.6	44.4	−58.4	−51.7	9.22	10.60
NITROGEN (see also **AMMONIA**)								
N$_2$ (g)	0	0	191.5	29.12	0	0	45.767	6.96
NO (g)	90.37	86.69	210.6	29.86	21.600	20.719	50.339	7.13
NO$_2$ (g)	33.85	51.84	240.4	37.9	8.091	12.390	57.47	9.06

Substance	Δh_f^0	Δg_f^0	s^0	c_p^0	Δh_f^0	Δg_f^0	s^0	c_p^0
	kjoules/mole		joules / mole · deg		kcal/mole		cal / mole · deg	
NITROGEN (cont.)								
NO$_3^-$ (aq)	−206.57	−110.5	146		−49.372	−26.41	35.0	
N$_2$O$_4$ (g)	9.66	98.29	304.3	79.1	2.309	23.491	72.73	18.90
HNO$_3$ (l)	−173.23	−79.91	155.6	109.9	−41.404	−19.100	37.19	26.26
OXYGEN								
O$_2$ (g)	0	0	205.03	29.36	0	0	49.003	7.017
O$_3$ (g)	142	163.4	238		34.0	39.06	56.8	9.12
PHOSPHORUS								
P (s, white)	0	0	44	25.5	0	0	10.6	6.10
P (s, red)	−18.4			25.1	−4.4			5.99
PO$_4^{\equiv}$ (aq)	−1284	−1025	−217		−306.9	−245.1	−52	
P$_4$O$_{10}$ (s)	−3012				−720.0			
HPO$_4^=$ (aq)	−1299	−1094	−36		−310.4	−261.5	−8.6	
H$_2$PO$_4^-$ (aq)	−1302	−1135	89	−311.3	−271.3	21.3		
H$_3$PO$_4$ (s)	−1281				−306.2			
PCl$_3$ (g)	−306.4	−286.3	311.7		−73.22	−68.42	74.49	
PCl$_5$ (g)	−398.9	−324.6	353		−95.35	−77.59	84.3	
POCl$_3$ (g)	−592	−545	324.6		−141.5	−130.3	77.59	
POTASSIUM								
K (s)	0	0	64	29	0	0	15.2	6.97
K$^+$ (aq)	−251.2	−282.28	103		−60.04	−67.466	24.5	
KCl (s)	−435.87	−408.32	82.7	51.5	−104.175	−97.592	19.67	12.31
KClO$_3$ (s)	−391.2	−289.9	143.0	100.2	−93.50	−69.29	34.17	23.96
KNO$_3$ (s)	−492.7	−393.1	132.9	96.3	−117.76	−93.96	31.77	23.01
KMnO$_4$ (s)	−813	−714	171.7	119	−194.4	−170.6	41.04	28.5
SILICON								
Si (s)	0	0	18.7	19.9	0	0	4.47	4.75
SiO$_2$ (s, quartz)	−859	−805	41.8	44.4	−205.4	−192.4	10.00	10.62
SiF$_4$ (g)	−1548	−1506	285	76	−370	−360	68.0	18.2
SILVER								
Ag (s)	0	0	42.70	254.9	0	0	10.206	6.092
Ag$^+$ (aq)	105.9	77.11	73.9	37	25.31	18.430	17.67	9
AgCl (s)	−127.03	−109.72	96.1	50.8	−30.362	−26.224	22.97	12.14
AgBr (s)	−99.5	−95.94	107.1	52.4	−23.78	−22.930	25.60	12.52
AgI (s)	−62.4	−66.3	114	54.4	−14.91	−15.85	27.3	13.01
AgNO$_3$ (s)	−123.1	−32.2	140.9	93.1	−29.43	−7.69	33.68	22.24
SODIUM								
Na (s)	0	0	51	28.4	0	0	12.2	6.79
Na$^+$ (aq)	−239.66	−261.87	60		−57.279	−62.589	14.4	
NaCl (s)	−411.00	−384.03	72.4	49.7	−98.232	−91.785	17.30	11.88

Substance	$\Delta h_f{}^0$	$\Delta g_f{}^0$	s^0	$c_p{}^0$	$\Delta h_f{}^0$	$\Delta g_f{}^0$	s^0	$c_p{}^0$
	kjoules/mole		joules mole · deg		kcal/mole		cal mole · deg	
SODIUM (cont.)								
Na₂SO₄ (s)	−1384.5	−1266.8	149.5	127.6	−330.90	−302.78	35.73	30.50
Na₂CO₃ (s)	−1131	−1048	136	110.5	−270.3	−250.4	32.5	26.41
NaNO₃ (s)	−466.7	−365.9	116	93.1	−111.54	−87.45	27.8	22.24
SULFUR								
S (s, rhombic)	0	0	31.9	22.6	0	0	7.62	5.40
S (s,monoclinic)	0.30	0.10	32.5	23.6	0.071	0.023	7.78	5.65
SO₂ (g)	−296.9	−300.4	248.5	39.7	−70.96	−71.79	59.40	9.51
SO₃ (g)	−395.2	−370.4	256.2	50.6	−94.45	−88.52	61.24	12.10
SO₄⁼ (aq)	−907.5	−742.0	17	16	−216.90	−177.34	4.1	4.0
H₂S (g)	−17.51	−33.0	205.6	34.0	−4.185	−7.892	49.15	8.12
H₂SO₄ (l)	−811.3			137.6	−193.91			32.88
SOCl₂ (l)	−206			121	−49.2			28.8
TIN								
Sn (s,gray)	−2.1	0.08	45	25.7	−0.49	0.02	10.7	6.16
Sn (s,white)	0	0	51	26.4	0	0	12.3	6.30
SnO (s)	−286	−257	56	44	−68.4	−61.5	13.5	10.6
SnO₂ (s)	−581	−520	52	52.6	−138.8	−124.2	12.5	12.57
SnCl₄ (l)	−545	−474	259	165	−130.3	−113.3	61.8	39.5
ZINC								
Zn (s)	0	0	41.6	25.1	0	0	9.95	5.99
Zn⁺⁺ (aq)	−152.4	−147.21	−106.5		−36.43	−35.184	−25.45	
ZnO (s)	−348.0	−318.2	44	40.2	−83.17	−76.05	10.5	9.62
ZnCl₂ (s)	−415.9	−369.26	108	77	−99.40	−88.255	25.9	18.3
ZnSO₄ (s)	−978.6	−871.6	125	117	−233.88	−208.31	29.8	28

appendix 3

Combination and Permutation Formulas

In this section the combination and permutation formulas used in Chapter 6 will be derived.

(1) The number of arrangements of N distinguishable objects on N sites is $N!$, for the first object can be placed on any one of the N sites, the second on any of the $N - 1$ remaining ones, and so on. Thus the total number of arrangements is

$$N(N - 1)(N - 2) \ldots 1 = N!$$

(2) The number of arrangements of N_1 indistinguishable objects of one type and N_2 indistinguishable objects of another type on $N_1 + N_2$ sites is given by

$$\frac{(N_1 + N_2)!}{N_1! N_2!} = \binom{N}{N_1} = \binom{N}{N_2}$$

where $N = N_1 + N_2$. To prove this, we note that if the objects were distinguishable, the number of arrangements would be $(N_1 + N_2)!$ by (1). Now consider any one arrangement; that is, any one specification telling which sites are to be occupied by each type of object. The N_1 objects of type 1 (temporarily regarded as distinguishable) can be placed on their sites in $N_1!$ different ways by (1); similarly the N_2 objects of type 2 can be placed on their sites in $N_2!$ ways. Thus this one arrangement of two types of indistinguishable objects corresponds to $N_1! N_2!$ arrangements which would be found if the objects could be distinguished. This is true of each arrangement. Therefore, the total number of arrangements which we could count if the objects were distinguishable, $(N_1 + N_2)!$, exceeds the actual number of arrangements by the factor $N_1! N_2!$. This leads directly to the expression for the number of arrangements given above.

This same formula also gives the number of arrangements of N_1 indistinguishable objects on N sites, where N exceeds N_1. For in this case we merely take the N_2 objects of type 2 to be blanks, and the sites to which they are assigned remain empty.

This is easily extended to any number of classes of objects. Thus if there are N_1 indistinguishable objects of type 1, N_2 of type 2, etc., then the number of arrangements is

$$\frac{N!}{N_1!N_2!\ldots}$$

where $N = N_1 + N_2 + \ldots$. As before, one of the classes of objects may be blanks, corresponding to sites left empty.

(3) If multiple occupancy is permitted, the number of ways r indistinguishable objects can be assigned to n sites is

$$\binom{n + r - 1}{r}$$

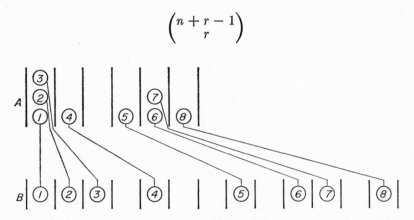

FIGURE 27. METHOD OF ESTABLISHING CORRESPONDENCE BETWEEN ARRANGEMENTS OF r OBJECTS ON n SITES WITH MULTIPLE OCCUPANCY, AND ARRANGEMENTS OF r OBJECTS ON $n + r - 1$ SITES WITHOUT MULTIPLE OCCUPANCY.

An arrangement of the type required is shown on Line A, Figure 27. In this figure the spaces between the vertical lines represent sites, the circles objects. Now number the objects from left to right, choosing any order for numbering objects on the same site. Next move the first object downward to the site directly below it in Line B; then move the second object down to Line B, simultaneously shifting it one site to the right; then move the third object downward and two sites to the right, and so on. Since the rth object will be moved $r - 1$ spaces to the right, no more than $n + r - 1$ spaces are needed in Line B. A little consideration of this process will show that any arrangement of the type shown on Line A — the type we wish to count — can be transformed into an arrangement of the type on Line B, and that arrangements of the latter type consist of r indistinguishable objects assigned to $n + r - 1$ sites with no more than one object in each site. Moreover, the process can be reversed, any arrangement of the type on Line B being transformed into one of the type on Line A. Thus the number of arrangements of the type on Line A is the same as the number of those of the type on line B, and by (2) this is given by the expression above.

The same expression can be derived by considering the $n - 1$ vertical lines in Line A (excluding the two end ones) as movable walls separating the sites, and considering the number of arrangements of r objects and $n - 1$ walls on $n + r - 1$ positions.

appendix 4

Stirling's Formula

The simple form of Stirling's formula used in Chapters 6 and 8 can be derived in a rather elementary manner. Since

$$\ln n! = \ln 1 + \ln 2 + \ln 3 + \ldots + \ln n$$

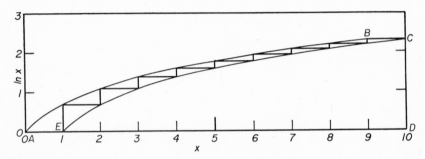

FIGURE 28. GRAPH ILLUSTRATING DERIVATION OF STIRLING'S FORMULA.

this quantity is given by the area under the step-shaped line of Figure 28 (which is drawn for $n = 10$). The smooth curves EC and AB have the equations

$$y = \ln x$$

and

$$y = \ln (x + 1)$$

respectively. Since

$$\text{Area } ECD < \ln n! < \text{Area } ABCD$$

we find

$$\int_1^n \ln x \, dx < \ln n! < \int_0^{n-1} \ln (x + 1) \, dx + \ln n$$

The two integrals are equal, as is seen by making the transformation $x' = x + 1$; evaluating them gives

$$n \ln n - n + 1 < \ln n! < n \ln n - n + 1 + \ln n$$

282

and so, a fortiori,

$$n \ln n - n < \ln < \ln n! < n \ln n - n + 1 + \ln n$$

Now for large n, $1 + \ln n$ is negligible; for example, if $n = 10^{10}$, $1 + \ln n$ is only about 24. Dropping this quantity gives

$$\ln n! = n \ln n - n$$

A more exact form of Stirling's formula is

$$\ln n! = (n + \tfrac{1}{2}) \ln n - n + \tfrac{1}{2} \ln (2\pi) + \frac{1}{12n} - \frac{1}{360n^3} + \dots$$

which, with only the terms shown, is correct to four significant figures even for $n = 2$. The derivation of this will not be given (see, for example, Bromwich[1]).

REFERENCE

1. Bromwich, T. J. I'A., "An Introduction to the Theory of Infinite Series," pp. 329-330, London, The Macmillan Co., 1926.

Evaluation of Integrals

In Chapter 6 several integrals were used with no indication of how they are evaluated. Knowing the techniques for evaluating these integrals is not necessary for understanding the uses to which they are put, but an outline of the methods for evaluating them is given here for the benefit of the student with enough curiosity to be interested.

1. Integrals of the Type $I_n \equiv \displaystyle\int_0^\infty x^n e^{-\alpha x^2}\, dx$

Integration by parts readily leads to the formula

$$I_{n+2} = \frac{n+1}{2\alpha}\, I_n$$

and so all others can be calculated from I_0 and I_1. Moreover, I_1 can be evaluated in an elementary manner by making the substitution $y = \alpha x^2$. We need therefore consider only I_0.

A double integral of the form

$$\int_0^\infty \int_0^\infty f(x)g(y)\ dx\ dy$$

can be factored into the product of two simple integrals, in the same manner as a double sum; for in the integration with respect to x, $g(y)$ is constant and can be taken outside the second integral sign, and then the entire integral with respect to x can be taken outside the first integral sign. Applying this fact, we find

$$\int_0^\infty \int_0^\infty e^{-\alpha(x^2+y^2)}\ dx\ dy = \int_0^\infty e^{-\alpha x^2}\ dx \int_0^\infty e^{-\alpha y^2}\ dy = I_0^{\,2}$$

The range of integration of the double integral is the entire first quadrant. We now change to polar coordinates, selecting instead of $dx\ dy$ the area element appropriate to these coordinates, $r \, dr \, d\theta$. The range necessary to cover the first quadrant is from 0 to ∞ for r and from 0 to $\pi/2$ for θ. This gives

$$I_0{}^2 = \int_0^{\pi/2} \int_0^\infty e^{-\alpha r^2} r \, dr \, d\theta = \int_0^{\pi/2} d\theta \int_0^\infty r e^{-\alpha r^2} \, dr = \tfrac{1}{2}\pi I_1$$

Evaluation of I_1 by elementary methods, as suggested above, leads to $I_1 = 1/(2\alpha)$, and so $I_0{}^2 = \tfrac{1}{4}(\pi/\alpha)$, and

$$I_0 = \tfrac{1}{2}\left(\frac{\pi}{\alpha}\right)^{\frac{1}{2}}$$

2. Integrals of the Type $J_n \equiv \displaystyle\int_0^\infty \frac{x^n}{e^x - 1} \, dx$

Of these integrals J_3 occurs in the Planck radiation theory and in the treatment of Debye's crystal model. J_1 and J_2 are needed in the one- and two-dimensional analogs of Debye's theory, and J_1 in the development of Fermi-Dirac statistics, a topic not pursued in this book. Only with n odd can these integrals be evaluated in simple terms; for even n numerical calculation is possible.

Since e^{-x} is less than 1 for positive values of x, we can use the geometric series to transform the denominator of J_n. Thus

$$\frac{1}{e^x - 1} = \frac{e^{-x}}{1 - e^{-x}} = e^{-x}(1 + e^{-x} + e^{-2x} + \dots) = \sum_{k=1}^\infty e^{-kx}$$

Therefore

$$J_n = \int_0^\infty x^n \sum_{k=1}^\infty e^{-kx} \, dx = \sum_{k=1}^\infty \int_0^\infty x^n e^{-kx} \, dx$$

The step involving the reversal of the order of summation and integration is readily justified for positive integrands (see, for example, Bromwich[1]). The integrals occurring in the last sum can be reduced to the elementary form

$$\frac{n!}{k^n} \int_0^\infty e^{-kx} \, dx = \frac{n!}{k^{n+1}}$$

by integrating by parts n times. This gives

$$J_n = n! \sum_{k=1}^\infty \frac{1}{k^{n+1}}$$

The function defined by this last series is known as the *Riemann zeta-function*, and so this equation may be written

$$J_n = n! \zeta(n + 1)$$

For even arguments the zeta-functions can be evaluated by a fairly elementary but tedious procedure involving Fourier series. First, x is expanded as a Fourier cosine series

$$x = b_0 + \sum_{k=1}^{\infty} b_k \cos kx$$

This is valid in the range from 0 to π, inclusive, if the coefficients are evaluated in the usual way by multiplying this equation by $\cos kx$ and integrating over this range. Thus

$$b_0 = \frac{1}{\pi} \int_0^{\pi} x \, dx = \frac{\pi}{2}$$

$$b_k = \frac{2}{\pi} \int_0^{\pi} x \cos kx \, dx = \frac{2}{\pi k^2} [(-1)^k - 1] = \begin{cases} 0 \text{ for even } k \\ -\dfrac{4}{\pi k^2} \text{ for odd } k \end{cases}$$

Therefore

$$x = \frac{\pi}{2} - \frac{4}{\pi} \left(\cos x + \frac{\cos 3x}{3^2} + \frac{\cos 5x}{5^2} + \ldots \right) \qquad (A5\text{--}1)$$

Substituting either $x = 0$ or $x = \pi$ leads to

$$1 + \frac{1}{3^2} + \frac{1}{5^2} + \ldots = \frac{\pi^2}{8}$$

If the series for $\zeta(2)$ is divided by four, the result is

$$\zeta(2) = 1 + \frac{1}{2^2} + \frac{1}{3^2} + \frac{1}{4^2} + \frac{1}{5^2} + \ldots$$

$$\tfrac{1}{4}\zeta(2) = \qquad \frac{1}{2^2} + \qquad \frac{1}{4^2} + \qquad \ldots$$

and by subtraction

$$\tfrac{3}{4}\zeta(2) = 1 \quad + \quad \frac{1}{3^2} \quad + \quad \frac{1}{5^2} + \ldots = \frac{\pi^2}{8}$$

This leads to $\zeta(2) = \pi^2/6$.

If Eq. (A5–1) is integrated twice, and the constants of integration are evaluated by setting $x = 0$ after the first integration and $x = \pi/2$ after the second, the result is

$$\frac{x^3}{6} = -\frac{\pi^3}{24} + \frac{\pi x^2}{4} + \frac{4}{\pi}\left(\cos x + \frac{\cos 3x}{3^4} + \frac{\cos 5x}{5^4} + \ldots\right)$$

and $\zeta(4)$ can be found from this equation in much the same manner as $\zeta(2)$ is found from Eq. (A5–1). The result is $\zeta(4) = \pi^4/90$.

The following more elegant methods may appeal to students with enough background in functions of a complex variable to follow them. Consider

$$\int_{S_k} \frac{dz}{z^{2n}(e^z - 1)}$$

where S_k denotes the square with vertices at $2\pi(k + \frac{1}{2})$ $(\pm 1 \pm i)$. The integrand has a pole of order $2n + 1$ at the origin; the residue there is

$$\frac{(-1)^{n-1}B_n}{(2n)!}$$

B_n being the *Bernoulli numbers*, defined by the expansion

$$\frac{1}{e^z - 1} = \frac{1}{z} - \frac{1}{2} + \sum_{r=1}^{\infty} \frac{(-1)^{r-1}B_r}{(2r)!} z^{2r-1}$$

The first few of these are $B_1 = 1/6$, $B_2 = 1/30$, $B_3 = 1/42$. The integrand also has simple poles of residue $(2\pi mi)^{-2n}$ at the points $\pm 2\pi mi$, where m is a positive integer. Therefore,

$$\frac{(-1)^{n-1}B_n}{(2n)!} + 2\sum_{m=1}^{k} \frac{(-1)^n}{(2\pi m)^{2n}} = \frac{1}{2\pi i}\int_{S_k} \frac{dz}{z^{2n}(e^z - 1)}$$

It can be shown by standard methods that as $k \to \infty$, the integral on the right approaches zero. This leads directly to

$$\zeta(2n) = \frac{B_n(2\pi)^{2n}}{2(2n)!}$$

Finally, J_{2n-1} can be evaulated without expanding to a Riemann zeta-function by integrating

$$\frac{z^{2n}}{e^z - 1} \, dz$$

around a rectangle with vertices at $\pm 2\pi i$ and $R \pm 2\pi i$, indented to exclude the poles of the integrand at the former points. Along the horizontal portions of the contour the term $(x \pm 2\pi i)^{2n}$ is expanded by means of the binomial theorem, and the contributions from these two portions are combined. The integral along the right vertical side approaches zero as $R \rightarrow \infty$; if the radii of the indentations are kept equal while they approach zero, the integral along the left side approaches a Cauchy principal value of

$$\frac{(-1)^n (2\pi)^{2n-1} i}{2n + 1}$$

Combining these with the contributions from the poles leads to the expression

$$\sum_{k=1}^{n} (-1)^{k-1} \binom{2n}{2k - 1} (2\pi)^{-2k} J_{2k-1} = \frac{2n - 1}{4(2n + 1)}$$

from which J_1, J_3, etc., can be evaluated successively.

REFERENCE

1. Bromwich, T.J.I.'A., "An Introduction to the Theory of Infinite Series,"p 500, London, The Macmillan Co., 1926.

The Frequency Distribution
In the Debye Crystal Model

In this section Eq. (6–51), giving the number of oscillators in a given frequency range in a Debye crystal, will be derived. This requires a study of the conditions for wave motion. The derivation is more easily understood if we start with a one-dimensional example, such as the transverse vibrations of a stretched string.

A wave moving with speed c in the x-direction satisfies the equation

$$\frac{\partial^2 y}{\partial x^2} = \frac{1}{c^2}\frac{\partial^2 y}{\partial t^2} \tag{A6-1}$$

This can be seen as follows: a solution of this equation is

$$y = f(x - ct)$$

where f is any function that has first and second derivatives. Now if a point is moving in the x-direction with speed c, $x - ct$ remains constant, and so the shape represented by the function $f(x - ct)$ is unchanged as the wave moves. Another solution is $f(x + ct)$, which represents a wave traveling in the $-x$-direction.

Standing waves, however, are more conveniently represented by functions of the type

$$y = X(x)T(t)$$

where X and T are functions of x alone and t alone, respectively. If we substitute this into Eq. (A6–1) and divide by XT, we find

$$\frac{X''}{X} = \frac{1}{c^2}\frac{T''}{T} \tag{A6-2}$$

the double prime indicating a second derivative. Now of course, we can watch how the position of a definite point changes with time; that is, we can let t vary while keeping x constant. But this keeps the left side of Eq. (A6–2) constant, and so the right side must be constant also, even though t is varying. Thus each side must be equal to a constant; moreover, this constant must be negative, or the solution will not represent periodic motion. Calling it $-\delta^2$, we have

$$T'' + (c\delta)^2 T = 0 \quad \text{and} \quad X'' + \delta^2 X = 0$$

for which the solutions are

$$T = A \sin (c\delta t) \quad \text{and} \quad X = B \sin (\delta x)$$

Where A and B are constants. A cosine term can be included in each of these solutions, but we do not need them. If the solution for T is to represent periodic motion of frequency ν, it must be

$$T = A \sin (2\pi\nu t)$$

and comparison shows that $c\delta = 2\pi\nu$, or

$$\delta = \frac{2\pi\nu}{c}$$

The solution for X then becomes

$$X = B \sin \frac{2\pi\nu}{c} x$$

Now if the string is clamped at both ends, we must have $X = 0$ at the points $x = 0$ and $x = l$, where l is the length of the string. The first is already satisfied because of the omission of the cosine term, but to satisfy the second we must have

$$\frac{2\pi\nu l}{c} = n\pi$$

where n is an integer, since the sine function is zero only at multiples of π. The only frequencies that are possible, then, are those given by

$$\nu = \frac{nc}{2l}$$

Each of these represents two possible modes of oscillation, since the string may vibrate either horizontally or vertically; vibration at any other angle would, of course, be regarded as the resultant of a horizontal and a vertical vibration.

The equation for wave motion in three dimensions, analogous to Eq. (A6–1), is

$$\frac{\partial^2 u}{\partial x^2} + \frac{\partial^2 u}{\partial y^2} + \frac{\partial^2 u}{\partial z^2} = \frac{1}{c^2}\frac{\partial^2 u}{\partial t^2}$$

To find a solution representing a standing wave we write

$$u = X(x)Y(y)Z(z)T(t)$$

where each of the functions represented by capital letters depends on one variable only. Substituting this into the equation and dividing by $XYZT$ gives

$$\frac{X''}{X} + \frac{Y''}{Y} + \frac{Z''}{Z} = \frac{1}{c^2}\frac{T''}{T}$$

An argument similar to that in the one-dimensional case shows that each of these terms must be separately constant, and that the constants must be negative. Thus we have

$$\frac{X''}{X} = -\alpha^2$$

$$\frac{Y''}{Y} = -\beta^2$$

$$\frac{Z''}{Z} = -\gamma^2$$

$$\frac{1}{c^2}\frac{T''}{T} = -\delta^2$$

and

$$\alpha^2 + \beta^2 + \gamma^2 = \delta^2 \tag{A6–3}$$

As in the one-dimensional case, we find $\delta = 2\pi\nu/c$. Now if the crystal is in the shape of a rectangular parallelopiped of sides A, B, and C, and we require that the surfaces be nodes, then X must be zero for $x = 0$ and for $x = A$. The solution of the X-equation is

$$X = D \sin \alpha x$$

the cosine term being omitted so that X will be zero when $x = 0$. If X is to be zero at $x = A$ also, we must have

$$\alpha A = \kappa \pi$$

or

$$\alpha = \frac{\kappa \pi}{A}$$

where κ is an integer. Similarly we find

$$\beta = \frac{\lambda \pi}{B}$$

and

$$\gamma = \frac{\mu \pi}{C}$$

where λ and μ are integers. Substituting in Eq. (A6–3) then gives

$$\frac{\kappa^2}{A^2} + \frac{\lambda^2}{B^2} + \frac{\mu^2}{C^2} = \frac{4 \nu^2}{c^2} \qquad \text{(A6–4)}$$

There are, then, as many modes of vibration of frequency ν as there are sets of positive integers, κ, λ, and μ, satisfying this equation.

The remaining part of the argument is essentially the same as that used in finding the number of translational states of a given energy in a gas (p. 125). Eq. (A6–4) can be rewritten

$$\frac{\kappa^2}{\left(\dfrac{2A\,\nu}{c}\right)^2} + \frac{\lambda^2}{\left(\dfrac{2B\,\nu}{c}\right)^2} + \frac{\mu^2}{\left(\dfrac{2C\,\nu}{c}\right)^2} = 1$$

which is the equation of an ellipsoid. The number of modes of vibration not exceeding a given frequency is given, except for trivial errors near the surface, by the volume of the first octant of this ellipsoid. This is

$$\Omega_l(\nu) = \frac{\pi}{6} \left(\frac{2A\,\nu}{c}\right)\left(\frac{2B\,\nu}{c}\right)\left(\frac{2C\,\nu}{c}\right) = \frac{4\pi\,\nu^3 V}{3c^3}$$

where V is the volume of the crystal.

So far this accounts for only one type of wave, for example, longitudinal, as indicated by the subscript l. But in solids transverse waves also occur; moreover, for these we must take into account the effect of polarization. Since any transverse wave can be resolved into two components polarized in mutually perpendicular directions, we must double this expression when applying it to transverse waves. This leads to

$$\Omega(\nu) = \frac{4\pi V}{3} \left(\frac{1}{c_l{}^3} + \frac{2}{c_t{}^3} \right) \nu^3$$

the subscript t referring to transverse waves. This is the number of modes having frequency no greater than a given frequency; the number of modes with frequency in a given infinitesimal range is found by differentiating this. The result is

$$\omega(\nu) \, d\nu = 4\pi V \left(\frac{1}{c_l{}^3} + \frac{2}{c_t{}^3} \right) \nu^2 \, d\nu$$

which is the same as Eq. (6–51).

Number of Independent Reactions in a Set

Although it is usually practical to determine by inspection how many reactions in a given set are independent, it is desirable to have a systematic method for the sake of completeness and for possible use in intricate cases.

The first step in this method is to write the reaction equations (or at least the coefficients) in a standard form, in which:

(1) All substances appear on the same side of the reaction arrow, reactants and products being distinguished by the sign of the coefficients;

(2) Every substance which appears in any of the equations appears in all of them, and in the same order, zero coefficients being used where necessary.

Thus the first two equations in the set on p. 193 are written

$$C + O_2 + 0H_2 + 0CO - CO_2 + 0H_2O \rightarrow 0$$

and

$$C + 0O_2 + 0H_2 - 2CO + CO_2 + 0H_2O \rightarrow 0$$

We then write the coefficients only, in the same order, as a matrix; for this set the matrix is

$$
\begin{array}{rrrrrr}
1 & 1 & 0 & 0 & -1 & 0 \\
1 & 0 & 0 & -2 & 1 & 0 \\
1 & 0 & -1 & -1 & 0 & 1 \\
0 & 1 & 2 & 0 & 0 & -2 \\
0 & 0 & -1 & 1 & -1 & 1
\end{array}
$$

The number of independent equilibria in the set is equal to the rank of this matrix.

The rank is defined as follows: select any k rows and any k columns of the matrix, and form a determinant of order k from the k^2 elements common to one of the selected rows and one of the selected columns, keeping their relative positions unchanged. If any of the determinants of order

k which can be formed in this manner differs from zero, but no non-vanishing determinant of order $k + 1$ can be formed in the same manner, the rank of the matrix is k.

Fortunately, it is not necessary to evaluate every determinant which can be formed from the matrix in order to determine the rank. Instead we can use the theorem that any multiple of the elements of any row (or column) can be added to the elements of another row (or column) without changing the rank. The first step in applying this theorem to the above matrix is to multiply the elements of the first row by -1 and add them to those of the second and third rows. This gives a new matrix,

$$\begin{array}{cccccc}
1 & 1 & 0 & 0 & -1 & 0 \\
0 & -1 & 0 & -2 & 2 & 0 \\
0 & -1 & -1 & -1 & 1 & 1 \\
0 & 1 & 2 & 0 & 0 & -2 \\
0 & 0 & -1 & 1 & -1 & 1
\end{array}$$

having the same rank as the original one, but having only one nonzero element in the first column. We next use the second row similarly to make all but one element of the second column zero. This requires adding the second row to the first and fourth rows, and subtracting it from the third. The result is

$$\begin{array}{cccccc}
1 & 0 & 0 & -2 & 1 & 0 \\
0 & -1 & 0 & -2 & 2 & 0 \\
0 & 0 & -1 & 1 & -1 & 1 \\
0 & 0 & 2 & -2 & 2 & -2 \\
0 & 0 & -1 & 1 & -1 & 1
\end{array}$$

Then the third row is subtracted from the fifth, and twice the third row is added to the fourth, leaving

$$\begin{array}{cccccc}
1 & 0 & 0 & -2 & 1 & 0 \\
0 & -1 & 0 & -2 & 2 & 0 \\
0 & 0 & -1 & 1 & -1 & 1 \\
0 & 0 & 0 & 0 & 0 & 0 \\
0 & 0 & 0 & 0 & 0 & 0
\end{array}$$

It is now unnecessary to go further, for clearly a determinant of order 3 formed from the nine elements in the upper left corner would have a value of 1, while any fourth-order determinant would have at least one row of zeroes. Thus the rank of the matrix is 3, and this is also the number of independent equilibria.

If necessary, this procedure can be continued by manipulating first rows and then columns (or vice versa) until all but k elements, no two of which are in the same row or column, are zero; the rank is then k.

This method is essentially an application of the theorem that out of a set of linear algebraic forms, the number that are linearly independent is the rank of their matrix. The mathematical background is discussed in books on simultaneous linear equations (see, for example, Thomas[1]).

REFERENCE

1. Thomas, J. M., "Theory of Equations," Chapters III and IV, New York, N.Y., McGraw-Hill Book Co., Inc., 1938.

appendix 8

Standard Half-Cell EMF Values

The following table gives the emf of some important half-cells, which are identified by the reaction which takes place when oxidation occurs in them. This reaction is given in the first column. The second column gives the half-cell emf, which is identical with the quantity called the "oxidation potential" by Lewis and Randall and Latimer. The third column gives the electrode potential, in the sense that this term is used in the IUPAC-CITCE recommendations; this is identical with the "reduction potential" of Lewis and Randall and Latimer. If the reaction is reversed, the electrode potential is unchanged, but the half-cell emf is changed in sign, becoming identical with the electrode potential.

The values in this table are taken mostly from Latimer, with some from Harned and Owen.

Reaction	Half-cell emf/v	Electrode Potential/v
$Li \rightarrow Li^+ + \epsilon$	3.045	−3.045
$K \rightarrow K^+ + \epsilon$	2.925	−2.925
$Ba \rightarrow Ba^{++} + 2\epsilon$	2.90	−2.90
$Sr \rightarrow Sr^{++} + 2\epsilon$	2.89	−2.89
$Ca \rightarrow Ca^{++} + 2\epsilon$	2.87	−2.87
$Na \rightarrow Na^+ + \epsilon$	2.714	−2.714
$Ce \rightarrow Ce^{+++} + 3\epsilon$	2.48	−2.48
$Mg \rightarrow Mg^{++} + 2\epsilon$	2.37	−2.37
$Al \rightarrow Al^{+++} + 3\epsilon$	1.66	−1.66
$Ti \rightarrow Ti^{++} + 2\epsilon$	1.63	−1.63
$Mn \rightarrow Mn^{++} + 2\epsilon$	1.18	−1.18
$Zn \rightarrow Zn^{++} + 2\epsilon$	0.7626	−0.7626
$Cr \rightarrow Cr^{+++} + 3\epsilon$	0.74	−0.74
$Fe \rightarrow Fe^{++} + 2\epsilon$	0.440	−0.440
$Cr^{++} \rightarrow Cr^{+++} + \epsilon$	0.41	−0.41
$Cd \rightarrow Cd^{++} + 2\epsilon$	0.403	−0.403
$Pb + 2I^- \rightarrow PbI_2 + 2\epsilon$	0.365	−0.365
$Pb + SO_4^= \rightarrow PbSO_4 + 2\epsilon$	0.356	−0.356

Reaction	Half-cell emf/v	Electrode Potential/v
$Co \rightarrow Co^{++} + 2\epsilon$	0.277	−0.277
$Pb + 2Cl^- \rightarrow PbCl_2 + 2\epsilon$	0.268	−0.268
$Ni \rightarrow Ni^{++} + 2\epsilon$	0.250	−0.250
$Ag + I^- \rightarrow AgI + \epsilon$	0.151	−0.151
$Sn \rightarrow Sn^{++} + 2\epsilon$	0.136	−0.136
$Pb \rightarrow Pb^{++} + 2\epsilon$	0.126	−0.126
$\frac{1}{2}H_2 \rightarrow H^+ + 2\epsilon$	0	0
$Ag + Br^- \rightarrow AgBr + \epsilon$	−0.0713	0.0713
$Cu + Cl^- \rightarrow CuCl + \epsilon$	−0.137	0.137
$Ag + Cl^- \rightarrow AgCl + \epsilon$	−0.2224	0.2224
$2Cl^- + 2Hg \rightarrow Hg_2Cl_2 + 2\epsilon$	−0.2676	0.2676
$Cu \rightarrow Cu^{++} + 2\epsilon$	−0.337	0.337
$Fe(CN)_6^{-4} \rightarrow Fe(CN)_6^{-3} + \epsilon$	−0.36	0.36
$Cu \rightarrow Cu^+ + \epsilon$	−0.521	0.521
$Pt + 4Br^- \rightarrow PtBr_4^= + 2\epsilon$	−0.58	0.58
$CuBr \rightarrow Cu^{++} + Br^- + \epsilon$	−0.640	0.640
$2Ag + SO_4^= \rightarrow Ag_2SO_4 + 2\epsilon$	−0.653	0.653
$Pt + 4Cl^- \rightarrow PtCl_4^= + 2\epsilon$	−0.73	0.73
$Fe^{++} \rightarrow Fe^{+++} + \epsilon$	−0.771	0.771
$2Hg \rightarrow Hg_2^{++} + 2\epsilon$	−0.789	0.789
$Ag \rightarrow Ag^+ + \epsilon$	−0.7991	0.7991
$Hg_2^{++} \rightarrow 2Hg^{++} + 2\epsilon$	−0.920	0.920
$Au + 4Cl^- \rightarrow AuCl_4^- + 3\epsilon$	−1.00	1.00
$Br^- \rightarrow \frac{1}{2}Br_2 \ (l) + \epsilon$	−1.0652	1.0652
$ClO_3^- + H_2O \rightarrow ClO_4^- + 2H^+ + 2\epsilon$	−1.19	1.19
$Mn^{++} + 2H_2O \rightarrow MnO_2 + 4H^+ + 2\epsilon$	−1.23	1.23
$2Cr^{+++} + 7H_2O \rightarrow Cr_2O_7^= + 14H^+ + 6\epsilon$	−1.33	1.33
$Cl^- \rightarrow \frac{1}{2}Cl_2 + \epsilon$	−1.3595	1.3595
$Au \rightarrow Au^{+++} + 3\epsilon$	−1.50	1.50
$Mn^{++} + 4H_2O \rightarrow MnO_4^- + 8H^+ + 5\epsilon$	−1.51	1.51
$PbSO_4 + 2H_2O \rightarrow PbO_2 + SO_4^= + 4H^+ + 2\epsilon$	−1.685	1.685
$Co^{++} \rightarrow Co^{+++} + \epsilon$	−1.82	1.82
$F^- \rightarrow \frac{1}{2}F_2 + \epsilon$	−2.65	2.65

Author Index

Subject Index